BRITISH BIRDS
IN THEIR HAUNTS

BRITISH BIRDS IN THEIR HAUNTS

By the late
REV. C. A. JOHNS, F.L.S.
Author of *Flowers of the Field*

Edited and Revised by
W. B. ALEXANDER, M.A. M.B.O.U.
Late Director of the Edward Grey Institute of Field Ornithology
in the University of Oxford.

Illustrated with 64 Coloured Plates (251 Figures) by
WILLIAM FOSTER, M.B.O.U.
and 5 Black-and-White Plates (18 Figures) by
ROLAND GREEN, M.B.O.U.

WITH A GLOSSARY OF COMMON AND PROVINCIAL NAMES AND
OF TECHNICAL TERMS

TWENTY-FIFTH EDITION

LONDON
ROUTLEDGE & KEGAN PAUL LIMITED
BROADWAY HOUSE : 68–74 CARTER LANE, E.C.4

Originally published in 1861
Revised several times since
Present revised edition 1948

Printed in Great Britain by Butler & Tanner Ltd., Frome and London

PREFACE TO THE TWENTY-FIFTH EDITION

ONE of the present editor's most cherished possessions as a boy was a copy of Johns' *British Birds in their Haunts* received as a Christmas present when he was seven years old. In those days he never dreamt that over fifty years later he would be asked to edit a new edition of this treasured work. The fact that it has continued popular for such a long period seems strong evidence that the anecdotal style of the author is specially attractive to the type of reader for whom it was intended, and the editor has therefore only made alterations when these seemed absolutely necessary in view of changed circumstances.

At the time when Johns wrote, the status and distribution of many species of birds in the British Isles was still imperfectly known. Nowadays these facts about the birds are almost as well known as their plumages and their eggs, so in this edition a brief summary of the status and distribution has been added at the end of the description of each species and its eggs.

For many years past it has been customary in zoological works, including the more scientific books on birds, to begin with the forms regarded as most primitive and end with those most highly developed. In almost all parts of the world outside Europe this arrangement has also been adopted in popular books on birds so that in America, Africa, India, and Australia the sequence of orders and families first promulgated by the late Dr. Gadow of Cambridge, and more recently revised by Dr. Wetmore of Washington, is now familiar. Recent lists of the birds of France, Italy, Denmark, and other European countries have followed this system, so it seems evident that it will soon be universally adopted. The editor has therefore rearranged the orders and families in this edition in accordance with this modern arrangement, though within each family the species have been left in the order in which Johns arranged them, as when dealing with nearly allied species he often gave particulars of habits common to the group under the first species dealt with and wrote more briefly concerning the remainder.

W. B. ALEXANDER.

OXFORD,
August, 1947.

SYNOPSIS OF THE ORDERS AND FAMILIES OF BIRDS INCLUDED IN THIS BOOK

1. ORDER COLYMBIFORMES. Large aquatic birds with strong, compressed, pointed bill ; large head and fairly long neck. Wings short, narrow and pointed, with eleven primaries. Tail very short. Legs very far back, short and flattened ; three front toes connected by webs. Food mainly fish, captured by pursuit under water. Eggs two, oily brown, spotted and blotched with grey and black, laid in a depression at the water's edge. Young covered with brownish down, unstriped.

Only *Family Colymbidæ* (Divers). Four species confined to northern portions of northern hemisphere, all on British list, three described below.
Page 1

2. ORDER PODICIPIFORMES. Aquatic birds with cylindrical, pointed bill ; rather long neck and head usually ornamented in the breeding plumage by coloured tufts of feathers. Wings short, concave, with twelve primaries. No stiff tail-feathers. Legs short, very far back, extraordinarily flattened ; the three front toes independently lobed with fringing membranes. Food fish and other aquatic creatures, captured by pursuit under water. Eggs white, laid on a pile of aquatic plants. Young in down, strikingly striped.

Only *Family Podicipidæ* (Grebes). About eighteen species distributed over the world, chiefly on fresh water. Five on British list, all described below.
Page 4

3. ORDER PROCELLARIIFORMES. Oceanic birds, with bill hooked at the tip and with the horny covering more or less divided into separate scutes. External nostrils tubular, the tubes sometimes uniting on the upper surface of the bill, sometimes opening independently at the sides. Wings long with ten primaries developed. Feet with the three front toes united by webs and the hind toe small or absent. Plumage with a strong, musky smell. Single egg white. Chick covered with down, remaining long in the nest. Includes four families.

Family Procellariidæ (Petrels, Shearwaters, and Fulmars). Comparatively large species with nostrils opening in separate tubes, legs comparatively short and characteristic gliding flight with long wings held rigid. Over fifty species, distributed over all the oceans ; eleven on British list, of which four are described below.
Page 8

Family Hydrobatidæ (Storm Petrels). Small species with nostrils combined in a single tube, legs comparatively long and very slender, and fluttering flight. About twenty species distributed over all the oceans ; five on British list, of which two are described below.
Page 10

4. ORDER PELECANIFORMES. Large aquatic birds with short legs and all four toes united by webs. Eggs usually unspotted, covered with a white chalky layer. Young, born blind, and usually naked, remaining long in the nest. Includes six families.

Family Sulidæ (Gannets). Sea-birds with stout, conical, pointed bills ; fairly short necks ; stout bodies ; long wings ; long wedge-shaped tails and short legs ; with areas on the face and a small throat-pouch unfeathered. They feed on fish obtained by diving from the air and subsequent pursuit under water. Nine species found in all oceans but North Pacific. One on British list described below.
Page 12

Family Phalacrocoracidæ (Cormorants). Birds with slender bill, terminating in a sharp hook ; long neck ; rather long wings and tail ; short legs set far back and very large feet. Parts of face and a small throat-pouch unfeathered. Food fish or crustacea obtained by pursuit under water. About thirty species found on coasts and inland waters of all countries except the Central Pacific Islands. Two British species described below.   *Page* 14

5. ORDER CICONIIFORMES. Wading birds, mostly of large size, with long neck and very long legs. Includes seven families.

Family Ardeidæ (Herons and Bitterns). Birds with long, pointed bill rounded above and compressed laterally ; body compressed and covered with loose feathers making them appear larger than their real size ; tail short ; toes long, the claw of the middle front toe serrated ; wings broad with eleven primaries. Eggs unspotted, usually bluish or greenish, sometimes buff or white. Young hatched with scanty covering of down, remaining long in the nest. About a hundred species, distributed in all countries. Ten on British list, of which three are described below.   *Page* 16

Family Ciconiidæ (Storks). Very large birds with long, stout bills ; wings very large with eleven or twelve primaries ; tail short ; front toes short, partially united by webs ; hind toe somewhat elevated. Eggs white and chalky. About twenty species distributed over most of the warmer parts of the world. Two on British list, of which one is described below.   *Page* 19

Family Threskiornithidæ (Ibises and Spoonbills). Large birds with long bill, either cylindrical and strongly curved downwards or flattened and dilated at the end ; wings with eleven primaries ; legs usually rather stout ; toes generally long, united by webs at the base. Eggs white, bluish or greenish, usually with reddish or brownish markings. Nestlings covered with down. About thirty species distributed over the world. Two on British list described below.   *Page* 19.

6. ORDER ANSERIFORMES. Large or moderate-sized birds, completely or partially aquatic in habits, with heavy bodies, long neck, small head ; bill covered with a soft, sensitive membrane ; front toes completely or partially united by webs. Eggs white, creamy, buffish or greenish, unspotted. Young covered with down, active soon after hatching. Includes two families.

Family Anatidæ (Ducks, Geese, and Swans). Aquatic birds with short legs set far back and small hind toe elevated ; wings large and somewhat pointed, all the quills moulted simultaneously so that the birds are temporarily flightless. Many species, found in all parts of the world Forty-two species on British list, of which twenty-nine are described below.   *Page* 20

7. ORDER FALCONIFORMES. Diurnal, carnivorous birds with strong, hooked beak with sharp cutting-edges and a ' cere ' or patch of fleshy skin at the base of the upper mandible ; feet with four toes, which usually have sharp, curved claws ; female larger than male. Eggs either pure white or white with red blotches. Young remain in the nest for a long period. Includes four families.

Family Accipitridæ (Eagles, Buzzards, Kites, Harriers, Vultures, and Osprey). Birds of prey, mostly of large size, with large, broad, somewhat rounded wings. Food usually includes carrion and dead animals as well as prey captured on the ground. Numerous species, found in all parts of the world. Seventeen on British list, of which twelve are described below.   *Page* 43

Family Falconidæ (Falcons and Kestrels). Birds of prey varying much in size, with long pointed wings and great powers of flight. Food obtained by ' stooping ' at great speed on their prey from the air and striking it with their talons, or by hovering over it and pouncing. Numerous species, found in all parts of the world. Seven on British list, of which four are described below.
Page 53

8. ORDER GALLIFORMES. Terrestrial or arboreal birds, usually of moderate or large size, with stout, arched bill, broad wings and strong legs and feet. Food mainly grain, berries, shoots of plants and other vegetable matter, supplemented by insects, snails, etc. Eggs numerous. Downy chicks active soon after hatching, becoming feathered and capable of flight before they are nearly full-grown. Includes seven families.

Family Tetraonidæ (Grouse). Nostrils covered by feathers and legs partly or completely feathered, without spurs. About twenty species, confined to the northern portions of the northern hemisphere. Four species in Britain, all described below.   *Page* 58

Family Phasianidæ (Fowls, Pheasants, Partridges, and Quail). Game birds with nostrils bare and legs unfeathered, often with spurs and with hind toe elevated. Many species, found throughout the world except the Pacific islands and southern South America. Four species in Britain, all described below. *Page* 65

9. ORDER GRUIFORMES. A diversified group of birds, either terrestrial or frequenting swamps and reed-beds, mostly of moderate or large size with fairly long necks and legs and with hind toe, when present, at a higher level than the three front ones. Includes twelve families.

Family Gruidæ (Cranes). Very large, terrestrial birds, with straight bill, long neck, large rounded wings with eleven primaries, short tail of twelve feathers, very long legs and three front toes stout and connected by webs at the base. About sixteen species, found in North America, Europe, Asia, Africa and Australia. One species on British list described below. *Page* 73

Family Rallidæ (Rails and Coots). Small or moderately-sized birds mostly frequenting reed-beds or dense vegetation with the body very much compressed, enabling them to traverse the narrow passages between the plant-stems. Bill stout, varying much in length, frequently with a horny shield extending from the base of the upper mandible upwards to the forehead ; wings short and rounded ; legs usually fairly long with long slender toes. Numerous species, found in all parts of the world. Eight species on British list, of which six are described below. *Page* 74

Family Otididæ (Bustards). Large or moderate-sized, terrestrial birds, with short, blunt, curved bill ; flattened head ; thick neck ; broad, rounded wings ; and fairly long, rounded tail. Legs stout ; no hind-toe ; three front toes short and stout with flat soles and flatish nails. About thirty species confined to the eastern hemisphere. Three on British list, of which one is described below. *Page* 79

10. ORDER CHARADRIIFORMES. A large group of birds mostly aquatic or frequenting the vicinity of water, very diversified in external appearance but agreeing in many anatomical characters. Includes sixteen families.

Family Hæmatopodidæ (Oyster Catchers). Large wading birds with very long, hard, compressed bill with tip rounded or truncate, not pointed. Legs fairly long and very stout ; hind toe absent, three short, stout, front toes partially connected by webs at base. Plumage black or black and white, bill and legs red or orange. About ten species distributed over the sea-coasts of the world. One species in Britain described below. *Page* 80

Family Charadriidæ (Plovers and Turnstones). Wading birds mostly frequenting sea-coasts, but sometimes grassy plains or moors inland. Bill comparatively short, hard at tip but softer at the base ; legs fairly long with hind toe small or absent. Eggs large, pear-shaped, usually four, greenish or buff with darker markings. Downy young active directly after hatching. About seventy species distributed throughout the world. Twelve species in British list, of which seven are described below. *Page* 81

Family Scolopacidæ (Snipe, Woodcock, Sandpipers, Curlews, Godwits, etc.). Wading birds varying greatly in size. Bill usually long and rather slender, straight or curved ; legs usually long, hind toe small or absent. Eggs usually four, resembling those of plovers. Downy young active directly after hatching. About eighty species distributed throughout the world, though a large proportion nest in high northern latitudes and disperse over sea-coasts at other seasons. Forty-one species on British list, of which twenty-three are described below. *Page* 90

Family Recurvirostridæ (Avocets and Stilts). Wading birds with very long, slender bill either straight or curved upwards ; long neck and long slender legs, front toes more or less united by webs at the base, hind toe rudimentary or absent. Eggs usually four, pear-shaped, buff with black or grey spots and markings. Downy young active soon after hatching. About seven species frequenting swamps and lagoons throughout the world. Two on British list, of which one is described below. *Page* 109

Family Phalaropodidæ (Phalaropes). Small maritime birds with straight slender bill, rather long neck, legs very much compressed and long toes with lobed, fringing webs. Female larger and more brightly coloured than male, the latter incubating the eggs and caring for the downy chicks, which are active soon after hatching. Three species widely distributed over the oceans except during the breeding season when they frequent the tundras and swamps of high northern latitudes. Two on British list described below. *Page* 110

Family Burhinidæ (Stone Curlews). Large terrestrial birds frequenting open plains, steppes, and downs, crepusculæ in habits. The bill is stout, head large, eyes very large, neck and wings long, legs very long and the feet have three toes. The plumage is mainly brown and buff, with markings of black and patches of white. Their two eggs are stone-coloured, blotched or scrawled with black, laid on the bare ground. About nine species, distributed throughout the eastern hemisphere and in tropical America and Haiti. One on British list described below. *Page* 111

Family Glareolidæ (Pratincoles and Coursers). Terrestrial birds with comparatively short bill, rather long wings, square or forked tail and long slender legs. Plumage mainly sandy or rufous but usually with conspicuous black and white markings on the wings. Two to four eggs, buff or grey, marked with various colours. Young active shortly after hatching. Numerous species found in the arid regions of the eastern hemisphere. Three on British list, of which two are described below. *Page* 112

Family Stercorariidæ (Skuas). Dark-plumaged, long-winged sea-birds with stout, hooked beak, with the basal portion of the upper mandible covered by a separate horny plate, or cere. Central tail-feathers slightly or very much longer than the others. Legs fairly short and front toes united by webs. Largely rapacious, much of their food being obtained by robbing other birds. Two to four eggs usually olive-brown with large spots of dark brown or purplish laid in a hollow on the ground. Young when hatched covered with brown down, dependent on their parents for food till they are fledged. Four species breeding in high northern or southern latitudes but distributed over the oceans at other seasons, all on British list and described below. *Page* 113

Family Laridæ (Gulls and Terns). Aquatic birds with long wings, short neck, and short legs, with webs uniting the three front toes and the hind toe small or absent. Bill usually nearly straight and rather slender, but stout and somewhat hooked in some of the larger species. The majority when adult have the plumage grey above and white below, mottled with brown in the young. The majority build fairly substantial nests on the ground, on cliffs or in trees. The eggs are from one to five in number, white, yellowish, brown, or greenish with darker markings of various colours. The young when hatched are covered with mottled down and are dependent on their parents for food until fledged. Almost all the species are sociable and nest in colonies. About ninety species found on sea-coasts throughout the world and also on fresh waters. Twenty-seven species on British list, of which sixteen are described below. *Page* 115

Family Alcidæ (Auks, Guillemots, and Puffins). Small or moderate-sized marine birds with short neck ; small, narrow wings with eleven primaries and very short tails of from twelve to eighteen feathers. Their legs are short and placed very far back near the tail and they have only three toes which are connected by webs. Their food consists of fish and crustaceans obtained by diving from the surface and pursuit under water by the aid of their wings. They congregate to breed on islands and cliffs, often in very large colonies, and deposit one, two, or three large oval or pear-shaped eggs on cliff-ledges or in crevices or holes. The young when hatched are covered with dark-coloured down and are dependent on their parents for food until they are fledged. About twenty species confined to the seas of the northern hemisphere. Seven on the British list, of which one, the Great Auk, is extinct and five are described below. *Page* 126

11. ORDER COLUMBIFORMES. Arboreal or terrestrial birds, mostly of moderate size, with eleven primaries in the wings and the legs generally feathered. They feed on seeds, berries, and fruits and are more dependent on water for drinking than most other birds. Unlike other birds they immerse their bills and take continuous draughts instead of sips. Includes three families.

Family Pteroclidæ (Sand-grouse). Terrestrial birds inhabiting open plains or deserts and associating in flocks, with short, stout arched bill ; long, pointed wings ; wedge-shaped tails and very short legs. They lay three eggs, whitish, buff or greenish with brown, reddish or violet markings in a hollow on the ground. About sixteen species found in Africa, southern Europe, western and central Asia, and India. One on the British list described below. *Page* 131

Family Columbidæ (Pigeons and Doves). Arboreal or, sometimes, terrestrial birds, varying considerably in size, with small head and short bill, the basal portion of which is covered with soft skin and the terminal portion hard, arched and somewhat enlarged. The tail is usually rather long, rounded or wedge-shaped, consisting of from twelve to twenty feathers and the feet have three toes in front and one behind. The majority build frail platforms of sticks and the eggs are invariably white and usually two in number. The young when hatched are naked, except for scattered hair-like bits of down. They remain in the nest till fledged and are fed on pigeon's milk, which is the partly-digested food regurgitated from the crops of their parents. Over five hundred species distributed throughout the world, but more than half occur in the islands of the Malay Archipelago and the South Pacific. Five on the British list of which four are described below. *Page* 131

12. ORDER CUCULIFORMES. Small or moderate-sized birds, mostly arboreal, varying considerably in appearance and habits. The feet have four toes of which two are directed forwards and two backwards. Includes two families.

Family Cuculidæ (Cuckoo). Arboreal, or, sometimes, terrestrial birds with bill compressed and somewhat curved at the tip and with no bristles at the base. The wings contain ten primaries and the long, rounded or wedge-shaped tail consists of ten (or eight) feathers. Numerous species occur throughout the world, but the majority are confined to the tropics. The New World species build nests of rude construction and incubate their eggs, but most of the Old World species deposit their eggs in the nests of other birds and leave them to be hatched and their young reared by the foster-parents. In many cases the egg bears a close resemblance to that of the species usually chosen as foster-parent and the young cuckoo, soon after hatching, throws out of the nest the eggs or young of the rightful owner. Four species on the British list of which one is described below. *Page* 138

13. ORDER STRIGIFORMES. Nocturnal, carnivorous birds with large head ; short, curved, hooked bill, and very large eyes both turned forward and surrounded by discs of feathers. The wings are long and rounded, containing eleven primaries ; the tail, usually short, consists of twelve feathers ; and the whole of the plumage is exceptionally soft so that the flight is absolutely noiseless. The legs are comparatively short and usually feathered and the four toes have sharp, curved claws used for seizing the prey : the outer toe can be turned forward or backward. The eggs are oval and pure white and are usually laid in a hollow in a tree, in the old nest of another species, or on the ground. The young are blind when hatched and are covered with down. Includes two families.

Family Tytonidæ (Barn Owls). Species of moderate or large size, buff or greyish above and white below. Bill longer and less curved than in other owls, facial discs more or less triangular, eyes comparatively small and claw of middle toe serrated. Only a few species but distributed throughout the world except New Zealand. One in Britain described below. *Page* 142

Family Strigidæ (Brown Owls). Species varying much in size, mostly with brown plumage, mottled or barred with black, grey, yellow, and white. Many have a tuft of feathers on each side of the head above the ears and the facial discs are more or less round. Many species throughout the world. Nine species on British list of which four are described below. *Page* 144

14. ORDER CAPRIMULGIFORMES. Nocturnal or crepuscular birds of moderate or fairly large size with wide bill surrounded by bristles and soft plumage mottled and pencilled with various shades of brown and rufous, usually with spots or patches of white. Includes five families.

Family Caprimulgidæ (Nightjars). Insectivorous birds of moderate size with flat head, very large eyes, long wings with ten primaries, tail of ten feathers, short legs and feet with three toes before and one behind, the long, middle front toe having a comb-like structure below. They catch crepuscular and nocturnal insects on the wing at dusk or during the night and lay two spotted eggs on the ground without making any nest. Numerous species found throughout the world except New Zealand and the Pacific islands. Four on British list of which one is described below. *Page* 147

15. ORDER APODIFORMES. Small or very small birds spending almost the whole of the day-time in the air and capable of extremely rapid flight. They have exceptionally elongated wings and extremely small legs and feet adapted only

for perching so that they are incapable of running or hopping on the ground. They lay from one to four white eggs. Includes three families.

Family Apodidæ (Swifts). Aerial birds with short, flat, triangular bill, very wide at the gape ; very long wings with ten primaries, of which the first is the longest ; tail of ten feathers, often rigid and pointed ; short legs, often feathered ; and feet in which all four toes point forward or three forward and one inwards. The plumage is hard and mainly dark brown or blue-black, usually with some white patches. Their insect food is obtained entirely on the wing and when they settle they cling to the face of a cliff or the bark of a tree-trunk. In most species the nest is largely composed of a glutinous substance secreted by the salivary glands in which are embedded straws, leaves, or feathers. Numerous species found in all parts of the world except New Zealand. Three on British list of which one is described below.

Page 150

16. ORDER CORACIIFORMES. Birds of diverse form and habits mostly with brilliant plumage and usually with three toes in front and one behind, the front ones generally more or less united at the base. They lay white eggs in holes. Includes nine families.

Family Alcedinidæ (Kingfishers). Birds with large head, frequently crested ; long, stout, straight bill ; short, rounded wings with eleven primaries, of which the first is small ; tail unusually short ; and legs and feet small and weak. Numerous species found throughout the world, but principally in the tropics and especially in New Guinea and the Malay Archipelago. One in Britain described below.

Page 151

Family Meropidæ (Bee-eaters). Birds of small or moderate size with long, slightly curved bill ; wings with eleven primaries of which the first is very short ; rather long tail of twelve feathers and very short legs and toes. The plumage in both sexes is brilliant, commonly exhibiting shades of blue, green, or copper. They are sociable, hawking for insects in the air in flocks and breeding in colonies in holes excavated in sand-banks. Numerous species found in Africa and tropical Asia, one visiting Australia and one southern Europe in summer. The latter on British list and described below.   *Page* 153

Family Coraciidæ (Rollers). Moderate-sized arboreal birds with strong, rather wide, curved, hooked bill ; long, rounded wings with ten primaries ; tail of twelve feathers and legs short. The plumage is generally blue of various shades, or green, often varied with reddish and they are noisy, active birds, frequently uttering harsh, chattering notes and remarkable for their habit of tumbling and rolling over in the air during flight. About twenty species found in Africa and tropical Asia, one visiting Australia in summer and one visiting Europe and northern Asia. The latter, on the British list, is described below.

Page 154

Family Upupidæ (Hoopoes). Moderate-sized arboreal birds with long, slender, slightly curved bill ; broad wings with ten primaries ; a square tail of ten feathers ; short legs and rather long toes. The head bears a crest of long feathers, which is fan-shaped when spread, and the plumage is cinnamon-coloured strikingly barred with black and white. The food consisting of worms and insects is mostly obtained on the ground. Three species in Africa, one of them also extending over most of Asia and Europe, on the British list, and described below.

Page 154

17. ORDER PICIFORMES. A considerable group of birds, almost all arboreal, varying much in appearance but all having two toes turned forward and two turned backward and all laying white eggs. Includes six families.

Family Picidæ (Woodpeckers). Arboreal birds, varying considerably in size, but almost all climb about the trunks and larger boughs of trees in search of insects. They have a large head, very muscular neck, and strong wedge-shaped bill with which they excavate holes in trees and pick off bark in search of wood-boring larvæ. The exceptionally long tongue is often barbed at the tip and is kept moist with a sticky secretion from large salivary glands ; it can be protruded far beyond the bill and by its aid they drag insects from their holes. They have short legs with strong feet and claws and a tail of twelve feathers, generally with stiff, spiny shafts, which helps to support the bird when pressed against a tree-trunk. Numerous species are found in all parts of the world except Madagascar, the eastern Malay islands, New Guinea,

Australia, New Zealand, and the Pacific islands. Four on the British list described below. *Page* 155

18. ORDER PASSERIFORMES. Small or moderate-sized birds whose chief external characteristic is the form of the feet. These have three toes before and one behind always inserted at the same level and usually at least as long as the longest (middle) front toe ; all the toes can be bent downwards to obtain a firm grasp of a twig, or even a wire, so that birds of this order are commonly called ' Perching-birds '. The species pre-eminent as song-birds are all members of this order. Perching-birds construct more or less elaborate nests and their young, when hatched, are naked and helpless, being completely dependent on their parents until they are fledged. The order contains between five and six thousand species, or about half the total number of birds, and they are commonly grouped in about sixty-five families but few of these admit of satisfactory definition.

Family Alaudidæ (Larks). Terrestrial birds, inhabiting open country, cultivated land, pastures, or desert. They are characterized by the fact that the sides of the tarsus are covered with scutes, not with an unbroken lamella, and the claw of the hind toe is straight, sharp and often very long. Their bills vary greatly, in some species being fairly slender and pointed, in others very stout. The plumage is usually brown or sandy in colour making them inconspicuous on the ground, where they run instead of hopping. Most of them rise into the air to sing and the majority rarely or never settle in trees. Their nests are almost always open cup-shaped structures on the ground and their eggs have a whitish ground-colour almost hidden by a profusion of spots and freckles. They are numerous in Africa and Asia, few in Europe and represented by only one or two species in North America and Australia. Eight species on the British list, of which three are described below.
Page 160

Family Hirundinidæ (Swallows). Small, insectivorous birds, which spend most of the daytime hawking about in the air for flying insects. They have flattened, triangular bills, very wide at the base ; very long, pointed wings with only nine visible primaries ; tails of twelve feathers, more or less forked, sometimes with the outer feathers greatly elongated ; very short legs and weak feet with the three-front toes more or less united at the base. They usually breed in colonies, many species using mud in the construction of the nest, others building in holes or excavating burrows. Their eggs are white, sometimes with spots. Numerous species found throughout the world except New Zealand, but those which breed in the higher latitudes of both hemispheres migrate to the tropics or beyond in winter. Four on the British list of which three are described below. *Page* 163

Family Oriolidæ (Orioles). Medium-sized birds with fairly long and straight bill with fine, short bristles at the base, and the nostrils partially covered by a membrane. The wings have ten primarie, of which the first is well-developed, being about half the length of the second and the tail consists of twelve feathers. The sexes are differently coloured, the males usually being largely yellow and the females greenish, while the young have striped breasts. Orioles build hammock-like nests of soft materials, suspended by their edges from two or more forking twigs, and lay from three to five eggs, white or pinkish with purplish or brown spots and streaks. They are found in tropical Africa, Asia, the Malay Archipelago, and Australia, the American birds called ' Orioles ' belonging to a different family. One species visits Europe, including the British Isles, in summer and is described below. *Page* 169

Family Corvidæ (Crows, Jays, etc.). Large perching birds with fairly long, powerful bills and the nostrils covered by bristles directed forward. The wings have ten primaries of which the first is always much shorter than the second. They are omnivorous and probably the most intelligent of birds, and in most countries are among the commonest. Their nests are usually stout, cup-shaped structures of sticks, strengthened with earth and lined with fine twigs, roots, etc. and are usually built in trees but sometimes in holes or on ledges of cliffs. The eggs, usually from three to six in number, are greenish or bluish with dark spots or mottlings. The young resemble their parents in plumage. Members of the family occur in almost all parts of the world. Nine on the British list all described below. *Page* 170

Family Paridæ (Tits). Small insectivorous birds with short, stout, rounded bill and fairly long rounded wings, in which the fourth or fifth primary is the longest and the first is small, sometimes rudimentary. The numerous species are distributed throughout the world except South America, the Pacific islands and New Guinea. Eight species in Britain all described below. *Page* 184

Family Sittidæ (Nuthatches). Small, arboreal birds with rather long, stout, straight bill ; longish wings ; short tails ; short legs and large feet, the toes with large, laterally-compressed claws. They run actively about on tree-trunks or branches indifferently upwards or downwards, clinging to the bark with their strong feet. They feed largely on nuts, but also eat insects and berries. The nuts are wedged into crevices in the bark and split open by hammering with the powerful bill. They are found in Europe, Asia, Australia, and North America. One species in Britain, described below. *Page* 191

Family Certhiidæ (Creepers). Small, insectivorous birds with long, slender bill, usually somewhat curved ; short legs ; toes unequal in length, the outer much longer than the inner, and very strong claws, that of the hind-toe as long as the toe itself. They climb upwards on tree-trunks or rocks probing crevices in search of lurking insects. Though the species are few they are distributed throughout the world except South America, Madagascar, New Zealand, and the Pacific islands. Two on the British list, of which one is described below. *Page* 194

Family Cinclidæ (Dippers). Moderate-sized birds with slender bill, plump body, short wings and tail, and rather long legs. They inhabit rivers and torrents in mountainous regions and, though they show no special structural peculiarities to adapt them to an aquatic life, they swim and dive readily and obtain their food, which consists mainly of the larvæ of aquatic insects, from the bottom of pools in rivers. They build bulky, domed nests of moss with the opening at the side, usually on rocks near waterfalls, and lay five or six pure white eggs. The few species occur in Europe, northern Asia, and western America from Alaska to Argentina. One in Britain, described below.
Page 195

Family Troglodytidæ (Wrens). Small birds with fairly long, slender, compressed bill ; short, rounded wings ; and comparatively long legs. The sexes are alike and the plumage is always some shade of brown, usually more or less barred, and generally lighter below. Numerous species distributed over Europe, Asia, Africa, and North and South America. One in Britain described below. *Page* 196

Family Turdidæ (Thrushes, Chats, etc.). Small or moderate-sized birds with slender or small bills. Their plumage varies greatly but the young in their first plumage are always spotted and different from the adults. Very numerous species distributed throughout the world except some of the Pacific islands. Twenty-four on the British list, of which fourteen are described below. *Page* 199

Family Sylviidæ (Warblers). Small birds, mostly with rather weak, slender bills and comparatively short wings. The majority are sombrely coloured, shades of brown, grey, or greenish predominating in their plumage, and they are mainly insectivorous, though some also eat berries. Very numerous species occur throughout the eastern hemisphere. The birds called ' Warblers ' in America belong to a different family. Thirty-seven on the British list, of which fourteen are described below. *Page* 216

Family Regulidæ (Kinglets). Very small, arboreal birds with thin, slender bill and comparatively long wings, rounded at the tip. Comparatively few species found in Europe, northern Asia, and North and South America. Two on the British list described below. *Page* 228

Family Muscicapidæ (Flycatchers). Small, insectivorous birds with flattened bill, wide at the base and surrounded by bristles. The feathers of young birds are mottled. Many species in the tropical portions of the eastern hemisphere with a few in New Zealand and the Pacific islands and a few visiting Europe and northern Asia in summer. The American ' Flycatchers ' belong to a very different family. Five on the British list, of which three are described below. *Page* 230

Family Prunellidæ (Accentors). Small birds with rather slender, but hard, bill, widened at the base ; rounded wings ; short legs and fairly strong feet. They mostly inhabit mountainous regions and hop about on the ground or over rocks picking up small insects, spiders, and seeds. They build open, cup-shaped nests and lay blue eggs. About a dozen species found in Europe, Asia, and North Africa. Two on the British list, of which one is described below. *Page 233*

Family Motacillidæ (Wagtails and Pipits). Small birds with thin, slender bill ; wings with only nine primaries, and secondaries nearly as long as the primaries ; and long tails of twelve feathers. They are mainly terrestrial, running on the ground instead of hopping, and generally keeping the tail in constant up-and-down motion. Their open, cup-shaped nests are either placed on the ground or in a hole in a bank or wall, and their eggs are spotted. They are mainly found in Europe, Asia, and Africa, only being represented in America, Australia, and New Zealand by a few species of Pipits. Ten on the British list, of which seven and three additional races, here treated as species, are described below. *Page 234*

Family Bombycillidæ (Waxwings). Moderate-sized birds with short, thick bill, wide at the base and slightly hooked at the tip ; long crest ; long wings ; short tail and very short legs. Only three species, one in North America, one in north-eastern Asia, and the third breeding in high latitudes in both hemispheres and wandering south in winter. The last is on the British list and is described below. *Page 241*

Family Laniidæ (Shrikes). Moderate-sized birds with strongly-hooked bill ; rounded wings ; fairly long tail of twelve feathers and rather short legs. Their food consists of large insects, frogs, reptiles, small birds, and small mammals and they have the curious habit of impaling their victims on thorns. Many species occur in Africa and tropical Asia and a few in Europe, northern Asia, and North America. Five on the British list, of which three are described below. *Page 242*

Family Sturnidæ (Starlings). Moderate-sized birds with fairly long, nearly straight bill, with exposed nostrils and with wings containing ten primaries, of which the first is very small. They are found in Europe, Africa, Asia, the Malay Archipelago, and the Pacific islands, one species visiting northern Australia in summer. Two on the British list, described below. *Page 245*

Family Ploceidæ (Weaver-birds and Sparrows). Small birds with finch-like conical bill and wings generally with ten primaries, of which the first is usually small and occasionally absent. The males usually have brilliant plumage and the females are generally duller. They feed almost exclusively on seeds and mostly build large, untidy nests of grasses more or less woven together, domed and sometimes with a projecting, tubular entrance. They frequently build in colonies and most species lay white eggs, though in some they are blue or green and in some they are also spotted or speckled. Numerous species in the warmer parts of the eastern hemisphere, especially Africa, but few in Europe. Three on the British list, of which two are described below. *Page 246*

Family Fringillidæ (Finches and Buntings). Small birds with conical, rather short bill, with the nostrils close to the feathers and either concealed by them or by a membrane ; with wings with only nine primaries, the first being absent ; and with tails of twelve feathers. The sexes almost always differ in plumage, the young being like the females. They are predominantly seed-eaters, but feed their young on insects. They almost all build open, cup-shaped nests and though their eggs vary in ground-colour they are nearly always spotted, speckled or streaked. Very many species distributed throughout the world except Australia and New Zealand, where, however, several European species have been acclimatized. Thirty-three on the British list, of which twenty are described below. *Page 249*

INDEX OF PLATES

INDEX OF PLATES

ORDER COLYMBIFORMES

FAMILY COLYMBIDÆ

THE GREAT NORTHERN DIVER COLYMBUS IMMER
(Plate I)

Bill, with the upper mandible, nearly straight, upwards of four inches in length; head and neck violet-black, with a double gorget white, barred with black; upper parts black spotted with white; under parts white; bill black; irides brown; feet dusky, the membranes whitish. Young very like the next, but distinguishable by their superior size and the direction of the bill. Length thirty-three inches. Eggs dark olive-brown, with a few spots of purplish brown. A winter visitor to the coasts of the British Isles, sometimes visiting inland waters, and occasionally found during summer, especially in northern Scotland, but not proved to breed.

THE name Divers is, on the sea-coast, loosely applied to a variety of sea-birds, including the Grebes, Cormorants, and other birds, which, when pursued, place their safety in diving rather than in flying. In works on natural history the term is, however, employed to designate the genus COLYMBUS, and with great propriety; for, however skilled any of the above birds may be in this mode of progression, the true divers surpass them immeasurably. First among these in size and dignity is the Great Northern Diver, a native of high latitudes in both hemispheres, visiting our waters chiefly during winter. The Northern Diver, or Imber or Ember Goose, is tolerably frequent in British waters. In Scotland it prefers salt-water lochs and sandy bays to the open sea, though occasionally seen some miles from land. It swims deep in the water, but advances rapidly. When in pursuit of prey it sinks beneath the surface without plunge or splash, the head disappearing last, and it traverses perhaps two or three hundred yards of water before it rises again. Montagu says that it propels itself by its feet alone; Audubon, on the contrary, states that it uses the wings under water. The latter author is most probably correct, for it dives more swiftly than the Grebes, and these birds undoubtedly make a vigorous use of their wings. Where shoals of small fish, such as sand-eels and sprats, abound, or where fish even of a much larger size are numerous, the Northern Diver finds a rich harvest. Occasionally while thus engaged it meets its death by dashing into the herring nets, and there getting entangled. A fine specimen was recently shown to me in the island of Islay, which had been thus captured. Though it has never been known to take wing in attempting to elude pursuit, it is often seen flying with strength and rapidity, outstripping even the Grebe, which, in proportion to its size, is furnished with far larger wings than itself.

The adult male, which is a very handsome bird, is of rare occurrence, most of those which visit our shores being young birds.

The nest is usually placed near the edge of a reedy lake or large river, having a well-beaten track leading to it from the water's edge. This is formed by the bird in its clumsy effort to walk, a feat which it only performs on such occasions. The nest itself is bulky, and is formed of the vegetable substances found in the immediate vicinity, such as grasses and other herbaceous plants. It contains two, and sometimes three, eggs. The young are able to swim and dive very soon after they are hatched, and are fed for about a fortnight by their parents, at the expiration of which time they have to hunt for themselves.

THE BLACK-THROATED DIVER COLYMBUS ARCTICUS
(Plate I)

Bill slightly curved upwards, with the middle of the lower mandible equal in width to the base, exceeding three inches in length ; head ash-grey ; throat and front of the neck black, lustrous with violet and green ; beneath the throat a narrow band streaked with white and black ; sides and front of the neck streaked with white and black ; back black, with a longitudinal patch of white and black bars on the upper part ; scapulars with twelve or thirteen transverse white bars ; bill dusky ; iris brown ; feet dusky, with whitish membranes. Young birds have the head and back of the neck greyer and the upper plumage dark brown, edged with bluish ash ; under plumage white ; cheeks white, spotted with ash ; upper mandible ash-grey, lower dull white. Length twenty-four to twenty-eight inches. Eggs dark olive-brown, spotted with purplish brown. Breeds in northern and western Scotland and the Outer Hebrides ; also a winter visitor to the coasts of all parts of the British Isles.

THIS Diver differs from the preceding species principally in being of inferior size. The predominant tints of the plumage are the same, and the habits of the two are so similar that a separate description is unnecessary. The present species is, however, far less common, though it breeds in the Outer Hebrides and in Scotland, and migrates southward in winter. It lays two eggs, near the edge of a fresh-water loch ; and Mr. Selby observed that a visible track from the water to the eggs was made by the female, whose progress upon land is effected by shuffling along upon her belly, propelled by her legs behind. In the breeding season the old birds are often seen on the wing, at which time also they have a peculiar and loud cry, which has been compared to the voice of a human being in distress.

THE RED-THROATED DIVER COLYMBUS SEPTENTRIONALIS
(Plate I)

Bill slightly curved upwards, with the edges of both mandibles much incurved, not exceeding three inches in length ; head, throat, and sides of the neck, mouse-

colour ; crown spotted with black ; neck both above and below marked with white and black lines ; on the front of the neck a large orange-coloured patch ; back dusky brown ; lower parts white. Young birds—*upper plumage mouse-colour, darker on the back, where it is marked by longitudinal white lines ; wings dusky ; feathers on the flanks dusky, some of them edged with white ; all the under plumage pure white. Length twenty-six inches. Eggs chestnut-brown, spotted with darker brown. Breeds in northern and western Scotland, the Shetlands, Orkneys, and Hebrides, and in Donegal ; also a winter visitor to the coasts of the British Isles generally.*

THE name 'Loon', given in some districts to the Crested Grebe, is elsewhere given to the Red-throated Diver. The term is an old one, for our countrymen, Ray and Willughby, quoting yet more ancient authorities, describe the Northern Diver under the name of 'Loon', and the Black-throated Diver under that of 'Lumme', the latter being the name of the bird in Iceland and Norway, and the former probably an English corruption of the same word, which in the original signifies 'lame'.

On no part of our coast must we expect to hear this bird popularly called by the name of 'Red-throated', for, though common on many parts of the coast, almost all the specimens observed are young birds of the year, which have the throat pure white. Several were brought to me by the seaside gunners on the coast of Norfolk. In May birds with red throats are noticed. A writer in the *Zoologist* [1] says that they are very numerous in winter off the coast of the Isle of Wight, passing and repassing in small flocks and in two lines about a mile apart. Of the hundreds which fell under his notice one only had a red throat, and this was captured under singular circumstances. On April 24, 1839, some fishermen observed an object floating which they imagined was a keg of spirits, but which proved to be a large fish of the kind known as the Fishing Frog, or Angler. On hauling it on board with their boathooks, the fishermen discovered that the animal had nearly choked himself by swallowing, tail foremost, an adult Red-throated Diver. The head of the bird protruded from the throat into the mouth of the captor, and, strange to say, it had not only survived its imprisonment, but was unhurt. It was extricated and presented to the Zoological Gardens, where it lived for six months.

This species, like the rest of the genus, obtains its food by diving ; when pursued it rarely tries to escape by taking wing, though it has the power of flying with great rapidity. During the breeding season especially, it often flies about over the water with its long neck out-stretched, and uttering a wailing scream.

I am informed by a friend, that while fishing in a boat in calm water off the coast of North Devon, he has many times seen Divers pass through the water, at a considerable depth below, propelling themselves by a free and active use of their wings.

From October to May only these Divers frequent the English coast. Towards the end of spring they withdraw northwards and build their nests, of coarse grass and other herbs, close to the edge of a fresh-water

[1] Vol. iii. p. 974.

loch. They lay two eggs, and the male takes his turn in the office of incubation.

ORDER PODICIPIFORMES

FAMILY PODICIPIDÆ

THE GREAT CRESTED GREBE PÓDICEPS CRISTÁTUS (*Plate II*)

Bill longer than the head, reddish, the tip white ; distance from the nostril to the tip seventeen or eighteen lines ; cheeks white ; crest and ruff dark brown and chestnut ; upper plumage dark brown ; secondaries white ; breast and under parts silky white ; irides red ; feet dull green. Female—*crest and ruff less conspicuous, colours generally less bright.* Young birds *have neither crest nor ruff. Length twenty-one inches. Eggs white. A resident in England, Wales, Ireland, and southern and central Scotland.*

THE Great Crested Grebe is thus described by Sir Thomas Browne, under the name of Loon : ' A handsome and specious fowl, cristated, and with divided fin-feet placed very backward. They come about April, and breed in the broad waters ; so making their nest in the water, that their eggs are seldom dry while they are set on.'

The movements of this bird in the water are most graceful ; in swimming it vies with the Swan, and it is a skilful diver. As seen perched up in a museum its form is ungainly, but in its native element it might serve as the standard of perfection among water birds. The legs, compressed so as to present a sharp edge, cut the water with a minimum of resistance ; the webbed feet are placed so far backwards that they fulfil at once the office of propellers and rudder ; the body is conical and covered with satiny plumage, which throws off water as perfectly as the fur of the otter ; the long neck tapers to exceedingly narrow dimensions and terminates in a small head produced into a slender bill. The conformation of the greyhound is not better adapted for fleet running than that of the Grebe for rapid diving. The chase, I need scarcely add, consists of fish ; but the Loon will feed on frogs, tadpoles, and any other small animals which fall in its way. It frequents fresh water during the summer months, but on the approach of winter repairs to the sea, not, it would seem, from any desire of varying its food, but to avoid being frozen up. It builds its nest among rushes or decaying weeds, but little above the level of the water, and lays four eggs, the male assisting his partner in the office of incubation.

The young can dive and swim immediately that they are hatched ; but if the mother be suddenly alarmed while they are with her, she takes them under her wing and dives with them.

The name Loon is supposed to be a corruption of the Finnish

designation, Leomme or Lem, ' lame ', given to several of the *Colymbidæ* on account of the awkwardness with which they advance on land.

The Loon rarely flies, except at the period of migration, when it passes swiftly through the air, with neck and feet extended to their full length.

THE RED-NECKED GREBE PÓDICEPS GRISEÍGENA (*Plate II*)

Bill as long as the head, black, yellow at the base ; distance from the nostrils to the tip eleven lines ; crest very short ; head and crest lustrous black ; cheeks and throat mouse-colour ; a black band along the nape ; breast bright rust-red ; lower parts white ; flanks spotted with dusky ; feet black, greenish yellow beneath. Young birds have the head, neck, and back dusky ; throat, cheeks, breast, belly, and abdomen, silky white ; sides of the breast spotted with grey. Length sixteen inches. Eggs dirty greenish white. A winter visitor, chiefly to the east coast of England.

THE Red-necked Grebe is smaller than the Loon, from which it differs also in wanting the elongated crest, in having a more robust bill in proportion to its size, and is further distinguished by the grey hue of its cheeks, on account of which last character it is known in France under the name of *Grèbe Jou-gris*. It is a native of the north-eastern parts of Europe, and is fairly common along the eastern coast of Great Britain from autumn to spring. In habits it differs little from the last described species, but is less common, occurring both in fresh-water lakes and along the sea-coast.

THE SLAVONIAN GREBE PÓDICEPS AURITUS (*Plate II*)

Bill strong, shorter than the head, compressed throughout its whole length, black. with the tip red ; eyes with a double iris, the inner yellow, the outer red ; distance from the nostrils to the tip of the bill six or seven lines ; head and bushy ruff glossy black ; two horn-like crests orange-red ; lore, neck, and breast, bright chestnut ; upper plumage dusky ; secondaries and under parts white. Young—crest and ruff wanting ; upper plumage and flanks dusky ash, under parts white ; irides white, surrounded by red. Eggs dirty white. Breeds in northern Scotland ; a winter visitor to other parts of the British Isles.

THE Slavonian, or Horned Grebe, approaches so closely in habits to the two preceding species that it is unnecessary to say more than that it inhabits the northern parts of America and Europe. It lays from three to seven eggs, and the male assists in the office of incubation.

THE BLACK-NECKED GREBE PÓDICEPS NIGRICOLLIS
(*Plate II*)

Bill short, rather broad at base, pointed and compressed at tip, upper mandible slightly, and lower sharply, tilted upwards, blue-grey with whitish tip ; eyes with inner ring of iris silvery and outer orange-pink ; head and ruff, chin and throat, jet black ; on sides of head behind eye tufts of long silky golden-chestnut feathers ; neck and upper plumage black ; flanks chestnut and black ; secondaries and under parts white. Eggs white. Breeds locally in England, Scotland, and Ireland ; also a winter visitor.

THE Black-necked, or Eared Grebe, is slightly smaller than the preceding, and in all states of plumage can be distinguished by its slender tip-tilted bill. In habits it is somewhat intermediate between the larger Grebes and the Dabchick, like the latter being secretive in the breeding season, frequenting reedy lakes and ponds. It sometimes nests in large colonies.

THE LITTLE GREBE OR DABCHICK PÓDICEPS FLUVIÁTILIS
(Plate XIII)

Bill very short, shining, compressed ; no crest or ruff ; distance from nostrils to tip of the bill five lines ; tarsus with a double row of serratures behind ; head black ; cheeks bright chestnut ; breast and flanks dusky, mottled with white ; upper parts dark brown, tinged with green ; primaries ash-brown ; secondaries white at the base and on the inner web, under parts dusky ash, tinged on the thighs with reddish ; bill black, whitish at the tip and base of the lower mandible ; irides reddish brown ; feet externally greenish brown, beneath flesh-colour. Young birds are ash-brown above, slightly tinged with red ; breast and flanks reddish white ; belly pure white ; bill brown and yellowish ash. Length nearly ten inches. Eggs dirty white. Resident throughout the British Isles, except the Shetlands.

THE Lesser Grebe, or, as it is more commonly called, the Dabchick, frequents rivers, ponds, and lakes, in all parts of the country, rarely flying, and still more rarely coming to land.

Rambling by the side of a sluggish river, the sides of which are lined with reeds or bulrushes, one may often descry, paddling about with undecided motion, what appears to be a miniature Duck no longer than a Blackbird. It does not, like the Moor-hen, swim with a jerking movement, nor when alarmed does it half swim and half fly in a direct line for the nearest bank of weeds. If you are unobserved, it swims steadily for a short distance, then suddenly disappears, making no splash or noise, but slipping into the water as if its body were lubricated. It is diving for its foods, which consist of water insects, molluscs, small fish, and worms. As suddenly as it dives so suddenly does it reappear, most likely not far from the spot where you first observed it :

> A di-dapper peering through a wave,
> Who, being looked on, ducks as quickly in.
>
> SHAKESPEARE.

Another short swim and it dives again ; and so it goes on, the time spent under the water being far in excess of that employed in taking breath. Advance openly or make a noise, it wastes no time in idle examinations or surmises of your intentions, but slips down as before, not, however, to reappear in the same neighbourhood. Its motives are different : it now seeks not food, but safety, and this it finds first by diving, and then by propelling itself by its wings under water in some direction which you cannot possibly divine ; for it by no means follows that it will pursue the course to which its bill pointed when it went down. It can alter its line of flight beneath the water as readily as a swallow can change its course of flight through the air. But wherever it may reappear, its stay is now instantaneous ; a trout rising at a fly is not more expeditious. You may even fail to detect it at all. It may have ensconced itself among weeds, or it may be burrowing in some subaqueous hole. That it has the power of remaining a long while submerged, I have no doubt. There is in the parish of Stamford, Dingley, Berkshire, a large and beautiful spring of water, clear as crystal, the source of one of the tributaries of the Thames. I was once bending over the bank of this spring, with a friend, watching the water, some five or six feet down, as it issued from a pipe-like orifice and stirred the sand around like the bubbling of a cauldron, when there suddenly passed between us and the object we were examining a form so strange that we were at first doubtful to what class of animals we should refer it. In reality, it was a Dabchick, which, alarmed probably by the noise of our conversation, was making for a place of safety. As it passed within two or three feet of our faces, we could distinctly see that it propelled itself by its wings ; but it appeared not to have observed us, for it kept on in a direct course towards the head of the spring. We searched long in the hope of discovering it again, but failed ; and as there were no weeds among which it could possibly hide above water, and we could examine the bottom of the spring almost as thoroughly as if it contained air only, we could but conclude that our apparition had taken refuge in a hole under the bank.

Early in spring, when Dabchicks leave the small streams and watercourses for broader pieces of water, they have been observed to fly ; and during the building season also they have been seen circling round in the air near the locality of their intended nest. The nest itself is constructed of weeds of all kinds, forming a thick mass raised but a few inches above the surface of the water, and invariably far enough from the bank to be inaccessible except by wading. The Dabchick lays five or six long-shaped eggs, pointed at either end, of a chalky white colour. These the bird, when she leaves the nest, covers with weeds for the purpose of concealment, and on her return continues the work of incubation without removing the covering, so that the eggs soon lose their white hue, and before the period of hatching have become very dirty. The young birds can swim and dive immediately on leaving the egg.

ORDER PROCELLARIIFORMES

FAMILY PROCELLARIIDÆ

THE FULMAR PETREL FULMARUS GLACIALIS (*Plate III*)

Head, neck, under plumage, and tail, white ; wings bluish ash, the primaries brownish grey ; beak, irides, and feet, yellow. Young of the year *grey tinged with brown, mottled on the back with deeper brown ; bill and feet yellowish ash. Length nineteen inches. Eggs white. An oceanic bird, which breeds on many parts of the coasts of the British Isles.*

THE Fulmar is essentially a sea-bird, and never comes to land except in the breeding season, when it builds its nest of herbage on the grassy shelves of the highest cliffs, and lays a single egg, if which be taken, it lays no more. The young birds are fed with oil by the parents, and on being molested spurt out through the throat and open mouth the same fluid, which, being of a rank smell, infects not only the nest, but the whole neighbourhood. The young birds, which are taken early in August, are boiled, and made to furnish a large quantity of fat, which is skimmed off and preserved for winter use. The old birds are considered great dainties.

In the Arctic regions the Fulmar is well known for its assiduity in attending on whale ships, keeping an eager watch for anything thrown over ; and when the operation of cutting up a whale is going on, helping itself most greedily to stray pieces of offal, and venturing so near as to be easily knocked down by a boathook or to be taken by hand.

In the British Isles the only breeding-station until 1878 was St. Kilda, where many thousands breed annually. In the year mentioned they began breeding in the Shetlands on the island of Foula. Since that time they have gradually spread southwards, reaching the Orkneys in 1900 and the northern mainland of Scotland two years later. In 1911 they bred on the west coast of Ireland and in 1922 at Flamborough Head, Yorkshire.

THE MANX SHEARWATER PUFFINUS PUFFINUS (*Plate III*)

Bill an inch and a half long ; tail rounded ; upper plumage brownish black, lustrous ; under, white ; sides of the neck barred with grey ; sides spotted with grey. Length fourteen inches. Eggs nearly round ; pure white. Breeds on islands off the west coast of Britain from Scilly Islands to Shetland and round Ireland.

THAT a bird whose generic name is *Puffinus* should sometimes be called a ' Puffin ' is not surprising ; and the reader who meets with the name

in books should satisfy himself whether the subject of his study be an
Auk or a Shearwater, before he admits as facts any statements about
the ' Puffin ' which may fall in his way.　Yarrell, for instance, gives
the name of Puffin to the bird described under the name of *Fratercula
Arctica*, while by Montagu that bird is described under the name of
' Coulterneb ', ' Puffin ' being given as a synonym for the Shearwater.
Off Cornwall it is called *skiddeu* and *brew*.

The Shearwater is so called from its mode of flight, in which it
' shears ' or skims the water ; and its distinctive name, Manx, it owes
to its having been formerly very abundant in the Calf [1] of Man, a
small island lying south of the Isle of Man.

The Manx Shearwater is, during the greater portion of the year,
an ocean-bird, and only ventures on shore during the breeding season.
It then repairs to some island, or portion of the coast little frequented
by man, and in society with other birds of the same species there takes
up its summer quarters.　A sandy or light earthy soil, scantily furnished
with vegetation, is preferred to any other station.　Its nest is a hole
in the ground, either the deserted burrow of a rabbit or a tunnel
excavated by itself, or less frequently it lays its one egg in the crevice
of a rock.　During the day Shearwaters, for the most part, remain
concealed in their holes, and lie so close that they will suffer themselves
to be dug out with a spade and make no attempt to escape.　Towards
evening they quit their hiding-places, and paddle or fly out to sea in
quest of food.　This consists of small fish and other marine animals
which swim near the surface, and are caught by the birds either
while they are floating or ' shearing ' the water.　No nest ever contains
more than one egg, but that one and the chick which it produces are
objects of the greatest solicitude.

Unfortunately for the poor Shearwaters, their young, though fed
on half-digested fish oil, are delicate eating ; consequently, some of
the stations of these birds have been quite depopulated, and in others
their numbers have been greatly thinned.

Willughby tells us that in his time ' Puffins ' were very numerous
in the Calf of Man, and that fully fledged young birds, taken from the
nests, were sold at the rate of ninepence a dozen.　He adds, that in
order to keep an accurate reckoning of the number taken, it was
customary to cut off, and retain, one of each bird's legs.　The consequence was that the state in which the birds were sent to market
was supposed to be their natural condition, and the Puffin was popularly believed to be a ' monopod ' (one-footed bird).

This station is now deserted ; but colonies still exist in Annet,
one of the Scilly Islands, on the coast of Wales, and in the Hebrides,
Orkneys, and Shetlands.　In the Scilly Islands the Shearwater is called
a Crew, from the harsh note uttered by the bird when its burrow is
invaded ; in the north, a Lyrie or Scrabe.

---

[1] ' Calf ', on many parts of the coast, is a name given to the smaller of two rocks
in proximity, of which the larger is called the ' Cow '.

THE GREAT SHEARWATER PUFFINUS GRAVIS (*Plate XXX*)

Bill two inches long ; tail pointed ; upper plumage dusky ; under, white. Length eighteen inches. An oceanic bird visiting the Atlantic coasts of the British Isles in summer and autumn, and sometimes also met with off the coast of Yorkshire.

THE only known breeding-place of the Great Shearwater is Tristan da Cunha in the South Atlantic. In the northern summer it ranges into the north Atlantic, sometimes congregating in large flocks where food is plentiful. In flight and habits it resembles the Manx Shearwater but, as its name implies, is considerably larger.

THE SOOTY SHEARWATER PUFFINUS GRISEUS (*Plate LXVII*)

Bill an inch and three-quarters long ; upper plumage sooty brown ; under, grey-brown ; under wing-coverts greyish white. Length sixteen inches. An oceanic bird occurring off British coasts chiefly in autumn.

THE Sooty Shearwater breeds on numerous islands in the southern hemisphere and during the southern winter migrates to the oceans of the northern hemisphere. Its habits are similar to those of other Shearwaters with which it frequently associates.

FAMILY HYDROBATIDÆ

THE STORM PETREL HYDROBATES PELÁGICUS (*Plate III*)

General plumage sooty-black, browner below ; rump white ; tail even at the extremity ; legs moderate ; membranes black. Length scarcely six inches. Egg white, usually with fine specks of red-brown at the large end. Frequents British seas throughout the year, breeding on islands off the west coast of Britain from the Scilly Islands to the Shetlands, and off the north and west coasts of Ireland.

UNDER the name of ' Mother Carey's Chickens ' the Petrels must be known to all readers of voyages. According to belief popular in the forecastle, these birds are invisible during calm or bright weather ; but when the sky lowers, and a storm is impending, suddenly, no one knows whence, forth come these ill-omened heralds of the tempest, inspiring more terror than would be caused even by the hurricane which they are supposed to commence. In reality, the Petrels are scarcely birds of the day ; they love to hide themselves in holes and behind stones. It is not, therefore, surprising that when the sea is calm, and the sun bright, they lurk in their hiding-places, if near enough to land ; or, if on the open ocean, lie asleep on the surface of the water, unnoticed, because still and of small size. An overcast sky, however, awakes them as twilight would, and they leave their hiding-places, or rise from their watery bed, not because a storm is impending, but because the cloud which accompanies the storm brings them the desired gloom. When in motion they are more conspicuous than when at rest, and they follow the wake of a ship for the same reason that other sea-fowl do, for the sake of the offal thrown overboard. They will sometimes accompany a ship for days, showing that they have untiring power of wing, and to all but the superstitious greatly relieving the monotony of the voyage.

The Petrel builds its nest, a rude structure of weeds and rubbish, either in the hole of a cliff or under stones on the beach, and lays a single egg. It rarely comes abroad by day, and if disturbed ejects from its mouth an oily matter, after the manner of the Fulmar. Towards evening it comes forth from its stronghold, and skims the sea in quest of food, which consists of floating animal matter of all kinds. Its name, Petrel, or Little Peter, is derived from its habit of occasionally skimming along so close to the surface of the sea as to dip its feet in the water, and present the appearance of walking ; but its ordinary flight is very like that of the Swallow.

The Storm Petrel breeds in the Orkney, Shetland, and Scilly Islands, and a few on the Welsh coast, also in the Channel Islands. It is frequently seen in the Atlantic and Mediterranean, and is some-times driven inshore or even inland during severe weather.

Its note is only heard during the season of incubation, when its retreat is often betrayed by a low twittering.

Storm Petrels are gregarious birds ; they breed in colonies, and skim the sea in small flocks.

THE FORK-TAILED PETREL OCEANODROMA LEUCORRHOA
(Plate III)

General plumage like the last ; tail forked ; legs moderate ; membrane dusky. Length seven and a quarter inches. Eggs white, marked with small rusty spots. Frequents British seas throughout the year, breeding in St. Kilda and other remote Hebridean islands and occasionally on islets off the west coast of Ireland.

THE Fork-tailed Petrel does not differ materially in habits from the other species. It ranges all over the North Atlantic and is perhaps more frequently driven inshore or inland in the British Isles than the Storm Petrel.

ORDER PELECANIFORMES

FAMILY SULIDÆ

THE GANNET sula bassana (*Plate VIII*)

Crown buff-yellow ; general plumage milk-white ; quills black ; bill bluish grey at the base, white at the tip ; orbits pale blue ; membrane prolonged from the gape and that under the throat dusky blue ; irides yellow ; feet striped with green, the membranes dusky ; claws white. Birds of the first year, *general plumage dusky brown, beneath greyish. In the* second year, *greyish black above, marked with numerous triangular white spots, whitish below. Length three feet. Eggs dull greenish white. Resident in British seas, breeding at about a dozen localities round the coasts.*

It would not be difficult to compile, from various sources, a description of the Gannet and its habits which would fill more pages than my readers, perhaps, would care to peruse. To avoid this contingency, I will limit myself to a statement of my own personal acquaintance with the bird and its ways, and a transcript of notes kindly furnished me by a friend who visited the Bass Rock, one of its favourite haunts in the breeding season.

Extract from my own Journal.—' August 27th. I lay for a long time to-day on the thick herbage which crowns the splendid cliffs, " the Gobbins ", near the entrance of Belfast Lough, watching through a telescope the proceedings of some Gannets, or Solan Geese. This bird, which is allied to the Pelicans rather than the Geese, is of a large size, much bigger than a Gull, from which, also, it may be distinguished at a distance by its greater length of neck, the intense whiteness of its plumage, and the black tip of its wide-spreading wings. But apart from all these distinguishing characters, its mode of fishing is, by itself, sufficient to mark it. In flight it is eminently wandering ; it circles round and round, or describes a figure of eight, at a varying elevation above the water, in quest of herrings, pilchards, or other fish whose habit is to swim near the surface. When it has discovered a prey, it suddenly arrests its flight, partially closes its wings, and descends head foremost with a force sufficient to make a *jet d'eau* visible two or three miles off, and to carry itself many feet downwards. When successful, it brings its prize to the surface, and devours it without troubling itself about mastication. If unsuccessful, it rises immediately, and resumes its hunting. It is sometimes seen swimming, perhaps to rest itself, for I did not observe that it ever dived on these occasions. My companion told me that the fishermen on the coast of Ireland say that, if chased by a boat when seen swimming, it becomes so terrified as to be unable to rise. The real reason may be that it is gorged with food. He was once in a boat on the Lough, when, a

Gannet being seen a long way ahead, it was determined to give chase, and ascertain whether the statement was correct. As the boat drew near, the Gannet endeavoured to escape by swimming ; but made no attempt either to dive or to use its wings. After a pretty long chase, the bowman secured it, in spite of a very severe bite which it inflicted on his hand, and carried it home in triumph. It did not appear to have received any injury, and when released, in the evening of the same day, swam out to sea with great composure. A fisherman in Islay told me that in some parts of Scotland a singular method of catching Gannets is adopted. A herring is fastened to a board and sunk a few feet deep in the sea. The sharp eye of the Gannet detects the fish, and the bird, first raising itself to an elevation which experience or instinct has taught it to be sufficient to carry it down to the requisite depth, pounces on the fish, and in the effort penetrates the board to which the fish is attached. Being thus held fast by the beak, and unable to extricate itself, it is drowned. Gannets are frequently caught in the herring-nets, at various depths below the surface. Diving after the fish, they become entangled in the nets, and are thus captured in a trap not intended for them. They perform good service to fishermen, by indicating at a great distance the exact position of the shoals of fish.'

Gannets breed in great numbers on several parts of our rocky coast ; from the extreme north to south-western Ireland and Grass-holm, off the coast of Pembrokeshire. On the east coast their principal breeding place is the Bass Rock, in the Firth of Forth. In circumference the island is about a mile ; on the northern side it rises to an elevation of eight hundred feet, whilst towards the south it shelves almost down to the sea. The isolated position of this rock, and the difficulty of landing on it, have rendered it a fit retreat for sea-fowl of various kinds. The discharge of a gun causes the whole of the colony to take wing ; and as they rise into the air, the eye of the spectator is dazzled by the mazy intercrossings of white wings, the ear bewildered by the discord of confused screamings. A visit paid at sunrise, when flocks of various kinds are wheeling about in all directions, will more than reward the early riser for his activity, for Scotland scarcely offers a more interesting sight. Of all the numerous birds which frequent the rock, the Solan Goose is the most abundant.

' The only parts of the island where they can be approached are on the south and west sides. They sit lazily and stupidly on and about their nests, which are composed of a mass of weeds and grass, and will suffer themselves to be stroked, patted, or knocked on the head, as the case may be, with a most philosophical gravity.'

The Gannet lays but one egg ; and the young bird is nourished on semi-liquid food disgorged by the parent. On its first exclusion from the egg its skin is naked, and of a bluish black hue, but is soon covered with a white down. Through this the true feathers appear, which are black, the adult plumage being pure white.

FAMILY PHALACROCORACIDÆ

THE CORMORANT PHALACRÓCORAX CARBO (*Plate VII*)

Tail of fourteen feathers. Winter—*head, neck, and all the under parts, black, with green reflections ; close to the base of the bill a broad white gorget ; on the neck a few faint whitish lines ; feathers of the back and wings bronze- colour bordered with black ; primaries and tail black ; beak dusky ; orbits greenish yellow ; irides green ; feet black.* Summer—*feathers of the head elongated, forming a crest ; on the head and neck numerous long silky white feathers ; on the thighs a patch of pure white.* Young birds *brown and grey, the gorget greyish white.* Length three feet. Eggs greenish white, chalky. Resident on British coasts and commonly visiting inland waters.*

PHALACRÓCORAX, the modern systematic name of the genus Cormorant, is given by Willughby as a synonym of the Coot, and with much propriety, for translated into English it means ' Bald Crow '. Applied to the Cormorant, it must be considered as descriptive of the semblance of baldness produced by the white feathers of the head during the breeding season. The Cormorant Willughby describes under the name of *Corvus aquaticus*, or Water Raven. The English name, ' Corvorant ', is clearly *Corvus vorans*, a voracious Raven ; and ' Cor- morant ' perhaps a corruption of *Corvus marinus*, Sea Raven.

Seaside visitors are pretty sure of seeing more than one specimen of this bird, if they care to look for them, for the Cormorant frequents all parts of the coast as well as lakes and rivers, and does not leave us at any period of the year. Often we may see two or three of these birds flying along together at a slight distance above the surface of the sea, distinguished by their black hue, long outstretched neck, and rapid waving of the wings. They fly swiftly in a straight line, and seem to be kept from dipping into the water by making ahead at full speed. Occasionally, while engaged in a boating expedition, we may encounter a party of three or four occupied in fishing. They are shy, and will not allow a near approach, but even at a distance they may be dis- tinguished by their large size, sooty hue, long necks, and hooked beaks. They sit low in the water, often dipping their heads below the surface, and in this posture advancing, in order that their search for food may not be impeded by the ripple of the water. A sheltered bay in which shoals of small fish abound is a choice resort, and here they make no long continuous stay in the swimming attitude, but suddenly and frequently dive, remaining below a longer or shorter time, according to the depth which they have to descend in order to secure their prey, but when successful, occupying but a very brief space of time in swallowing it. Not infrequently they may be discerned from the shore similarly occupied, floating or diving in the midst of the very breakers. Sometimes, but rarely, one settles on a rail or stump of a tree close to the water in a tidal river. The capture of fish is still its object, and it is quite as expert in securing its prey from such a station as when roving at large on the open sea.

All along our coast there is at various intervals a rock popularly distinguished in the neighbourhood by the name of ' Shag rock '. Such a rock is generally low, isolated, and situated at a safe distance from land ; or, if near the shore, is close to the base of a steep cliff. Hither the Cormorants, when their hunger is appeased, repair for the threefold purpose of resting, digesting their food, and drying their wings. The process of digestion is soon completed, but the time consumed in drying their thoroughly drenched wings depends on the amount of sunshine and air moving. Of these, whatever they may be, they know how to avail themselves to perfection. They station themselves on the highest ridge of the rock, wide apart, and in a row, so as not to screen one another, raise their bodies to their full height, and spread their wings to their utmost extent. No laundress is more cunning in the exercise of her vocation. Indeed, they can hardly fail to recall the idea of so many pairs of black trousers hung out to be aired.

Cormorants do not confine their fishing expeditions to the sea, but frequently ascend tidal rivers, and follow the course of streams which communicate with fish-ponds and lakes, where they commit great havoc ; for the quantity of fish which they devour at a meal is very great.

Most people are familiar with a representation of a fishery with the help of Cormorants conducted by the Chinese ; but it is not so generally known that a similar method once was practised in England. Willughby, quoting Faber's *Annotations on the Animals of Recchus*, says : ' It is the custom in England to train Cormorants to catch fish. While conveying the birds to the fishing-ground the fishermen keep the heads and eyes of the birds covered to prevent them from being alarmed. When they have reached the rivers, they take off the hoods, and having first tied a leather strap loosely round the lower part of the neck, that the birds may be unable to swallow down what fishes they catch, throw them into the water. They immediately set to work and pursue the fish beneath them with marvellous rapidity. When they have caught one they rise to the surface, and, having first pinched it with their beaks, swallow it as far as the strap permits, and renew the chase until they have caught from five to six each. On being called to return to their master's fist, they obey with alacrity, and bring up, one by one, the fish they have swallowed, injured no farther than that they are slightly crushed. The fishing being brought to an end, the birds are removed from the neighbourhood of the water, the strap is untied, and a few of the captured fish, thrown to them as their share of the booty, are dexterously caught before they touch the ground.'

THE SHAG PHALACRÓCORAX ARISTOTELIS (*Plate VII*)

Tail graduated, of twelve feathers. In winter, *general plumage deep greenish black ; feathers of the back glossy with black borders ; orbits and pouch greenish yellow ; bill dusky ; irides green ; feet black. In* summer, *head crested.* Young birds *greenish brown above ; light grey below. Length twenty-eight inches. Eggs greenish blue, chalky. Resident on British coasts, chiefly in the vicinity of cliffs or rocks.*

EXCEPT in the smaller size and differences of plumage mentioned above, there is little to distinguish the Shag from the Cormorant. Both, too, are of common occurrence, and often frequent the same localities ; except that the Shag is more disposed to be gregarious : it does not, however, commonly resort to tidal rivers, and is still more rarely found on inland lakes ; its food and method of obtaining it are precisely similar, so that a description of one bird will suit the other almost equally well. The Shag is called sometimes the Green Cormorant, from the tint of its plumage ; but this name is not in common use. In Scotland a common name for it is Scart, applied also to the Great Cormorant.

ORDER CICONIIFORMES

FAMILY ARDEIDÆ

THE HERON ÁRDEA CINÉREA (Plate V)

A crest of elongated bluish black feathers at the back of the head ; similar feathers of a lustrous white hanging from the lower part of the neck ; scapulars similar, silver-grey ; forehead, neck, middle of the belly, edge of the wings, and thighs, pure white ; back of the head, sides of the breast, and flanks, deep black ; front of the neck streaked with grey ; upper plumage bluish grey ; beak deep yellow ; irides yellow ; orbits naked, livid ; feet brown, red above ; middle toe, claw included, much shorter than the tarsus. In young birds the long feathers are absent ; head and neck ash-coloured ; upper plumage tinged with brown ; lower, spotted with black. Length three feet two inches. Eggs uniform sea-green. Resident throughout the British Isles, except the Shetlands ; also a winter visitor.

THE Heron, though a large bird, measuring three feet in length from the point of the beak to the extremity of the tail, and four feet and a half in breadth from the tip of one wing to the other, weighs but three pounds and a half. Consequently, though not formed for rapid flight, or endued with great activity of wing, its body presents so large a surface to the air, that it can support itself aloft with but a slight exertion. It is thus enabled, without fatigue, to soar almost into the regions assigned to the Eagle and Vulture ; and when pursued by its natural enemies, the Falcons, to whom it would fall an easy prey on account of the largeness of the mark which its body would present to their downward swoop if it could only skim the plains, it is enabled to vie with them in rising into the air, and thus often eludes them.

The Heron, though it neither swims nor dives, is, nevertheless, a fisher, and a successful one, but a fisher in rivers and shallow waters only, to human anglers a very pattern of patience and resignation. Up to its knees in water, motionless as a stone, with the neck slightly stretched out, and the eye steadily fixed, but wide awake to the motion of anything that has life, the Heron may be seen in the ford of a river, the margin of a lake, in a seaside pool, or on the bank of an estuary, a faultless subject for the photographer. Suddenly the head is shot forward with unerring aim ; a small fish is captured, crushed to death, and swallowed head foremost ; an eel of some size requires different treatment, and is worth the trouble of bringing to land, that it may be beaten to death on the shingle ; a large fish is impaled with its dagger-like beak, and, if worth the labour, is carried off to a safe retreat, to be devoured at leisure. If observers are to be credited, and there is no reason why they should not, a full-grown Heron can thus dispose of a fish that exceeds its own weight. A frog is swallowed whole ; a water rat has its skull split before it discovers its enemy, and speedily is undergoing the process of digestion. Shrimps, small crabs, newts, water beetles, all is fish that comes to its comprehensive net ; but if, with all its watchfulness, the look-out be unsuccessful, it rises a few feet into the air, and slowly flaps itself away to some little distance, where perhaps, slightly altering its attitude, it stands on one leg, and, with its head thrown back, awaits better fortune. While thus stationed it is mute ; but as it flies off it frequently utters its note, a harsh, grating scream, especially when other birds of the same species are in the neighbourhood. On these occasions it is keenly on the alert, descrying danger at a great distance, and is always the first to give notice of an approaching enemy, not only to all birds feeding near it on the shore, but to any Ducks which may chance to be paddling in the water.[1]

During a great portion of the year the Heron is a wanderer. I have frequently seen it at least fifty miles distant from the nearest heronry ; but when it has discovered a spot abounding in food, it repairs thither day after day for a long period.

In the month of January, if mild, but as a rule in February, Herons show a disposition to congregate, and soon after repair to their old-established breeding-places, called Heronries. These are generally lofty trees, firs or deciduous trees in parks, or even in groves close by old family mansions. The nests, huge masses of sticks, a yard across, lined with a little grass, and other soft materials, are placed near each other, as many, sometimes, as a hundred in a colony,[2] or, more rarely, they are placed among ivy-clad rocks, ruins, or even on the ground. Each nest contains three to four eggs, on which the female sits about three weeks, constantly fed by her partner during the whole period of incubation. The power of running would be of little use to a young bird hatched at an elevation of fifty feet from the ground ; the young Herons are consequently helpless till they are sufficiently fledged to perch on the branches of the trees, where they are fed by their parents. Indeed, the favourite position of these

---

[1] A Heron in captivity has been known to perch on an old carriage-wheel, in the corner of a courtyard, and to lie in wait for Sparrows and Martins. One of the latter it was seen to pierce while flying, and immediately descending with outspread wings to run to its trough, and, having several times plunged in its prey, to swallow it at a gulp.

[2] Pennant counted eighty in one tree.

birds, both old and young, is, during a considerable portion of the day, on the upper branches of a lofty tree, whither, also, they often repair with a booty too large to be swallowed at once.

By a statute of Henry VIII the taking of Herons in any other way than by hawking, or the long bow, was prohibited on a penalty of half a mark ; and the theft of a young bird from the nest was visited with a penalty of ten shillings.

Not to be acquainted with the noble art of Falconry was deemed degrading : so that the saying, ' He does not know a Hawk from a Heronshaw ', was a common expression of contempt, corrupted into the proverb, ' He does not know a Hawk from a handsaw '.

THE NIGHT HERON NYCTÍCORAX NYCTÍCORAX (*Plate V*)

Head, back, and scapulars, black, with blue and green reflections ; on the back of the head three very long narrow white feathers ; lower part of the back, wings, and tail, pearl-grey ; forehead, streak over the eyes, and all the lower parts, white ; beak black, yellow at the base ; irides red ; feet yellowish green. Young birds have no crest ; the upper plumage is dull brown streaked with yellow ; wing-coverts and primaries marked with fish-shaped streaks, which are yellowish ; under parts dull white, mottled with brown and ash ; bill greenish ; irides and feet brown. Length twenty-one inches. Eggs pale blue. An occasional visitor to the British Isles, chiefly to southern and eastern England and Ireland.

THE Night Heron is a bird of wide geographical range ; but, on account of its nocturnal habits and the rarity of its occurrence in this country, it has been little observed.

It passes the day concealed among the thick foliage of trees and shrubs, and feeds only by night. It builds its nest in trees, and lays four or five eggs.

THE BITTERN BOTAURUS STELLÁRUS (*Plate IV*)

Moustaches and crown black ; upper plumage yellowish rust-red, spotted with dusky ; the feathers of the neck elongated, marked with brown zigzag lines ; primaries barred with rust-red and dusky grey ; plumage beneath paler, marked with oblong dusky streaks ; upper mandible brown, edged with yellow ; lower, orbits, and feet, greenish yellow ; irides bright yellow. Length two feet four inches. Eggs dingy green. Resident in the broads and fens of eastern England ; elsewhere in the British Isles an irregular visitor, chiefly in winter. Formerly a widespread resident.

THE Bittern frequents extensive reed-beds on the borders of lakes, or the dense vegetation of swamps and fens, feeding on fish, especially eels, and other creatures found in such localities, including frogs, voles, and aquatic insects. From its secretive habits it is rarely seen, but its presence during the breeding season is known by the loud, vibratory, boom of the male bird, which is audible for a distance of a mile or more. This usually commences early in February and continues till

June and may be heard at all hours of the day and night, but especially at dusk and shortly before dawn.

It is called Botaurus, because it imitates *boatum tauri*, the bellowing of a bull. Of 'Botaurus', the names 'Bitour' and Bittern are evident corruptions; and the following names, in different languages, are all descriptive of the same peculiar note : Butor, Rordump, Myredromble, Trombone, Rohrtrummel, Rohrdommel, and Rordrum.

The Bittern builds its nest on the ground, and lays four brown eggs, which are tinged with ash or green. The old bird, if wounded, defends itself in the same way as the Heron.

FAMILY CICONIIDÆ

THE WHITE STORK CICÓNIA CICÓNIA (*Plate V*)

General plumage white ; scapulars and wings black ; bill and feet red ; orbits naked, black ; irides brown. Young birds have the wings tinged with brown and the beak reddish black. Length three feet six inches. Eggs white tinged with ochre. An occasional visitor, chiefly to eastern and southern England, usually in spring.

THE Stork is so rare a visitor with us, that I have no scruple in referring my readers, for a full account of the habits of so interesting a bird, to some more comprehensive work on the subject.

It is recorded that in 1416 a pair nested on St. Giles' Church in Edinburgh, but at least since 1544, when Turner wrote that it was quite unknown in England in the wild state, it has only been an irregular visitor to Great Britain.

FAMILY THRESKIORNITHIDÆ

THE SPOONBILL PLATALÉA LEUCORODIA (*Plate IV*)

General plumage white ; a large patch of reddish yellow on the breast ; a crest of long narrow white feathers pendent over the neck ; lore, orbits, and naked space on the neck, pale yellow ; bill black, tipped with yellow ; irides red ; feet black. Young birds want the yellow patch on the breast and the occipital crest ; portions of the wing black. Length thirty-one inches. Eggs white, spotted with light red. A regular visitor to the coasts of Norfolk and Hampshire, fairly frequently met with on other parts of the south and east coasts of England, but elsewhere in the British Isles only an occasional straggler. Formerly nested in England and Wales.

SPOONBILLS do not appear to have been common at any time ; for though Sir Thomas Browne enumerates them among the birds of Norfolk and Suffolk, where they built in heronries, his contemporary,

Willughby, knew them only as natives of Holland. This bird is not infrequent in East Anglia, and it is met with now and again along the south coast, and has wandered up the Thames valley.

In Europe the Spoonbill is a migratory bird, retiring in autumn to Africa. It is remarkable not only for the singular conformation of its bill, but for ' being one of the very few which have been found to possess no true muscles of the organ of voice ; and no modulation of a single tone appears to be possessed by the bird '.[1]

It builds its nest in high trees, or, when these are wanting, among reeds and rushes ; and lays four eggs.

THE GLOSSY IBIS PLEGADIS FALCINELLUS (*Plate LXV*)

General plumage dusky ; back, wings, and tail, glossed with metallic green and purple ; head, neck, and under parts, reddish ; bill dark brown ; irides hazel ; naked skin round eyes dull blue ; legs and feet greenish. Young birds have the head and neck mottled with greyish white and lack the gloss on the upper parts. Length twenty-two inches. Eggs deep greenish blue. An irregular visitor to the British Isles, chiefly in autumn and usually to the southern and eastern coasts of England, sometimes in small parties.

THE only representative of the Ibises which ever occurs in the British Isles, with its curved bill and dark plumage, looks like a large black Curlew, and is said to have been called by this name in former days when it was a sufficiently frequent visitor to be known to shore gunners. The Glossy Ibis breeds in swamps in various localities in southern Europe and in the late summer individuals or parties, chiefly of young birds, wander in all directions from their breeding-haunts, sometimes reaching this country, before migrating south to Africa for the winter.

ORDER ANSERIFORMES

FAMILY ANATIDÆ

THE GREY LAG GOOSE ANSER ANSER (*Plate VI*)

Folded wings not reaching to the extremity of the tail ; bill strong, orange-yellow, the nail whitish ; upper plumage ash-brown, many of the feathers bordered with greyish white ; under plumage in front light ash-grey, barred on the flanks and belly with brown, behind pure white ; irides deep brown ; legs dull flesh-colour. Eggs ivory white. Length two feet ten inches. Resident in the northern Highlands and some of the Hebrides ; also a winter visitor, chiefly to Scotland, north-western England and Ireland. Formerly nested in the fens of eastern England.

[1] Yarrell's *British Birds*.

THE Geese are characterized by having a large, ovate body, a long neck and a short and stout beak, high at the base and bent down at the tip, adapted for cropping vegetable food ; the wings are large and powerful ; the legs, placed under the centre of the body, afford some facility in walking, and the webbed feet are eminently fitted for paddling, but rarely employed in diving. They spend the greater portion of the year in high latitudes, where their arrival is celebrated with great rejoicings, as an indication of returning summer. They are eminently gregarious, flying generally in the form of a half-opened pair of compasses, with the angle in front, or in an irregular wavy line, and uttering a loud harsh cry, which may often be heard some time before the birds themselves are in sight.

The present species, which is the ancestor of the domestic Goose, was formerly of common occurrence in Great Britain, but is now much less frequent. It breeds in northern Scotland, coming south from autumn to spring. On their arrival in autumn, they resort to marshes and swamps, meadows, cornfields, and turnip-fields, especially such as are remote from human dwellings. There they feed by day on such vegetable substances as fall in their way, but they are said to prefer the young shoots of corn to any other kind of food. So wary are they and difficult of approach, that a ' Wild Goose chase ' is a proverbial expression for an unsuccessful enterprise. At night they retire to the broad flats near the sea, or to the mouths of rivers, where they roost on the ground.

THE WHITE-FRONTED GOOSE ANSER ALBIFRONS (*Plate VI*)

Folded wings reaching a little beyond the tail ; bill orange-yellow, the nail white ; a large space on the forehead pure white, surrounded by a dusky band ; upper plumage ash-brown, varied with grey, dull white, and bluish black ; under plumage in front brownish white, with patches and bars of black, behind white ; irides dark brown ; feet orange. Length two feet three inches. Eggs white, tinged with buff. A winter visitor to the British Isles.

A REGULAR visitor to the British Isles, coming late in the autumn to stay till spring, usually seen in small flocks of from eight to twenty birds ; it is entirely graminivorous, and, when undisturbed, usually rests at night in any grass-field where it may have been feeding in the afternoon.

Its habits, during its stay in these latitudes, are similar to those of the other species, but it prefers low and marshy districts, and in these localities subsists on the aquatic grasses, being very seldom seen to frequent corn or stubble fields. It has never been observed to remain with us after April, when it betakes itself to the regions bordering on the Arctic circle.

THE BEAN GOOSE ANSER FABALIS (*Plate VI*)

Folded wings exceeding the tail in length ; bill long, orange, the base and nail black ; upper plumage ash-brown ; the wings darker, edged with greyish white ; under plumage in front dirty white, behind pure white ; irides dark brown ; legs orange. Length thirty-four inches. Eggs white. A winter visitor to the British Isles.

THE Bean Goose was formerly regarded as the commonest of the grey geese visiting the British Isles, but it seems certain that it was often confused with the Pink-footed Goose, and perhaps with the Grey Lag. At the present time it is the rarest species of the genus in this country, single individuals or small parties sometimes being met with in flocks of the commoner kinds and sometimes independently. In Scotland, where it is more frequent than in England or Ireland, it shows a partiality for upland pastures and fresh-water lochs.

THE PINK-FOOTED GOOSE ANSER BRACHYRHYNCHUS (*Plate VI*)

Folded wings not reaching to the extremity of the tail ; bill shorter than the head, narrow and much contracted towards the tip, pink, with the nail and base black ; head and neck reddish brown ; rest of the upper plumage ash-grey, edged with greyish white ; under plumage in front fawn-colour, behind white ; irides dark brown ; feet pink, tinged with vermilion. Length two feet four inches. Eggs dull yellowish white. A winter visitor to Great Britain, only very occasional in Ireland.

THE Pink-footed Goose was for long confused with the Bean Goose, of which some authorities regard it as only a racial form. The numbers visiting this country have undoubtedly considerably increased and in many localities on the east coast it is now the commonest of the grey geese, occurring in very large flocks.

THE CANADA GOOSE BRANTA CANADENSIS (*Plate LXV*)

Head and neck black, with a broad white patch on the throat extending upwards to the cheeks ; upper parts grey-brown, darkest on the wing quills ; breast brownish-white ; belly and upper and under tail-coverts pure white ; rump and tail black ; irides dark brown ; bill black ; legs and feet grey-black. Length three feet. Eggs white or creamy. An introduced resident, now occurring in a wild condition in various parts of the British Isles in the vicinity of lakes and meres.

As its name implies, this handsome goose is a native of North America, breeding in Canada, Newfoundland, and some of the northern United States, and migrating south to winter in the United States as far south as the Gulf of Mexico. It was introduced to this country in the seventeenth century and has long been kept in a semi-domesticated

state in many parks containing lakes. From these, flocks often wander
to considerable distances, especially in winter, and in several districts
numerous pairs breed in a completely wild state.

THE BERNACLE GOOSE BRANTA LEUCOPSIS (*Plate VII*)

*Forehead, sides of the head, and throat, pure white ; a dark streak between the
eyes and bill ; head, neck, quills, and tail, black ; rest of the upper plumage
undulated transversely with ash-grey, black, and dull white ; lower plumage
white, tinged on the flanks with grey ; irides dusky brown ; bill and feet black.
Length two feet one inch. Eggs greenish white. A winter visitor to the
Hebrides, the Solway district and parts of northern and western Ireland ;
occasionally to other districts of the British Isles.*

THIS beautiful bird occurs chiefly on the west side of Great Britain in
winter. ' It then more frequently retires to the sea than to the lakes
during its periods of repose, or when driven from its feeding-grounds.
A large flock then presents a beautiful spectacle, as the birds sit lightly
on the water, and when advancing elevate their necks. Not less
beautiful do they seem when on wing ; now arranged in long lines,
ever undulating ; at one time extending in the direction of their flight ;
at another obliquely, or at right angles to it, sometimes in an angular
figure, and again mingling together. Their voice is clear, and rather
shrill, and comes agreeably on the ear when the cries of a large flock
come from a considerable distance.' The mythical fragment of ancient
natural history, that the Bernacle is the product of a tree, is too trite
to require repetition here.

THE BRENT GOOSE BRANTA BERNICLA (*Plate VII*)

*Head, beak, neck, breast, feet, quills, and tail, black ; on each side of the
neck a patch of white with a few black feathers intermixed ; upper plumage
dingy ; all the tail-coverts white ; belly brownish grey, barred on the flanks
with greyish white. Length twenty-two to twenty-three inches. Eggs greyish
white. A winter visitor to the coasts of the British Isles, rarely occurring inland.*

THE Wild Geese which we have hitherto been considering feed on
grass, clover, and grain, in quest of which they resort to inland marshes,
meadows, and arable land ; but the Brent is a decidedly marine bird.
During its annual visits to our shores it stays out at sea by night,
cradled by the billows, and at early dawn repairs to the muddy flats
and sand-banks, where it feeds exclusively on marine plants, especially
laver and zostéra. As soon as these are left bare by the ebbing tide,
the Brents are taught by their instinct that they have no time to lose,
and hasten in ' skeins ' or ' gaggles ' making in their flight a trumpet-
like noise, which, heard at a distance, resembles that of a pack of
harriers or fox-hounds in full cry. They prefer to take their stand on
these parts of the ooze which are least intersected by creeks, and there,
if left undisturbed, they continue to feed without intermission till the

rising tide lifts them off their feet. Then, away to sea again, or, if the weather be boisterous, they seek for shelter in the rivers and estuaries. They are local in their attachments, returning annually to the same feeding-grounds. They do not associate from choice with other species, for though they may be frequently seen feeding in the vicinity of various Waders, they form no society with them, and are, indeed, in quest of different food. Seaside fowlers are well acquainted with the peculiarity of their habits, and not only know where to look for them when they are settled, but at what points they can most easily be intercepted, going and returning. It is the custom of the fowler to conceal himself behind some lurking-place, natural or artificial ; or, if this be wanting, to stretch himself on the ground. Then, as a skein, unconscious of danger, approaches, he suddenly shows himself ; the birds, panic-stricken, huddle together before they alter their line of flight, and the sportsman fires into the midst of them.

They are the most abundant of all the Geese which frequent our shores. They come to us in November and remain till late in February, when they begin to migrate in successive flights. They never remain to breed, but repair to the Arctic regions, and make their nests of withered herbage on islands or rocky elevations in the tundra.

THE MUTE SWAN CYGNUS OLOR (*Plate LXV*)

Whole plumage pure white, head and neck often with a rusty stain ; bill with a black knob and black base, rest mostly orange ; feet dark grey ; irides hazel ; tail of twenty-two or twenty-four feathers. Length five feet. Eggs white with greyish or greenish tinge. A semi-domesticated resident throughout the British Isles.

THE familiar tame or Mute Swan was formerly supposed to have been introduced to this country, traditionally from Cyprus by Richard Cœur-de-Lion. It is now known, however, that it was already domesticated prior to A.D. 1186, and it is highly probable that it was originally wild in this country, as it still is in Denmark and Sweden, and that the birds were gradually domesticated. From the thirteenth to the eighteenth century all Swans were the property of the Crown or of communities and individuals authorized to keep them by royal licence. Since the eighteenth century the customs connected with their private ownership have gradually died out, except on the Thames and in the vicinity of Norwich, and the birds have reverted to their wild state.

THE WHOOPER SWAN CYGNUS CYGNUS (*Plate VIII*)

Whole plumage pure white, the head and nape sometimes slightly tinged with yellow ; lower half of the bill quadrangular, yellow ; upper, black ; lore and a great portion of the edge of the upper mandible yellow ; irides brown ; legs black ; tail of twenty feathers. Young birds have the plumage grey ; lore flesh-colour. Length five feet ; breadth seven feet ten inches. Eggs dull white, tinged with greenish. A winter visitor to the British Isles : a few pairs remaining to breed in the western Highlands of Scotland.

THE ancient fable that Swans sing most sweetly before their death did not survive the age which invented it. Pliny disbelieved it, and, though the assertion may have been resuscitated from time to time as a poetic fiction, it has found no place in works on natural history.

The Swan is not musical ; it rests its claims to our admiration on other grounds, unchallenged and indisputable ; the unsullied white of its plumage is an apt emblem of purity, and the elegance of its movements in the water has become proverbial. The present species, which owes its name to its powerful voice, is said to be not quite so graceful as the tame Swan, but on land it is far more active. A bird which has been winged by a sportsman, and has fallen on the land, can only be overtaken by smart running. In Iceland, one of the summer resorts of these birds, they are much sought after for the sake of their down. In the month of August, when the old birds, having cast their quill-feathers, are unable to fly, the natives assemble in bodies in the places where the Swans collect, and mounted on small but active horses chase them through the marshes, and ride many of them down ; but the greater number are caught by the dogs, which always seize the birds by the neck, and so encumber them that they are then easily overtaken. But it is not the habit of Swans to remain much on land ; the perfect ease with which they float and swim indicates that the water is their element, and a glance at their long necks tells at once that their nature is to feed in shallow water or on the margin of deep lakes, where with their strong bills they either tear up the stems and roots of aquatics from the bottom, or crop at their pleasure from the banks. To this kind of food they add such insects, molluscs, and worms as come within their reach ; and (when sailing in salt water) sea weeds, and especially the long, ribbon-like leaves of zostéra. During summer they frequent the most secluded swamps and lakes in the wooded districts of the north, and build a very large nest in a spot unapproachable by human feet.

After they have recovered from their summer moult, they migrate southwards, and arrive in Scotland, sometimes in large flocks, early in October. Mr. St. John, in his *Wild Sports of the Highlands*, gives an interesting account of their habits while in this country. He went in pursuit of a flock which had selected for their winter feeding-place some fresh-water lochs about half a mile from the sea. They passed the day mostly on the salt water, and in the evening came inland to feed. He found them on one of the smaller lochs, some standing high and dry on the grassy islands trimming their feathers after their long voyage, and others feeding on the grass and weeds at the bottom of the loch, which in some parts was shallow enough to allow of their pulling up the plants which they fed on as they swam about, while numbers of wild Ducks of different kinds, particularly Wigeons, swarmed round them, and often snatched the pieces of grass from the Swans as soon as they had brought them to the surface, to the great annoyance of the noble birds, who endeavoured in vain to drive away these most active little depredators, who seemed determined to profit by their labours. ' I observed ', he says, ' that frequently all their heads were under the water at once, excepting one—but invariably *one* had kept his head and neck perfectly erect, and carefully watched on every side to prevent their being taken by surprise ; when he wanted to feed, he touched any passer-by, who immediately relieved him in his guard, and he in his turn called on some other Swan to take his place as sentinel.'

When disturbed on the water they generally huddle together and utter a low cry of alarm before they take flight. Owing to their great weight, they have not the power of rising suddenly into the air, but flap along the water, beating the surface with their great wings, some twenty or thirty yards. The flapping noise made while this process is going on, may be heard at a great distance.

In severe winters, flocks of Whoopers, Whistling Swans, or Elks, as they are variously called, come farther south, and may be observed from time to time on different parts of the coast.

BEWICK'S SWAN CYGNUS BEWICKII (*Plate VIII*)

Whole plumage pure white ; bill black, yellow at the base ; irides dark ; feet black ; tail of eighteen feathers. Young birds *greyish brown ; immature specimens tinged on the head and belly with rust-red. Length three feet nine inches ; breadth six feet one inch. Eggs dull white, tinged with brown. A winter visitor to the British Isles, especially to Ireland.*

BEWICK'S Swan is distinguished from the Whooper, not only by the characters given above, but by strongly marked anatomical features, which were first pointed out by Mr. Yarrell, who, with the modesty and generosity for which he was noted, gave it its present name ; ' Thus devoting it to the memory of one whose beautiful and animated delineations of subjects in natural history entitle him to this tribute.'

In severe winters it is fairly frequent on the coasts of England, and even abundant in Scotland. In the case of distant flocks the only criterion is size ; and as this species is one-third less than the Whooper, there is little probability of an experienced observer being mistaken in the identity.

In their habits they closely resemble their congeners, but are less graceful in their movements on the water, and spend a larger portion of their time on land.

THE SHELDRAKE TADORNA TADORNA (*Plate IX*)

Head, throat, and upper back, black, with green reflections ; lower parts of the neck and back, flanks, rump and tail (except the black tip), white ; from the shoulders a broad band of bright chestnut, which meets on the breast, passing into a broad, blotched, black band, which passes down the abdomen nearly to the tail ; under tail-coverts pale reddish yellow ; scapulars black ; wing-coverts white ; secondaries chestnut ; primaries black ; speculum bronzed green and purple ; bill, and protuberance at the base, red ; irides brown ; feet crimson-red. The female wants the red protuberance on the bill, and the colours generally are somewhat less bright. Length twenty to twenty-two inches. Eggs white, tinged with green. Resident on suitable parts of the coast throughout the British Isles : uncommon on fresh water.

THE Sheldrake is the largest and among the handsomest of the British Ducks, and if easy of domestication would be no doubt a common ornament of our lakes and rivers. It is, however, a marine bird. Numerous attempts have been made to familiarize it with inland fresh-water haunts to which some other species readily take, but they have rarely succeeded, while to induce it to breed at a distance from its seaside home has proved yet more difficult.

It differs from the majority of the Duck tribe in remaining on the coast of Britain throughout the year. In South Wales, for example, it is seen in winter and early spring, but about the breeding season it disappears for a few weeks. During this interval it is employed in incubation, but when its brood is hatched it is seen again, accompanied by a troop of ducklings, feeding in the creeks and marshy places. When thus discovered, the young broods are commonly hunted down by seaside idlers for the sake of being sold to any one who cares to try the experiment of rearing them.

On the coast of Norfolk it is more usual to search for the nests, in order to secure the eggs and place them under a tame Duck or domestic Hen. The male and female keep together, not only during incubation, but until the young are able to provide for themselves. It derives the name 'Burrow Duck', by which it is also known, from its custom of making its nest either in the burrow of a rabbit or in a hole hollowed out by itself. The nest is constructed of such herbage as abounds in the neighbourhood ; it is lined with down plucked from the breast of the parent bird, and contains from ten to twelve eggs.

Pennant (vol. ii. p. 257) says of these birds : ' They inhabit the sea-coasts and breed in rabbit-holes. When a person attempts to take their young, the old birds show great address in diverting his attention from the brood ; they will fly along the ground as if wounded, till the former can get into a place of security, and then return and collect them together.'

From this instinctive cunning, Turner, with good reason, imagines them to be the *chenalōpex*, or *Fox-Goose*, of the ancients ; the natives of the Orkneys to this day call them the *Sly-Goose*, from an attribute of that quadruped.

Sheld means parti-coloured. ' Shelled ' is still current in the eastern counties of England. Shelled duck is the more proper appellation.

THE SHOVELER SPATULA CLYPEATA (*Plate IX*)

Head and neck glossy green ; breast pure white ; belly and flanks chestnut ; back brown ; lesser wing-coverts pale blue ; scapulars white, speckled and spotted with black ; speculum brilliant green ; bill lead colour ; irides yellow ; feet reddish orange. Female—head pale reddish brown, streaked with dusky ; upper plumage dusky brown, edged with reddish white ; under plumage reddish with large brown spots ; the blue and green of the wings less bright. Length twenty inches. Eggs greenish buff. A summer resident, breeding in small numbers in many parts of the British Isles ; also a passage migrant and winter visitor.

THE Shoveler is well distinguished among all the British Ducks by the form and structure of its bill, which in old birds is dilated near the extremity into a form approaching that of a spoon, and is furnished with a fringe of slender lamellæ, resembling a comb. Towards the end of the bill these are not conspicuous as long as the mouth of the bird is closed, but along the narrower part they are prominent under all circumstances. So singular an apparatus obviously indicates that the habit of the Shoveler is to sift water and mud for the sake of securing the insects and worms which they contain. It resorts, therefore, to the margins of fresh-water lakes, ponds, and ditches, and is rarely seen at sea, nor does it ever dive after its food in deep water, but frequently comes to land in quest of slugs, snails, and worms. It is met with from time to time in many parts of England ; a tolerable number remain to breed with us, especially in the eastern counties. Its distaste for the sea disqualifies it for inhabiting the Arctic Regions ; consequently it breeds in temperate countries ; and flies farther to the south in winter, visiting tropical Africa, southern Asia, and central America. The nest, usually placed in a tuft of grass, is made of dry grass mixed with down which the female plucks from her own body, and contains eight or nine eggs.

The male annually undergoes a moult, or change of feathers, similar to that described as taking place in the Mallard.

THE GADWALL ANAS STRÉPERA (*Plate IX*)

Head and neck light grey, speckled with brown ; back and breast dark grey, the feathers ending in crescent-shaped whitish lines ; belly white, speckled with brown ; small wing-coverts and tip of the wing chestnut ; greater coverts, rump, and tail-coverts, black ; speculum white ; bill black ; irides brown ; feet orange. Female less distinctly marked. Length twenty inches. Eggs buffy white, tinged with green. Breeds regularly in Norfolk and Suffolk and in a few districts of Scotland, and occasionally elsewhere in England, Scotland, and Ireland : also a scarce winter visitor.

ITS food and habits closely resemble those of the Wild Duck ; it is active, and both swims and flies rapidly, preferring fresh-water lakes to the sea, and resorting principally to such pieces of water as afford it ready concealment. By day they mostly swim about in the open water, and come near the shore to feed in the evening. They breed in the great northern marshes of both hemispheres.

THE PINTAIL DUCK ANAS ACÚTA (*Plate X*)

Two central tail-feathers much elongated, black ; head and neck rich dark brown ; back and flanks marked with zigzag black and grey lines ; front of the neck, and a line on each side, white ; speculum lustrous with green and purple, bounded above by reddish brown, below by white ; bill lead-colour and black. Female—*central tail-feathers scarcely elongated ; head and neck reddish brown, speckled with dusky ; upper feathers dusky, edged with reddish white ; lower plumage reddish yellow, spotted with brown ; speculum dull yellowish brown ; no white line on the side of the neck. Length twenty-six inches. Eggs dull greenish white. A resident in small numbers, breeding locally in Scotland and Ireland and occasionally in England : also a numerous passage migrant and winter visitor.*

THE Pintail Duck is a northern bird which visits our shores in small parties. In form it is the most elegant of all the Ducks, and its movements are active and graceful. Yarrell states that on the coast of Dorsetshire and Hampshire it is so well known as to have acquired a local name, ' Sea Pheasant '.[1] For this it is indebted to the length of its tail, in which respect it differs from all the common Ducks. It arrives early in autumn, and remains either on the coast or in the inland marshes, until the return of spring ; differing, indeed, little in its habits from the common Wild Duck. It is occasionally taken in decoys in Norfolk, and has often been observed to associate with Wigeons. Its note is described by Montagu as being ' extremely soft and inward '.

The Pintail Duck has a wide geographical range, as it either breeds in or pays winter visits to the greater part of the northern hemisphere. The male annually assumes in summer the plumage of the female, resembling in this respect the Mallard. The flesh is considered excellent, on which account it is much sought after by wild-fowl shooters, both on the coast and in the fens.

THE WILD DUCK ANAS PLATYRHYNCHOS (*Plate IX*)

Head and neck dark green ; at the base of the neck a white collar ; upper parts marked with fine zigzag lines of ash-brown and grey ; breast chestnut ; lower parts greyish white, marked with fine zigzag ash-brown lines ; speculum dark blue with purple and green reflections, bordered above and below with black and white ; four middle feathers of the tail curled upwards, bill greenish yellow ; irides red-brown ; feet orange. Length twenty-four inches. Female smaller ; plumage mottled with various shades of brown and grey ; throat whitish ; speculum as in the male *; all the tail-feathers straight. Eggs greenish white. A common resident throughout the British Isles ; also a plentiful winter visitor.*

[1] Willughby calls it the ' Sea Pheasant ', or ' Cracker '.

Its size, abundance, and value as an article of food, have given to
the Wild Duck an importance which belongs to few other British
birds ; and the modes of capturing it are so varied and interesting
that they are often described in works not exclusively devoted to natural
history. For this reason I shall in great measure confine my notice
of this bird to such particulars in its history as the reader may probably
have an opportunity of verifying by his own observation in the course
of his rambles among places which it habitually frequents.

The term ' Wild Duck ', properly applicable to the female bird
only (' Mallard ' being the distinctive name of the male), is generally
employed to include both sexes. The difference in the plumage of
the two is very great, as, indeed, is the case with all those varieties
of the same bird which, under the name of ' Tame Ducks ', have
altered the least from their natural wild type. Yet in the summer
months, when both sexes moult,[1] the Mallard puts off the whole of
his characteristic gay plumage, and appears in the sober brown
garb of the Duck. It is only, in fact, from October to May that the
Mallard can be distinguished from his partner by his markings. At
this season, too, young birds, so far as they are fledged, are of the
same tone of colouring. Domesticated birds are subject to the same
change ; but a reason for this singular metamorphosis no naturalist,
as far as I am aware, has ventured to assign.

Wild Ducks hold a prominent place among birds of the most
extensive distribution, being ' indigenous to the greater part of the
northern hemisphere '.[2] In consequence of this wide range they must
of necessity frequent many districts highly favourable to their preserva-
tion ; they are therefore numerous. Equally well adapted for travelling by sea and through the air, and capable of enduring great variations of heat and cold, their presence may be expected wherever a tract
of country occurs calculated to supply them with food and opportunities for nidification. As long as England abounded in marshes, and
her rivers ran through wastes rarely frequented by man, Wild Ducks
were numerous in many counties where they are now but rarely seen.
Many have retired before draining and civilization, yet they never
totally desert us. In most districts where there are rivers lined with
reeds, even not so very far removed from the sound of the steam-engine,
one may, by cautiously and quietly guiding one's steps, fall in with a
brood of active ducklings sifting the ooze, with the instinct of their kind,
for minute insects ; flapping along the water in chase of a fly, or
paddling among the reeds on the look-out for anything good to eat.
The matron of the party, with a proud consciousness of her dignity
as sentinel and protector, preserves a more stately demeanour, but,
with this slight difference, is similarly occupied. As you approach
she is the first to descry you ; with a homely ' quack ', differing in no
respect from the note of the domesticated bird, she sounds an alarm,
and the whole family, mother and children, are quickly concealed
among the reeds. It is possible, by long-continued persecution, to
induce her to rise, but she does so reluctantly, and even then, unless

[1] Formerly spelt ' mute ', from the Latin *muto*, to change.
[2] Yarrell, vol. iii. p. 273.

you are such a barbarian as to shoot her, all is yet safe. The young will hide themselves securely until danger is past, and she, not far off, though unseen, is circling round her helpless brood. In an islet, probably, of the river ; in a tuft of reeds surrounded by quagmire ; among thick bushes near the bank ; under the stump of an alder, or even high up among the branches, she formerly had her nest, composed of grass, and lined with down from her own breast ; and at no great distance from this her offspring are yet lingering. The latter could swim immediately that they left the egg, but their bodies are large and heavy in proportion to the size of their wings, so that they will be unable to fly until nine or ten weeks old, when they will be thoroughly fledged, and only distinguishable from their parent by their smaller size.

From the rapidity with which young Ducks 'scutter' along the surface of the water, using both feet and wings, they are called by sportsmen, 'flappers' ; and from the same habit, no doubt, the children's game of 'Ducks-and-drakes' was named. The word is one with which I have been familiar, like most other people, from my earliest years, yet I never thought of its etymology until I was passing, a few weeks since, in a steamer down Loch Tarbet. The boat disturbed a party of 'flappers' which were feeding near the shore, and as they half flew, half paddled away at a rapid rate, the sport and the name suggested themselves to my mind together.

In marshy districts, both in England and Scotland, these birds remain all the year round ; but their numbers are greatly augmented in winter by the arrival of large flocks from the north. These fly mostly by night, in long lines, and proceed to the fens and salt marshes, where they feed until daylight. They then put out to sea, and rest, floating on the water, until dusk ; and it is while they are on their way to and from these feeding-grounds that the seaside gunners do the greatest execution among them. They fly mostly in small parties, and utter no note ; but if after dusk a shot be fired in the vicinity of a marsh or of a piece of reclaimed land intersected by ditches, it is followed by a concert of 'quacks' from all sides, which proves that, however small the parties may have been, the number of Ducks collectively must be very great.

When it is desired to construct a decoy,[1] a quiet, shallow pond is selected, edged with reeds, and having an extent of from two to fifty acres or more. From the edge of this are dug, at various points, curved creeks, called 'pipes', broad at the mouth, and contracting till the banks meet. Over each of these pipes is thrown a net, supported on arches made of hoops ; the first about ten feet high, the others diminishing in size, and the whole ending in a bag-net, or 'purse'. On each bank of the pipes are erected screens made of reeds, high enough to conceal a man. Previously to commencing operations the

[1] Decoy, a corruption of Duck-coy, from the Dutch *kooi*, a cage or pen. See *Ray and Willughby's Ornithology*, p. 286, where, mention being made of a method of capturing wild-fowl which had been introduced into England from Holland, the following passage occurs : 'Piscinas hasce cum allectatricibus et reliquo suo apparatu *Decoys* seu *Duck-coys* vocant, allectatrices *Coy-ducks*.'

decoy-man has let loose on the pond a few tame Ducks, closely resembling wild birds in plumage, who are familiar with his person and have
been trained to come at his call.   Accompanied by a little dog, a
' piper ', he stations himself behind a screen, near the mouth of a pipe
which faces the wind, choosing this position because Ducks prefer to
swim against the wind and to feed on a lee shore.   When the pond is
well stocked with birds he throws some corn on the water near the
mouth of a pipe, and makes a low whistle.   At the familiar sound the
' coy-ducks ' hasten to the spot, and, if all be well, are followed by a
portion of the wild birds.   The piper is then let loose, and immediately
runs to the water's edge.   The Wild Ducks, either from curiosity, or
some unknown motive, paddle towards him.   The ruse succeeding so
far, the piper is made to appear for a moment beyond the next screen,
and so on until a party of Ducks have been lured so far up the pipe
as to be out of sight of those remaining in the pond.   The decoy-man,
who has all the while been lying hid near the first screen, then shows
himself to his intended victims, who, in their flight, hurry on to the
' purse ', and are caught and dispatched at leisure.   All this time
the coy-ducks, if well trained, have remained at the mouth of the
pipe, feeding, and unconsciously enticing new-comers into the snare.

That this method of capturing wild-fowl is effective, may be inferred from the fact that decoys of a precisely similar kind have been
worked ever since the time of Willughby (1676), who describes them
at length.   A Son of the Marshes gives a fuller account of Duck decoys
in *Wild-Fowl and Sea-Fowl*.

THE GARGANEY ANAS QUERQUÉDULA (*Plate X*)

Crown dusky ;   over the eye a white band extending down the neck ;   throat
black ;   neck chestnut-brown streaked with white ;   breast pale yellowish brown,
with crescent-shaped black bars ;   back mottled with dusky grey and brown ;
speculum greyish green, bordered above and below with white ;   bill dark brown ;
irides brown ;   feet grey.   Length sixteen inches.   Eggs buff.   A summer
visitor to the British Isles, breeding regularly in small numbers in eastern and
southern England and occasionally in other parts of England, Wales, and southern
Scotland.   A rare straggler only in Ireland and the north of Scotland.

THIS elegant little duck visits us in March and April and is sufficiently
well known in the eastern counties to have acquired the provincial
name of ' Summer Teal '.   Young birds are commonly seen on the
Broads of Norfolk in July and August, distinguishable from young Teal
by the lighter colour of their plumage, more slender habit, and greater
length of neck.

THE TEAL ANAS CRÉCCA (*Plate X*)

Head and neck bright chestnut ;   on each side of the head a broad green band
edged with buff, enclosing the eye and extending to the nape ;   lower part of the
neck, back, and flanks, marked with numerous black and white zigzag lines ;

Red-throated Diver Winter and Summer.

Little Auk   Black-throated Diver *imm.* and *ad.*

Great Northern Diver

I

Red-necked Grebe

Horned or Slavonian Grebe   Black-necked or Eared Grebe

Great Crested Grebe (Winter, Summer)

II

Manx Shearwater

Storm Petrel　　　　　　　　　　　　　　　Fork-tailed Petrel

Fulmar

III

Spoonbill   Moorhen

Coot   Bittern

IV

Crane   Stork

Heron   Night Heron

V

Pink-footed Goose

White-fronted Goose

Grey Lag Goose

Bean Goose

VI

Shag

Bernacle Goose

Brent Goose

Cormorant

VII

Gannet

Whooper Swan   Bewick's Swan

VIII

Sheldrake   Shoveler ♂

Gadwall ♂   Mallard or Wild Duck ♂ ♀

IX

Garganey ♂

Teal ♂ ♀

Wigeon ♂

Pintail ♂

X

Eider Duck ♂ ♀♂

Velvet Scoter ♀♂   Long-tailed Duck ♂ ♀

Common Scoter ♂ ♀

XI

Pochard ♂ ♀

Seaup ♂

Tufted Duck ♂

Golden-eye ♂ ♀

XII

Merganser ♂   Smew ♂ ♀
Goosander ♂   Dabchick

XIII

Osprey   Golden Eagle

Sea Eagle   Spotted Eagle, *imm.*

XIV

Rough-legged Buzzard

Kite

Common Buzzard

Honey Buzzard

Marsh Harrier ♂

Merlin ♂

Sparrowhawk ♀

Hobby

XVI

breast reddish white, with roundish black spots ; speculum black, green, and purple, edged with white ; bill dusky ; irides brown ; feet ash. Female— *upper plumage dusky brown, mottled with reddish grey ; throat, cheeks, and a band behind the eyes, yellowish white, spotted with black ; speculum black and green. Length fourteen inches and a half. Eggs yellowish white. A resident breeding throughout the British Isles, but only in limited numbers in southern England and Ireland : also a plentiful winter visitor.*

THE Teal is the smallest, and by no means the least beautiful, among the British Ducks. It is decidedly an indigenous species, as it breeds in many parts both of Great Britain and Ireland, especially in the eastern counties, in Welsh bogs, and northern mosses. It is domesticated, too, without difficulty, and is generally to be found on artificial and other pieces of water where the breed of water-fowl is encouraged. Its favourite summer resorts in England are lakes which are lined with rushes, boggy places on the moors, and sedgy rivers. It is an active bird, rising from the water with great facility, and having a rapid flight. The few Teal which remain all the year with us pair early in spring. I have observed them in couples on the Kennet, in Berkshire, before winter had well departed. They appear to have a strong attachment to any place on which they have once fixed to build their nest, and return to the same locality year after year ; and the young brood remain in the neighbourhood of their birthplace until pairing time in the following year. The nest is usually placed among coarse herbage by the bank of a lake or river, and is constructed of decayed vegetable matter, lined with down and feathers, and contains from ten to fifteen eggs. The number, however, of these birds to be found with us in summer is as nothing compared with the immense flocks which visit our inland lakes and swamps in winter. They are then much sought after for the table, being considered more delicate eating than any others of the tribe. In some parts they repair to salt marshes and the seashore, where they share the fate of the Wild Duck.

Willughby tells us that in his time the Teal and Wigeon, considered as marketable goods, were classed together as ' half-fowl ', their value being only half that of the Wild Duck. In the fen counties they are still ranked together as ' Half Ducks ', and for the same reason.

The Teal has two notes, one a kind of quack, the other, uttered by the male only during winter, which has been compared to the whistle of the Plover. Its food consists of water insects, molluscs, worms, and the seeds of grass and sedge.

THE WIGEON ANAS PENÉLOPE (*Plate X*)

Male—*head and upper part of the neck chestnut, the cheeks and crown speckled with black ; a broad cream-coloured band extending from the bill to the crown ; throat nearly black ; a narrow collar of white and black wavy lines extending over the back and flanks ; lower part of the neck and sides of the breast chocolate-colour ; scapulars velvet-black, edged with white ; wing-coverts white ; quills ash-brown ; speculum glossy green, with a black band above and below ; tail wedge-shaped, two middle feathers pointed, and the longest, dusky ash ; under*

B.B.   C *tail-coverts black ; bill bluish grey, the tip black ; irides hazel ; feet dusky grey. Female—head and neck reddish brown, speckled with dusky ; back and scapulars dusky brown, the feathers edged with rusty red ; wing-coverts brown, edged with whitish ; speculum without the green gloss ; flanks reddish brown. Length twenty inches. Eggs brownish white. A plentiful winter visitor to the British Isles, numerous pairs remaining to breed in northern Scotland and small numbers nesting irregularly farther south.*

THE name Whew Duck, or Whewer, by which this bird is known in some parts of England, was given to it on account of its emitting a shrill whistle while flying. The name is an old one, for Ray and Willughby describe it under the name of ' Whewer '. Its French name *Siffleur*, ' Whistler ', has reference to the same peculiarity, and by this note the bird may often be distinguished from others of the same tribe, when so far off that the eye fails to identify it. The Wigeon ranks next to the Teal and Wild Duck as an article of food, and is among the best known of all the Ducks which frequent our shores.

Flocks of Wigeons repair to our shores in autumn, and either betake themselves to inland lakes and morasses, or keep to the coast, especially where there are extensive salt marshes. In winter their numbers are greatly increased, especially in the south ; and as they feed by day as well as by night, they offer themselves a ready prey to the fowler. Their food consists of marine and fresh-water insects, small shellfish, seaweed, and grass. Their nidification differs little from that of the Teal.

THE EIDER DUCK SOMATERIA MOLLISSIMA (*Plate XI*)

Prolongations of the bill flat ; upper part of the head velvet-black, with a central whitish band ; lower, greenish white ; neck and back white ; breast tinged with red ; lower plumage black ; bill and feet greenish grey ; irides brown. Female—general plumage reddish brown, with transverse black bars ; wing-coverts black, bordered with dark reddish brown ; two whitish bars across the wing ; belly brown, barred with black. Length twenty-five inches. Eggs shining greenish grey. Resident on the coasts of Scotland, Northumberland, and northern Ireland, occasionally occurring farther south in winter.

THE Eider Duck differs from all the birds of the same tribe hitherto described, in being essentially and absolutely a sea-bird. Rarely found on inland waters, it does not even visit the fresh-water lochs which, in many places in the north, are only separated from the sea by a bar of sand and shingle. It spends the greater part of its time on the water, and feeds on fish, molluscs, and other animal matter which it can obtain by diving. In the latter art it is very expert, and when pursued by the fowler generally manages to escape, as it can remain a long time under water, and on rising to the surface is ready to descend again almost instantly. Though a northern bird, it is subjected to no privations by the freezing of lakes and marshes, since it finds its rest and food on the open sea. Consequently it is not migratory, and stray specimens only visit the southern shores of England. Where it was bred, there, probably, or not far off, it remains all the year round. The Farne Islands, off the coast of Northumberland, are the extreme southern limit of its breeding-ground. In the Hebrides, the Orkneys and Shetland Islands, it is plentiful. It is rare on the Irish coast.

In the Arctic regions, in Iceland, and on the rocky coasts of Norway and Sweden, Eider Ducks are very numerous. In Labrador, Audubon informs us, they begin to form their nests about the end of May or the beginning of June. ' For this purpose some resort to islands scantily furnished with grass ; others choose a site beneath the spreading boughs of stunted firs, and, in such places, five, six, or even eight are sometimes found beneath a single bush ; many are placed on the sheltered shelvings of rocks a few feet above highwater mark. The nest, which is sunk as much as possible into the ground, is formed of seaweeds, mosses, and dried twigs, so matted and interlaced as to give an appearance of neatness to the central cavity, which rarely exceeds seven inches in diameter. In the beginning of June the eggs are deposited, the male attending upon the female the whole time. The eggs, which are regularly placed on the moss and weeds of the nest without any down, are generally from five to seven. When the full complement of eggs has been laid, the female begins to pluck some down from the lower part of the body ; this operation is daily continued for some time, until the roots of the feathers, as far forward as she can reach, are quite bare. This down she disposes beneath and around the eggs. When she leaves the nest to go in search of food, she places it over her eggs to keep up their warmth.'

Sir W. J. Hooker, in his interesting *Journal of a Tour in Iceland*, describes the nests as he saw them in the little island of Akaroe, where, as on other uninhabited islands, the Eider Ducks breed in great numbers. ' On our landing on the rocky island, we found the Eider fowls sitting upon their nests, which were rudely formed of their own down, generally among the old and half-decayed seaweed, that the storms had cast high up on the beach, but sometimes only among the bare rocks. It was difficult to make these birds leave their nests, and so little inclined were many of them to do it, that they even permitted us to handle them, whilst they were sitting, without their appearing to be at all alarmed. Under each of them were two or four eggs ; the latter is the number they lay, but from many of them two had been taken for food by the natives, who prefer those which have young ones in them. *June 24th.*' A few days later (June 27) he visited the island of Vidöe, the residence of the ex-governor, where, he says, ' we were shown the immense number of Eider Ducks which lived on Vidöe, and which were now sitting on eggs or young ones, exhibiting a most interesting scene. The ex-governor made us go and coax some of the old birds, who did not on that account disturb themselves. Almost every little hollow place between the rocks is occupied with the nests of these birds, which are so numerous that we were obliged to walk with the greatest caution, to avoid trampling upon them ; but, besides this, the ex-governor has a number of holes cut in the smooth and sloping side of a hill in two rows, and in every one of these, also, there is a nest.　No Norfolk housewife is half so solicitous after her poultry as the ex-governor after his Eider Ducks, which by their down and eggs afford him a considerable revenue ; since the former sells for three rix-dollars (twelve shillings) a pound.　Cats and dogs are, at this season of the year, all banished from the island, so that nothing may disturb these birds.'　I need scarcely add that the Eider down of commerce is taken from these nests, not in a pure state but mixed with fragments of plants.　Pennant says that if the nest and eggs be taken ' the Duck lays again, and repeats the plucking of her breast, if she is robbed after that, she will still lay, but the drakes must supply the down, as her stock is now exhausted ; if her eggs are taken a third time, she wholly deserts the place.'　The quantity of down found in one nest weighs about three-quarters of an ounce, and may be compressed into a ball two inches in diameter, but on being shaken out will fill a large hat.

The young brood take to the water immediately on being hatched. To effect this they are often obliged to travel a considerable distance, and if difficulties present themselves, insurmountable in any other way, the parent bird carries the young in her bill.　Once clear of the rocks, they are liable to no further molestation from land robbers. But the sea is not without its dangers, for the rapacious Black-backed Gull frequently attacks them, and, but for the self-devotion and bravery of the mother bird, would commit great havoc among them. At his appearance the young dive in all directions, while the mother counterfeits lameness to distract his attention from them to herself, or springs from the water and attacks the Gull until he is compelled to retire from the contest.

THE VELVET SCOTER MELANITTA FÚSCA (*Plate XI*)

General plumage velvet-black ; below the eyes a white crescent ; speculum white ; bill orange, protuberance at the base, nostrils, and edge of mandibles, black ; irides and feet red, the membranes of the latter black.　Female smaller ; upper plumage sooty brown ; under parts light grey, streaked and spotted with dusky brown ; between the bill and eye a whitish spot, and another over the ear ; bill dusky ash ; irides brown ; feet dull red.　Length twenty-three inches.　Eggs buff.　A winter visitor to the coasts of England, Wales, and Scotland, rare in Ireland.

THE Velvet Scoter, an inhabitant of the extreme northern regions of Asia and Europe, appears in the British Isles as a winter visitor only, being sometimes seen on the eastern coast of Scotland, in large flocks, but not generally extending its migration to our southern shores except in the severest weather.　It may be distinguished from the Common Scoter by its larger size, and yet more strikingly by the conspicuous white bar across the wing.

The habits and food of the Velvet Duck differ in no material respect from those of the Common Scoter, or Black Duck.

THE BLACK (OR COMMON) SCOTER OIDEMIA NIGRA (*Plate XI*)

General plumage deep black ; quills dusky brown on the inner web, glossy grey beneath ; disk of the upper mandible orange-yellow ; protuberance at the base black ; no speculum on the wings. Female—general plumage brown of several shades ; bill without the protuberance ; nostrils, and a spot towards the tip, yellowish. Length eighteen inches. Eggs pale buff. A common winter visitor to the coasts of the British Isles, some non-breeding birds remaining during summer. Breeds in small numbers in northern Scotland and in one locality in Ireland.

THIS bird is well known along the eastern coast of England under the name of Black Duck. Although scattered specimens or flocks may be observed from time to time during summer, in most parts it must be considered as a winter visitant only. Being the only entirely black Duck which frequents our shores, it is distinguished among other species by its colour alone. Small or large parties of these birds may be seen on different parts of the coast, swimming and diving at a short distance outside the surf, or flying at an elevation of a few feet above the surface of the sea. They fly rapidly in a straight line, and when diving remain a long time under water. Their food consists of mussels and other shellfish, in quest of which they often ascend the creeks and arms of the sea, but they are rarely seen in fresh water.

The flesh of the Black Duck is said to be oily and fishy ; on this account it is in some Roman Catholic countries classed with fish, and allowed to be eaten during Lent. In some parts of the Continent, where it is consequently in demand, fishermen take advantage of its diving propensities, and spread their nets over the mussel banks to which they have observed that these birds resort, and capture them in large numbers. A few of this species remain to breed in the north of Scotland. The nest is a hollow in the peat, lined with grasses and down and sheltered by heather, on moors, generally within a few yards of a loch or pool. The eggs are usually five to seven in number, sometimes more.

THE POCHARD AYTHYA FERÍNA (*Plate XII*)

Head and neck bright chestnut ; breast, upper part of the back, and rump, black ; back, scapulars, flanks, and abdomen, greyish white, marked with numerous fine wavy lines ; no speculum ; bill black, with a broad lead-coloured transverse band ; irides bright orange ; feet lead-colour, the membranes black. Female—smaller ; head, neck, and breast, reddish brown ; throat white, mottled with reddish ; large brown spots on the flanks ; wavy lines on the back less distinct. Length nineteen inches. Eggs greenish white. A resident, breeding in small numbers in many parts of the British Isles : also a common winter visitor.

A HARDY northern bird of wide geographical range, with considerable power of flight, a skilful diver, and not particular as to diet, the Pochard is an abundant species. It breeds in some districts. But it is principally as a winter visitant that it is known in the south of Europe. In Norfolk ' Red-headed ' Pochards are perhaps more numerous than any other kind of Duck which falls to the gun of the seaside fowler. Small parties of these birds may frequently be seen by day flying over the sea, or swimming securely in the offing ; and in the evening great numbers resort to the fens and salt marshes, where they feed on various kinds of animal matter, and the roots and leaves of grasses and aquatic plants. As they are considered good eating, and command a ready sale, they contribute to the support of the seaside population, who, when thrown out of work by the severe weather, wander about the shore by day and lie in wait by night, armed with guns of various calibre, for the chance of securing in one or two Ducks the substitute for a day's wages.

They are variously known in different places by the name of Pochards, Pokers, Dunbirds, and Red-eyed Pochards. On some parts of the coast of Norfolk I found that they are included with the Wigeon under the common name of ' Smee-Duck '.

The Pochard builds its nest among reeds, and lays twelve or thirteen eggs.

THE SCAUP DUCK AYTHYA MARÍLA (*Plate XII*)

Head and upper part of the neck black, with green reflections ; breast and rump black ; back and scapulars whitish, marked with numerous fine wavy black lines ; belly, flanks, and speculum, white ; bill blue, the nail and edges black ; irides bright yellow ; feet ash-grey, with dusky membranes. Female—*a broad whitish band round the base of the bill ; head and neck dusky brown ; breast and rump dark brown ; back marked with fine wavy lines of black and white ; flanks spotted and pencilled with brown ; irides dull yellow. Length twenty inches. Eggs clay-buff. A common winter visitor to the coasts of the British Isles, uncommon on inland waters. Pairs occasionally remain to breed in the north of Scotland.*

THE Scaup is so called from its feeding on ' scaup ', a northern word for a bed of shellfish.[1] It is a northern bird, arriving on our coasts in October and November, and remaining with us till the following spring. During this time it frequents those parts of the coast which abound in shellfish, mostly diving for its food after the manner of the Scoters. On the coast of Norfolk, where Scaups often appear during winter in large flocks, they are called ' Mussel Ducks ', a name no less appropriate than Scaup ; for mussels, and indeed many other kinds of shellfish, as well as insects and marine plants, seem equally acceptable to them. It is generally distributed along the shores of Great Britain, excepting on the south coast of Ireland. In August, 1861, I observed two birds swimming sociably on a small fresh-water loch in the island of Islay, which, upon examination through a telescope, appeared to me to be, one, a kind of Goose, the other decidedly a Duck of some kind. On inquiry I found that the former was a

---

[1] ' Avis hæc *the Scaup Duck* dicta est quoniam *scalpam*, i.e. pisces testaceos fractos seu contritos, esitat.'—WILLUGHBY, p. 279.

Bernacle Goose, which had been caught in a neighbouring island in the previous winter, and had been given to the laird's keeper, who pinioned it and turned it out on the loch to shift for itself. Of the Duck nothing was known, nor had it been observed before. It eventually proved to be an adult male Scaup Duck, but what had induced it to remain there all the summer in the society of a bird of a different tribe, is a question which I did not attempt to solve.

The Scaup Duck is very abundant in Holland during winter, covering the inland seas with immense flocks. It is found more sparingly in other continental countries. It breeds in the extreme north, both in the eastern and western hemispheres.

THE TUFTED DUCK AYTHYA FULIGULA (*Plate XII*)

Feathers on the back of the head elongated ; head, neck, breast, and upper plumage, black, with purple, green, and bronze reflections ; speculum and under plumage white, except the abdomen, which is dusky ; bill blue, nail black ; irides bright yellow ; feet bluish, with black membranes. Female—smaller, the crest shorter ; upper plumage dull black, clouded with brown ; under plumage reddish white, spotted on the breast and flanks with reddish brown. Length seventeen inches. Eggs greenish white. A resident, breeding locally in most parts of the British Isles : also a common winter visitor.

THE Tufted Duck is now the commonest of the diving ducks on inland waters in almost all parts of this country, though when Johns wrote it was only a winter visitor, none remaining to breed. The nest is placed close to the water's edge on the banks of lakes and ponds in a tussock or under a bush and contains from six to fourteen or even more eggs.

THE LONG-TAILED DUCK OR 'CALLOO' CLANGULA
HYEMALIS (*Plate XI*)

Winter plumage—head, neck, elongated scapulars, under parts, and lateral tail-feathers, white ; a large patch of chestnut-brown on each cheek ; flanks ash-grey ; rest of the plumage brownish black ; two central tail-feathers very long ; bill black, with a transverse orange band ; irides orange ; feet yellow with dark membranes. Length, including the tail, twenty-two inches. The female wants the white scapulars and elongated tail ; head and neck dark brown and greyish white ; below the ear-coverts a patch of brown ; neck in front light brown, clouded with darker brown ; upper plumage generally dark brown ; under, white. Length sixteen inches. Eggs greenish white, tinged with buff. A plentiful winter visitor to the coasts of Scotland, much less common on the coasts of England and Ireland, and only occasionally found on inland waters.

THOUGH a few specimens of this beautiful bird are obtained from time to time in various parts of England, especially on the coast of the eastern counties, it cannot be considered other than a rarity. ' Among the northern islands of Scotland, and along the coasts of the mainland,' Macgillivray tells us, ' these birds make their appearance in October, in small flocks, which gradually enlarge by the accession of new families. In the Bay of Cromarty, where they are very common, it is pleasant to see them in small flocks scattered over the water. They are most expert swimmers, and live on bivalve shellfish and crustacea, which they obtain by diving in shallow or moderately deep water. The male in swimming raises his tail obliquely, in rough water almost erects it, and is remarkable for the grace and vivacity of his movements. Their flight is rapid, direct, and generally performed at the height of a few feet. They rise easily from the water, especially when facing a breeze, and alight rather abruptly. Sometimes during the day, but more frequently at night, they emit various loud and rather plaintive cries, as well as cacklings of shorter guttural notes.' Mr. Hewitson, who met with many of them in Norway, considers their note to be strikingly wild and most interesting. Farther north the Long-tailed Duck is yet more abundant. Mr. Dunn says, ' This species (Calloo) is very abundant in both Orkney and Shetland, arriving about the middle of October, and departing again in the month of March. It is to be met with in all the inlets or voes, generally in large flocks, never far from the land, feeding upon small shellfish and star-fish. When on the wing it utters a musical cry, something like " Calloo ", which may be heard at a great distance. From this cry it derives its provincial name.' In the Arctic regions of both continents these birds are so numerous as to be known by the name of ' Arctic Ducks '. They build their nests among rushes near the shore of fresh-water lakes, and line them with down from their breasts, like the Eider Duck. Iceland appears to be the extreme southern limit of their breeding-ground.

The Long-tailed Duck is described by Willughby under the name of *Anas caudacuta Islandica*, by the natives called *Havelda*.

THE GOLDEN EYE BUCEPHALA CLANGULA (*Plate XII*)

A white patch under the eye ; head and neck black, lustrous with violet and green ; back black ; scapulars, great wing-coverts, speculum, and under parts, white ; bill black ; irides golden yellow ; feet orange, with black membranes. Female —all the head and neck dark brown ; feathers of the back dusky, bordered with dark ash ; greater wing-coverts white, tipped with black ; speculum and under parts white ; tip of the bill yellowish, irides and feet pale yellow. Length eighteen and a half inches. Eggs buffy white. A common winter visitor to the British Isles.

THIS pretty, active little Duck is a regular winter visitant to the British shores, from autumn to spring, resorting to most of the localities frequented by other species, and frequently falling to the sportsman's gun, though little prized for the table. Females and young birds, called Morillons, are most numerous in England. They are very strong of flight, and are remarkable for making with their wings as they cleave the air a whistling sound, thought to resemble the tinkling of bells, whence the German name *die Schelle Ente*, Bell Duck, the Norfolk provincial name Rattle-Wing, and the systematic name *Clangula*. The young male does not make this noise, and having also dissimilar plumage from the adult, has been described by some authors as a distinct species under the name of Morillon.

The food of the Golden Eye varies with its haunts. In estuaries it feeds on crustaceous and molluscous animals and small fish, which it obtains by diving. In rivers and lakes it feeds principally on the larvæ and pupæ of insects, for which also it dives in clear deep water. The call-note is an unmelodious quack or croak.

The Golden Eye breeds only in high latitudes, and builds its nest in holes of trees, often at the height of twelve or fifteen feet from the water, into which it has been seen to convey its young one by one, holding them under the bill, and supported on its neck. The Lapps, in order to supply themselves with eggs, are in the habit of placing in the trees, on the banks of the rivers and lakes frequented by these birds, boxes with an entrance hole, which, though invariably robbed, are visited again and again.

The Golden Eye is found in many countries of Europe, in northern Asia, and in North America.

THE SMEW MERGUS ALBELLUS (*Plate XIII*)

Crest, neck, scapulars, smaller wing-coverts, and all the under parts, white ; cheeks and back of the head greenish black ; two crescent-shaped marks advancing from the shoulders on each side to the breast black ; tail ash-coloured ; bill and feet bluish grey, the membranes black ; irides brown. Length seventeen inches. Female smaller ; head and cheeks reddish brown ; under parts white, clouded on the breast, flanks and rump, with ash-grey ; upper plumage and tail greyish black ; wings variegated with black, white, and grey. Eggs cream or pale buff. A regular winter visitor to England, but only occasionally to Scotland, Wales, and Ireland.

THE birds of this genus, though placed among the Anatidæ, or Duck tribe, are so strongly marked by the conformation of the bill that a simple examination of the head alone will enable the student to distinguish either of the species from the true Ducks already described. On the coast of Norfolk the popular name ' Smee Duck ' includes several kinds of Ducks, and I presume the present species ; but the bill, in the form of an elongated and almost cylindrical cone, with the edges of both mandibles furnished with saw-like teeth pointed backwards, cannot fail to distinguish the genus *Mergus*.

The Smew, or Smee, properly so called, is a winter visitor with us, more impatient of cold than the Duck tribe generally, and consequently frequenting the southern more than the northern parts of the island. In open weather it resorts to our rivers and fresh-water lakes, where it feeds on small fish and other aquatic animals, which it obtains by diving. In severe frosts it either flies farther south or repairs to tidal rivers and harbours. Though not a rare bird, it is sparingly distributed. It is found on many of the continental rivers, even those which are far distant from the sea, but is not often killed, as it is shy of being approached, readily takes wing, flies swiftly, and as a diver is most rapid and expert. It is, however, little sought after, for, in spite of its relationship, its strong fishy flavour prevents it from passing muster as a Duck. In the north of Devon it is called, according to Montagu, ' Vare Wigeon ', from the supposed resemblance of its head to that of a ' vare ' or weasel. I have also heard it called the ' Weasel Duck ' in Norfolk, and on the south coast the ' Weasel-headed '. It breeds in northern Europe and Asia, nesting in holes of trees like the Golden Eye, and laying from six to nine eggs.

THE RED-BREASTED MERGANSER MERGUS SERRATOR
(Plate XIII)

Head, crest, and neck, black, with greenish reflections ; a white collar round the neck ; breast reddish brown, spotted with black ; near the insertion of the wing several white spots, edged with black ; speculum white, divided by two transverse black bars ; back black ; belly white, barred on the flanks and rump with wavy grey lines ; bill and irides red ; feet orange. Length twenty-two inches. Female *smaller ; head and crest reddish brown ; breast mottled with ash and white ; upper plumage and flanks deep ash-colour ; speculum with one black bar ; bill and feet dull orange ; irides brown. Eggs whitish ash. A resident in Scotland and Ireland and a winter visitor to the coasts of England.*

THIS large and handsome bird is not uncommon in the estuaries and rivers of Great Britain, but is most frequent in the north. It is resident in Scotland and Ireland. The adult male is less frequently seen than females and young males, which closely resemble one another in size and plumage, both being inferior to the first in brilliancy of colouring. Their food consists of fish, especially sand-eels, and, when they find their way into fresh-water lakes and rivers, of eels and trout, which they capture by diving, and retain with ease by the help of their strong bills notched throughout like a saw.

In birds of the first year the tuft of feathers on the head is barely perceptible, and there is but a slight tinge of red on the lower part of the neck. Most of the Mergansers which resort to our shores during winter visit us from high latitudes ; but a few remain to breed in the Scottish and Irish lakes, making their nests of dry herbage and moss mixed with down from their own breasts.

The name Merganser, that is, ' Diving Goose ', has reference to the size of the bird and its habit of diving for its food. Its flight is strong and rapid, but differs somewhat from that of the Ducks, the neck being not stretched out to its full length, but slightly folded back. After the young are hatched the male deserts the female and leaves her to bring off her brood without assistance.

THE GOOSANDER MERGUS MERGANSER (Plate XIII)

Head and crest greenish black ; back black ; speculum (not barred with black), under parts, wing-coverts, outer scapulars, and some of the quills, buff ; bill red, the ridge and nail black ; feet vermilion. Length twenty-four to twenty-eight inches. Female *and* young—*head and crest reddish brown ; breast and flanks pale buff ; upper plumage dark ash ; bill and feet dull red. Eggs dull white. A resident in Scotland, breeding commonly in the Highlands and in a few localities in the Lowlands ; also a frequent winter visitor to Scotland and England but only occasionally to Ireland.*

THE Goosander is a regular winter visitor to the shores of Great Britain, frequenting bays and estuaries, but preferring fresh-water rivers and lakes, where it makes great havoc among trout and other fish. It is far more abundant in the north than in the south, and though it now breeds regularly in Scotland the general summer residence of this species is much farther to the north, both in the eastern and western hemispheres. The habits of the Goosander and Merganser are so much alike that further detail is unnecessary.

The females and young birds of the Goosander and Merganser are popularly called Dun-divers.

ORDER FALCONIFORMES

FAMILY ACCIPITRIDÆ

THE GOLDEN EAGLE ÁQUILA CHRYSAËTOS (*Plate XIV*)

Tail longer than the wings, rounded ; plumage of the head, back of the neck and legs, lustrous reddish brown, of the rest of the body dark brown ; primaries nearly black ; secondaries brownish black ; tail dark grey, barred and tipped with brownish black ; beak bluish at the base, black at the extremity ; iris brown ; cere and feet yellow ; claws bluish black. Length of the male *three feet, that of the* female *more ; breadth eight feet. Eggs dirty white, mottled with pale reddish brown. Resident in the Highlands of Scotland and the Hebrides ; elsewhere a very rare straggler.*

THE fable of the Eagle soaring to a great height in order to enjoy a gaze at the sun in his unclouded brilliancy, is founded probably on a belief of the ancients, thus stated by the naturalist Pliny : ' Before its young are as yet fledged, the Eagle compels them to gaze at the rays of the sun, and if it observes one to wink or show a watery eye casts it from the nest as a degenerate offspring ; if, on the contrary, it pre- serves a steady gaze, it is saved from this hard fate, and brought up.'

' The Golden Eagle ', says Macgillivray, ' seems to prefer live prey to carrion, and easily secures Grouse, in searching for which it flies low on the moors, sailing and wheeling at intervals. Hares, roes, and even red deer, it also attacks, but it does not haunt the shores for fish so much as the Sea Eagle does. There seems very little probability that Eagles have the sense of smell very acute, but that their vision is so is evident. I am not, however, inclined to think that they perceive objects from the vast height to which they sometimes soar, because I never saw one descend from such an elevation in a manner indicating that it had observed a carcase or other eatable object ; whereas, on the other hand, I have very frequently seen them flying along the sides of the hills, at a small height, obviously in search of food, in a manner somewhat resembling that of the Sparrow-Hawk, but with much less rapidity.'

The Golden Eagle breeds only in the Highlands. Those birds which have been recorded as visiting England were generally not this species but the White-tailed or Sea Eagle in immature plumage. It prefers mountains or extensive forests, building its eyrie either on rocks or lofty trees. In France, Sweden, Spain, and Switzerland, it is frequently observed. Its note, called in the Highlands a ' bark ', is sharp and loud, resembling at a distance, as, on the only occasion I ever heard it, it seemed to me, the croak of a Raven. It lays two or sometimes three eggs, and feeds its young, which are very voracious, on birds and the smaller quadrupeds.

THE SPOTTED EAGLE AQUILA CLANGA (*Plate XIV*)

General colour reddish brown ; tail brown above ; legs feathered in front of the toes. Length twenty-six inches. Eggs greyish white, sometimes spotted or blotched with dark brown. A rare straggler to the British Isles.

THE WHITE-TAILED (SEA) EAGLE HALIÆTUS ALBICILLA (*Plate XIV*)

Tail not longer than the wings ; upper plumage brown, that of the head and neck lightest, lower, chocolate brown ; tail white ; beak, cere, and feet, yellowish white ; claws black. In young birds the tail is dark brown, and the beak and cere of a darker hue. Length of the male, two feet four inches ; of the female, two feet ten inches. Eggs dirty white, with a few pale red marks. Formerly resident, now only a rare visitor to the British Isles in winter.

THE White-tailed Eagle, known also by the name of the Sea Eagle, is about equal in size to the Golden Eagle, but differs considerably in character and habits ; for while the latter has been known to pounce on a pack of Grouse and carry off two or three from before the very eyes of the astonished sportsman and his dogs, or to appropriate for his own special picking a hunted hare when about to become the prey of the hounds, the White-tailed Eagle has been observed to fly terror-struck from a pair of Skua Gulls, making no return for their heavy buffets but a series of dastardly shrieks. The ordinary food, too, of the nobler bird is living animals, though, to tell the truth, he is always ready to save himself the trouble of a chase, if he can meet with the carcase of a sheep or lamb ; but the White-tailed Eagle feeds principally on fish, water-fowl, the smaller quadrupeds, and offal, whether of quadrupeds, birds, or fish. On such fare, when pressed by hunger, he feeds so greedily that he gorges himself till, unable to rise, he becomes the easy prey of the shepherd's boy armed but with a stick or stone. It inhabits Greenland, Iceland, Norway, and Sweden, where it frequents the vicinity of the sea and large lakes. In winter it appears to leave the high latitudes and come farther south, not perhaps so much on account of cold as because, its ordinary prey being driven to seek a genial climate, it is compelled to accompany its food. It builds its nest either in forests, choosing the summit of the loftiest trees, or among inaccessible cliffs overhanging the sea. The materials are sticks, heath, tufts of grass, dry seaweed, and it lays two eggs. The young are very voracious, and are fed by the parent birds for some time after they have left the nest, but when able to provide for themselves are driven from the neighbourhood to seek food and a home elsewhere.

THE OSPREY PANDION HALIÆTUS (*Plate XIV*)

Wings longer than the tail ; feathers of the head and neck white, with dark centres ; on each side of the neck a streak of blackish brown, extending downwards ; upper plumage generally deep brown ; under, white, tinged here and there with yellow, and on the breast marked with arrow-shaped spots ; tail-feathers barred with dusky bands ; cere and beak dark grey ; iris yellow. Length two feet ; breadth five feet. Eggs reddish white, blotched and spotted with dark reddish brown. Formerly a summer visitor, breeding in Scotland, now only a scarce passage migrant through Great Britain.

' ENDOWED with intense keenness of sight, it hovers high in the air, and having descried a fish in the sea, it darts down with great rapidity, dashes aside the water with its body, and seizes its prey in an instant.' So says the ancient naturalist Pliny, describing a bird which he calls *Haliaëtus*, or Sea Eagle. Eighteen centuries later, Montagu thus described a bird, which, when he first observed it, was hawking for fish on the river Avon, near Aveton Gifford, in Devonshire : ' At last ', he says, ' its attention was arrested, and like the Kestrel in search of mice, it became stationary, as if examining what had attracted its attention. After a pause of some time, it descended to within about fifty yards of the surface of the water, and there continued hovering for another short interval, and then precipitated itself into the water with such great celerity as to be nearly immersed. In three or four minutes the bird rose without any apparent difficulty, and carried off a trout of moderate size, and instead of alighting to regale upon its prey, soared to a prodigious height, and did not descend within our view.' There can be no reasonable doubt that the bird thus described at such distant intervals of time is the same, and that the Sea Eagle of the ancients is the Osprey of the moderns. Wilson thus eloquently describes its habits under the name of the ' Fish Hawk ' : ' Elevated on the high dead limb of some gigantic tree, that commands a wide view of the neighbouring shore and ocean, the great White-headed Eagle seems calmly to contemplate the motions of the various feathered tribes that pursue their busy vocations below. High over all these hovers one whose actions instantly arrest all his attention. By his wide curvature of wing, and sudden suspension in air, he knows him to be the Fish Hawk settling over some devoted victim of the deep. His eye kindles at the sight, and balancing himself with half-open wings on the branch, he watches the result. Down, rapid as an arrow from heaven, descends the distant object of his attention, the roar of its wings reaching the ear as it disappears in the deep, making the surges foam around. At this moment the eager looks of the Eagle are all ardour ; and, levelling his neck for flight, he sees the Fish Hawk once more emerge struggling with his prey, and mounting in the air with screams of exultation. These are the signals for our hero, who, launching into the air, instantly gives chase, soon gains on the Fish Hawk : each exerts his utmost to mount above the other, displaying in the rencontres the most elegant and sublime aërial evolutions. The unincumbered Eagle rapidly advances, and is just on the point of reaching his opponent, when, with a sudden scream, probably of despair and honest execration, the latter drops his fish ; the Eagle, poising himself for a moment, as if to take a more certain aim, descends like a whirlwind, snatches it in his grasp ere it reaches the water, and bears his ill-gotten booty silently away to the woods.'

The Osprey has been observed on various parts of the coast of Great Britain and Ireland, especially in autumn, and is known in Sussex and Hampshire as the Mullet Hawk, because of its liking for that fish. It may be considered as a citizen of the world, for it occurs in various parts of Europe, Africa, India, and Australia. In North America, we have already seen, it is abundant. It builds its nest of sticks on some rock or ruin, generally near the water, and lays two or three eggs.

THE SPARROW-HAWK ACCIPITER NISUS (*Plate XVI*)

Upper plumage dark bluish grey, with a white spot on the nape of the neck ; lower, reddish white, transversely barred with deep brown ; tail grey, barred with brownish black ; beak blue, lightest at the base ; cere, irides, and feet, yellow ; claws black. Female—upper parts brown, passing into blackish grey ; lower, greyish white, barred with dark grey. Length, male twelve inches, female fifteen inches ; breadth, male twenty-four inches, female twenty-eight inches. Eggs bluish white, blotched and spotted with deep rusty brown. A common resident in wooded districts of the British Isles ; also a passage migrant, chiefly along the east coast.

SINCE the introduction of firearms, the Goshawk and Sparrow-Hawk have lost much of their reputation, every effort being now made to exterminate them, for carrying on, on their own account, the same practices which in bygone days they were enlisted to pursue on behalf of others. For hawking, it must be remembered, was not exclusively a pastime followed by the high and noble for amusement's sake, but was, in one of its branches, at least, a very convenient method of supplying the table with game ; and that, too, at a period when there were not the same appliances, in the shape of turnips, oil-cake, etc., for fattening cattle and producing beef and mutton in unlimited quantities, that there are now. The produce of the fish-ponds, woods, and fields was then a matter of some moment, and much depended on the training of the Hawks and diligence of the falconer whether the daily board should be plentifully or scantily furnished. In recent times, even, some idea of the intrinsic value of a good Hawk may be gathered from the fact that, in Lombardy, it was thought nothing extraordinary for a single Sparrow-Hawk to take for his master from seventy to eighty Quails in a single day. In the Danubian Provinces and in Hungary, the practice of hunting Quails with Sparrow-Hawks is still in vogue ; but with us, the agile bird is left to pursue his prey on his own account. And right well does he exercise his calling. Unlike the Kestrel, which soars high in air and mostly preys on animals which when once seen have no power of escape, the Sparrow-Hawk is marked by its dashing, onward flight. Skimming rapidly across the open fields, by no means refusing to swoop on any bird or quad-ruped worthy of its notice, but not preferring this kind of hunting-ground, it wings its easy way to the nearest hedge, darts along by the side, turns sharply to the right or left through an opening caused by a gate or gap, and woe to any little bird which it may encounter, either perched on a twig or resting on the ground. Unerring in aim, and secure of its holdfast, it allows its victims no chance of escape ; one miserable scream, and their fate is sealed. And even if the prey detects its coming enemy, and seeks safety in flight, its only hope is to slip into the thick bushes and trust to concealment ; resort to the open field is all but certain death. Nor is it fastidious in its choice of food —leverets, young rabbits, mice, partridges, thrushes, blackbirds, sparrows, larks, pipits, and many others are equal favourites. It resorts very frequently to the homestead and farmyard, not so much in quest of chickens, which, by the way, it does not despise, as for the sake of the small birds which abound in such places. There it is a bold robber, little heeding the presence of men, suddenly dashing from behind some barn or cornrick, and rapidly disappearing with its luck-less prey struggling in its talons, pursued, perhaps, by the vociferous twitter of the outraged flock, but not dispirited against another onslaught. This coursing for its prey, though the usual, is not the only method of furnishing his larder pursued by the Sparrow-Hawk. He has been known to station himself on the branch of a tree in the neighbourhood of some favourite resort of Sparrows, concealed himself, but commanding a fair view of the flock below. With an intent as deadly as that of the fowler when he points his gun, he puts on the attitude of flight before he quits his perch, then selecting his victim, and pouncing on it all but simultaneously, he retires to devour his meal and to return to his post as soon as the hubbub he has excited has subsided somewhat. At times he pays dear for his temerity. Pouncing on a bird which the sportsman has put up and missed, he receives the contents of the second barrel ; making a swoop on the bird-catcher's call-bird, he becomes entangled in the meshes ; or dashing through a glazed window at a caged Canary bird, he finds his retreat cut off.

As is the case with most predaceous birds, the female is larger and bolder than the male, and will attack birds superior to herself in size. Though a fierce enemy, she is an affectionate mother, and will defend her young at the risk of her life. She builds her nest, or appropriates the deserted nest of a Crow, in trees, or if they be wanting, in a cliff, and lays four or five eggs. The young are very voracious, and are fed principally on small birds, the number of which consumed may be inferred from the fact that no less than sixteen Larks, Sparrows, and other small birds, were on one occasion found in a nest, the female parent belonging to which had been shot while conveying to them a young bird just brought to the neighbourhood of the nest by the male ; the latter, it was conjectured, having brought them all, and deposited them in the nest in the interval of nine hours which had elapsed between their discovery and the death of his partner.

THE RED KITE MILVUS MILVUS (*Plate XV*)

Upper parts reddish brown ; the feathers with pale edges ; those of the head and neck long and tapering to a point, greyish white, streaked longitudinally with brown ; lower parts rust-coloured, with longitudinal brown streaks ; tail reddish orange, barred indistinctly with brown ; beak horn-coloured ; cere, irides, and feet, yellow ; claws black. Female—upper plumage of a deeper brown ; the feathers pale at the extremity ; head and neck white. Length twenty-five inches ; breadth five feet six inches. Eggs dirty white, spotted at the larger end with red-brown. Formerly a common resident in Great Britain, now only breeding in south-central Wales, and a rare straggler elsewhere.

' THE Kite ', Pliny informs us, ' seems, by the movement of its tail, to have taught mankind the art of steering—nature pointing out in the air what is necessary in the sea.' The movement of the bird through the air indeed resembles sailing more than flying. ' One cannot ', says Buffon, ' but admire the manner in which the flight of the Kite is performed ; his long and narrow wings seem motionless ; it is his tail that seems to direct all his evolutions, and he moves it continuously ; he rises without effort, comes down as if he were sliding along an inclined plane ; he seems rather to swim than to fly ; he darts forward, slackens his speed, stops, and remains suspended or fixed in the same place for whole hours without exhibiting the smallest motion of his wings.' The Kite generally moves along at a moderate height, but sometimes, like the Eagle, rises to the more elevated regions of the air, where it may always be distinguished by its long wings and forked tail.

In France, it is known by the name ' Milan Royal ', the latter title being given to it not on account of any fancied regal qualities, but because in ancient times it was subservient to the pleasures of princes. In those times, hawking at the Kite and Heron was the only kind of sport dignified with the title of ' Chase Royal ', and no one—not even a nobleman—could attack the Kite and Heron without infringing the privileges of the king.

Though larger than the noble Falcons, it is far inferior to them in daring and muscular strength ; cowardly in attacking the strong, pitiless to the weak. It rarely assails a bird on the wing, but takes its prey on the ground, where nothing inferior to itself in courage seems to come amiss to it. Moles, rats, mice, reptiles, and Partridges, are its common food ; it carries off also goslings, ducklings, and chickens, though it retires ignominiously before an angry hen. When pressed by hunger, it does not refuse the offal of animals, or dead fish ; but being an expert fisherman, it does not confine itself to dead food of this kind, but pounces on such fish as it discerns floating near the surface of the water—carries them off in its talons, and devours them on shore.

The Kite is more abundant in the northern than the southern countries of Europe, to which latter, however, numerous individuals migrate in autumn. It builds its nest of sticks, lined with straw and moss, in lofty trees, and lays three or four eggs.

THE COMMON BUZZARD BUTEO BUTEO (*Plate XV*)

Upper plumage, neck and head, dark brown ; lower, greyish brown, mottled with darker brown ; tail marked with twelve dark transverse bands ; beak lead-coloured ; cere, iris, and feet, yellow. Length twenty to twenty-two inches. Eggs white, variously marked with pale greenish brown. A resident breeding in western England, Wales, and Scotland, but not in the Orkneys and Shetlands ; formerly in Ireland but now exterminated. Also a winter visitor, chiefly to the eastern counties of England and Scotland.

THE Buzzard is deficient in the graceful activity which characterizes the Falcons. In sluggishness of habits it approaches the Vultures, and in its soft plumage and mode of flight the Owls ; but differs from the former in feeding on live prey as well as carrion, and from the latter in its diurnal habits. In form indeed it resembles neither, being a bulky broad-winged Hawk, with stout legs and a short much-curved beak. It can fly swiftly enough when occasion requires, but its favourite custom is to take its station on some withered branch, or on the projecting corner of a rock, whence it can both obtain a good view of the surrounding country, and, when it has digested its last meal, sally forth in quest of a new one as soon as a victim comes within its range of observation. It pounces on this while on the ground, and pursues its chase with a low skimming flight, keeping a sharp look-out for moles, young hares and rabbits, mice, reptiles, small birds, and insects. At times it rises high into the air, and, soaring in circles, examines the surface of the ground for carrion. It has neither the spirit nor daring of the noble Falcons, submitting patiently to the attacks of birds much less than itself, and flying from the Magpie or Jackdaw. As an architect the Buzzard displays no more constructive skill than other birds of its tribe, building its nest of a few sticks, either on a rock or in a tree, and not infrequently occupying the deserted nest of some other bird. It has, however, a redeeming point, being a most assiduous nurse. The female sits close, and will allow the near approach of an intruder before she leaves her eggs. In captivity, strange to say, though by nature having a strong inclination for the flesh of chickens, she has been known to sit on the eggs of the domestic hen, to hatch a brood, and to rear them with as much solicitude as their natural mother could have shown, distributing to them morsels of raw meat, not comprehending, of course, their repugnance to such fare, and bearing with extreme patience and good humour their unaccountable preference for barley and crumbs of bread. The male bird is scarcely less affectionate as a parent : an instance being recorded of one, which, on the death of his partner, completed the period of incubation and reared the young brood by himself. The Buzzard rarely molests game, and more than compensates for the mischief it does work, by the destruction of undoubted vermin ; yet the hostility shown by gamekeepers against all birds except those which it is their business to protect, has so thinned its numbers that the Buzzard, though once common, is now extinct in Ireland and most parts of England.

THE ROUGH-LEGGED BUZZARD BUTEO LAGÓPUS
(Plate XV)

Tarsi feathered to the claws ; plumage yellowish white, variegated with several shades of brown ; a broad patch of brown on the breast ; tail white in the basal half, the rest uniform brown ; beak black ; cere and irides yellow ; feathers on the legs fawn-coloured, spotted with brown ; toes yellow ; claws black. Length twenty-six inches. Eggs whitish, clouded with reddish brown. A winter visitor to the British Isles chiefly to the eastern counties of Scotland and England.

THIS bird, which is distinguished from the preceding by having its legs thickly clothed with long feathers, is a native of the colder countries of both Continents, being only an occasional visitor in Great Britain during autumn and winter. It is sometimes seen in large flights on the Yarmouth Denes in October and November, at the same time with the Short-eared Owl. It mostly frequents the banks of rivers, where it feeds on vermin, reptiles, and the carcases of animals brought down by the floods. In softness of plumage and mode of flight, it resembles the Owls even more than the preceding species, and often extends its hunting expeditions until far into the evening. When not alarmed, it flies slowly and deliberately, and seemingly has neither the inclination nor the power to attack living birds, unless they have been previously disabled by wounds or other cause. The Rough-legged Buzzard builds its nest in lofty trees, and lays three or four eggs ; but there are no well-authenticated instances of its breeding in this country.

THE HONEY BUZZARD PERNIS APIVORUS (Plate XV)

Lores or spaces between eyes and bill are covered with feathers. The head of male is ash-grey, his upper parts brown ; three blackish bars cross the tail ; upper parts white-barred and spotted with brown on the breast. Length twenty-two to twenty-five inches ; female slightly the larger. Eggs white, usually heavily washed or blotched with purplish or reddish brown. A rare summer visitor, now only occasionally nesting in England ; also an uncommon passage migrant.

THIS species visits us during May and June, and a few stay to nest, placing the nest upon the remains of that of some other large bird. Wasps, wild bees, and larvæ form their food in summer, but other insects are eaten, and sometimes birds, mice, other small mammals, worms, and slugs. From two to four eggs are laid, both male and female taking part in the incubation. The sitting bird is regularly fed by the other.

The Honey Buzzard has bred from the New Forest up to Aberdeenshire. Unfortunately, as much as £5 having been offered for a couple of well-marked eggs of this species in the New Forest by collectors, their numbers have become very few. Nearly £40 has been offered by extravagant collectors for a good pair of the birds. By the year 1870 nearly all were driven away from that district.

THE MARSH HARRIER CIRCUS ÆRUGINOSUS (*Plate XVI*)

Head, neck, and breast, yellowish white, with numerous longitudinal brown streaks ; wing-coverts reddish brown ; primary quills white at the base, the rest black ; tail and secondaries ash-grey ; lower plumage reddish brown ; beak bluish black ; cere, irides, and feet, yellow ; claws black. Length twenty inches. Eggs white. Formerly widespread in the British Isles, but now almost exterminated. A few pairs breed in the Broads district of Norfolk, but elsewhere it only occurs as a straggler.

THE Harriers are bold predatory voracious birds, having somewhat of the appearance and movements of the Hawks. On a closer inspection, however, they are seen to approach nearer in character to the Owls. In the first place, they hunt their prey more in the morning and evening than at any other time of day. In the next place, these twilight habits are associated with a large head, and a somewhat defined face formed by a circle of short feathers ; while the plumage generally is soft and loose, and their mode of hunting resembles that of the nocturnal predatory birds, rather than that of the Falcons. They are remarkable for the great difference which exists between the plumage of the two sexes, which has made the task of discriminating the number of species very difficult. Less active than the Falcons, they yet carry on a formidable war against small birds, reptiles, and mice. The Harriers or Harrows are so called from their *harrying* propensities. Of similar import is the etymology of the English word ' havoc ', which may be clearly traced to the Anglo-Saxon *hafoc*, or hawk. The habit of the Marsh Harrier is not to station itself on a tree or rock, thereon to explore the country ; but while hunting, it is always on the wing, skimming along the ground, and beating about the bushes with a noiseless, unsteady flight, and always taking its prey on the ground. Rabbit-warrens afford this bird a favourite hunting-ground, where it either pounces on such living animals as it can surprise, or performs the office of undertaker to the dead bodies of rabbits killed by the weasels, burying them in the grave of its craw. On the seashore, the Marsh Harrier commits great depredations among young water-fowl, and is often mobbed and driven from the neighbourhood by the assembled old birds. The Partridge and Quail often, too, fall victims to its voracity, so that the Marsh Harrier receives no quarter from gamekeepers. It places its nest generally near water, in a tuft of rushes, or at the base of a bush, constructing it of sticks, rushes, and long grass, and lays three or four eggs.

It was formerly known as the Moor Buzzard.

THE HEN HARRIER CIRCUS CYÁNEUS (*Plate XVII*)

Tail longer than the wings ; third and fourth primaries of equal length ; upper plumage of the male *bluish grey ; lower white. Upper plumage of the* female *reddish brown ; lower, pale reddish yellow, with deep orange-brown longitudinal streaks and spots. Rump white in both sexes. Beak black ; cere greenish yellow ; irides reddish brown ; feet yellow ; claws black. Length,* male *eighteen inches ;* female *twenty inches. Eggs white. Formerly common, now only breeds regularly in the Orkneys and Outer Hebrides and occasionally elsewhere. As a passage migrant and winter visitor it occurs in small numbers throughout the British Isles.*

THE Hen Harrier and Ringtail were formerly considered distinct species ; and no wonder ; for not only are they different in size, but dissimilar in colour, one having the upper parts grey, the lower white ; and the other the upper parts reddish brown, and various parts of the plumage of a light colour, barred and streaked with deep brown. The experienced ornithologist, Montagu, suspecting that they were male and female of the same species, undertook to clear up the matter by rearing a brood taken from the same nest. The result was that at first there was no great difference except in size, all having the dark plumage of the Hen Harrier ; but after the first moult, the males assumed the grey and white plumage, while the larger birds, the females, retained the gayer colouring, and the latter was the Ringtail. In habits both birds resemble the Marsh Harrier, but do not confine themselves to damp places. They frequent open plains, hillsides, and enclosed fields, hunting a few feet above the surface of the ground, and beating for game as skilfully as a well-trained spaniel. The moment that the Harrier sees a probable victim he rises to a height of twenty feet, hovers for a moment, and then comes down with unerring aim on his prey, striking dead with a single blow, Partridge or Pheasant, Grouse or Blackcock, and showing strength not to be expected from his light figure, and slender, though sharp talons. Not unfrequently he accompanies the sportsman, keeping carefully out of shot, and pouncing on the birds, killing them, and carrying them off to be devoured in retirement. He preys exclusively on animals, killed by himself, destroying a great quantity of game, small mammals, birds, and reptiles. It is met with occasionally in most countries of Europe and Asia, and in various parts of the British Isles. It is far from improbable that this bird may frequently be seen, without being recognized as belonging to the Hawk tribe ; indeed, the beautiful form and light blue and white plumage, might cause it to be mistaken for a

Gull. It builds a flattish nest of sticks, just raised above the ground, in a heather, or furze-bush, and lays four to six eggs.

MONTAGU'S HARRIER CIRCUS PYGARGUS (*Plate XVII*)

Wings a little longer than the tail ; third primary longer than the fourth and second ; upper plumage bluish grey ; primaries black, secondaries with three transverse dark bars ; lateral tail-feathers white, barred with reddish orange ; under plumage white, variously streaked with reddish orange. Female—upper plumage brown of various tints ; under, pale reddish yellow, with longitudinal bright red streaks. Beak black ; cere deep yellow ; irides hazel ; feet yellow ; claws black. Length seventeen inches. Eggs bluish white. A summer visitor breeding in various parts of southern and eastern England and in Wales ; elsewhere in the British Isles only an occasional straggler.

THIS bird, which is of rare occurrence in Britain, resembles the Hen Harrier very closely, both in appearance and habits, although it is smaller and more slender, and the wings are longer in proportion. On the Continent, especially in Holland, it is more frequent. It received its name in honour of Colonel Montagu, who was the first to ascertain the identity of the Hen Harrier and Ringtail, and to separate the present species from both.

FAMILY FALCONIDÆ

THE PEREGRINE FALCON FALCO PEREGRINUS (*Plate XVII*)

Tail not longer than the wings ; upper plumage dark bluish grey with darker bands ; head bluish black, as are also the moustaches descending from the gape ; lower plumage white ; breast transversely barred with brown ; beak blue, darker at the point ; cere yellow ; iris dark brown ; feet yellow ; claws black. Female—upper plumage tinged with brown, lower with reddish yellow. Length fifteen inches ; female seventeen inches. Eggs dull light red, spotted and blotched with deep red. A resident, breeding in mountainous and hilly districts of the British Isles, and on sea-cliffs ; in winter more widely distributed.

THE Peregrine Falcon occupies among the ' noble ' birds of prey a place second only in dignity to the Gyr Falcon. Indeed, from its being more generally diffused and therefore more easily obtained, it is a question whether it was not considered, in England at least, the special bird of falconry. In France it appears to have been used almost exclusively as the Falcon of the country ; and as the number of Gyr Falcons imported to England must have fallen far short of the demand when the gentle science was in full vogue, here also the Peregrine must be considered the bird of falconry. The ' noble ' Falcons were those which flew fearlessly on any birds, no matter how much larger they were than themselves, and at once deprived their prey of life by pouncing on a vital part, devouring the head before they lacerated the carcase. The name Peregrine (foreigner) was given to this bird on account of its wide dispersion through most regions of the globe, and for the same reason it has long borne in France the name of *Pèlerin* (pilgrim), and not on account of its wide range in search of quarry. It is a bird of haughty aspect and rich colouring, sagacious, powerful, and daring ; a type of the chivalry of the Middle Ages, a veritable knight-errant, always armed, and ready to do battle in any cause against all comers.

In France the Peregrine Falcon is most abundant in the marshy districts of the north, which are much frequented by Snipes and Wild Duck ; with us it is most commonly seen in those parts of the sea-coast where sea-fowl abound. The high cliffs of the Isle of Wight, Beachy Head, North Wales, and the Scottish coast are favourite haunts. It makes its eyrie in the most inaccessible part of the cliff, constructing no nest, but laying two to four eggs in a cavity of a rock where a little loose earth has been deposited ; sometimes in the deserted nest of the Raven or Carrion Crow. If either of the old birds happens to be shot during the period of breeding, it is incredible in how short a space of time the survivor finds a new mate. Within a short distance from their nest they establish a larder well supplied with Puffins, Jackdaws and, above all, Kestrels ; while the immediate neighbourhood is strewed with bones. Remarkable as are both male and female bird for muscular power and high courage, the latter, which is also considerably larger, is by far the superior. The female was, consequently, in the days of falconry flown at Herons and Ducks, and she was the falcon proper among falconers ; the male, termed a Tiercel or Tiercelet, was flown at Partridges and Pigeons. In their native haunts they seem to cause little alarm among the Puffins and Razorbills by which they are surrounded, but the sudden appearance of a pair in a part of the cliff frequented by Jackdaws, causes terrible consternation ; while any number of intruders on their own domain are driven away with indomitable courage. When pressed by hunger, or desirous of changing their diet, they condescend to attack and capture birds so small as a Lark, and it is remarkable that however puny may be the prey, the Falcon preserves its instinctive habit of dealing a deadly blow at once, as if afraid that under all circumstances the natural impulse of its quarry were to stand on the defensive. Even in ordinary flight the movement of its wings is exceedingly quick, but when it stoops on its prey its rapidity of descent is marvellous, accompanied too, as it is, by a sound that may be heard at a distance of two hundred yards. Perhaps no bird has had more written about it than this Falcon ; numerous treatises have been composed on the art of ' reclaiming ' it, or training it for hawking, and the proper method of conducting the sport. We have at present space only to add a few words on the latter subject. The art of the falconer is to intercept the Herons when flying against the wind. When a Heron passes, *a cast* or couple of Falcons are thrown off, which dart into the air, flying in a spiral direction to get above the Heron. As soon as the first has attained the necessary elevation, she makes a stoop, and if she misses, a second stoop is made by the other in her turn. When one has succeeded in striking its prey, the other joins in the attack, and all three birds come to the ground together, buoyed in their descent by their expanded wings. The falconer now comes to the rescue, for though the Heron makes no resistance in the air, as soon as it reaches the ground it uses its formidable beak in defence, and unless prevented may work much mischief to its pursuers.

> As when a cast of Faulcons make their flight
> At an Heronshaw that lyes aloft on wing,
> The whyles they strike at him with heedlesse might
> The wary foule his bill doth backward wring.
> On which the first, whose force her first doth bring,
> Herselfe quite through the bodie doth engore,
> And falleth downe to ground like senselesse thing,
> But th' other, not so swift as she before,
> Fayles of her souse, and passing by doth hurt no more.
>
> *Faerie Queene.*

In France the ' cast ' consisted of three Falcons, which were trained to perform particular duties, the first to start the game in the required direction, the second to keep guard over it, and the third to deal the fatal swoop.

THE HOBBY FALCO SUBBUTEO (*Plate XVI*)

Wings longer than the tail ; upper plumage bluish black ; beneath, reddish yellow, with longitudinal brown streaks ; moustaches broad, black ; lower tail-coverts and feathers on the leg reddish ; beak bluish, darker at the tip ; cere greenish yellow ; iris dark brown ; feet yellow ; claws black. Female— all the colours duller, and the streaks below broader. Length twelve to fourteen inches ; breadth about two feet. Eggs yellowish white, speckled with reddish brown. A summer visitor breeding in England and Wales, chiefly in the south ; only a rare straggler to Scotland and Ireland.

The Hobby is a less common bird in England than in France, where it is said to be a constant companion of the sportsman, and to be endowed with enough discrimination to keep out of shot. Not satisfied with appropriating to its own use wounded birds, it pursues and captures those which have been fired at unsuccessfully, and not unfrequently even those which have been put up but have not come within shot. It is frequently taken, too, in the nets spread for Larks, or inveigled into the snare of the fowler who pursues his craft with limed twigs and the imitated cry of the Owl. It is a bird of passage, both on the Continent and in England, arriving and taking its departure at about the same time with the Swallow. In form and colouring it somewhat resembles the Peregrine Falcon, but is much smaller and more slender ; the wings, too, are larger in proportion, and the dark stripes beneath are longitudinal instead of transverse. Its natural prey consists for the most part of Larks and other small birds, beetles, and other large insects. It has been trained for hawking small birds ; but owing, perhaps, to its migratory habits, it was found to be impatient of captivity, and was not much prized. Hobbies frequently hunt in pairs, and an instance has been recorded where one hunted a Lark in company with a Hen Harrier ; but the latter, a bird of heavier flight, was soon compelled to give up the chase. It builds its nest, or appropriates a deserted one, in high trees, and lays three or four eggs.

THE MERLIN FALCO COLUMBARIUS (*Plate XVI*)

Tail longer than the wings ; upper plumage greyish blue ; lower, reddish yellow, with longitudinal oblong dark brown spots ; tail barred with black ; beak bluish, darker at the tip ; cere yellow ; irides dark brown ; feet yellow, claws black. Female—*above tinged with brown ; below, yellowish white. Length eleven to twelve inches ; breadth two feet. Eggs mottled with two shades of dark reddish brown. A resident, breeding in moorland districts of the British Isles ; in winter also occurring in lowlands.*

THE Merlin, or Stone Falcon (so called from its habit of alighting on stones to watch the flight of the small birds which it intends to make its prey), is a beautiful little bird, but notwithstanding its small body ranks among the ' noble ' Falcons. Associated with the Sparrow-Hawk, it was, on the Continent, anciently trained to hunt Quails—and the old falconers are loud in its praises. In England, it was accounted especially the Ladies' Hawk. In a state of nature, it has been observed to attack the Partridge, Magpie, Starling, Blackbird, etc., but its favourite prey is the Lark ; and it was to fly at this bird principally, that it was formerly trained. In hawking with Merlins, three of these birds were assigned to the Magpie, two to the Lark, and in the chase of the Quail and Land-Rail, the Sparrow-Hawk was associated with it. The Merlin is more frequent in the northern than in the southern part of Great Britain, and is seen more frequently in winter than in summer, but is nowhere common. It occasionally, perhaps generally, breeds in Northumberland, Cumberland, and North Wales, placing its nest upon the ground amongst the heather, and laying four or five eggs.

THE KESTREL FALCO TINNÚNCULUS (*Plate XVII*)

Wings shorter than the tail ; upper plumage, neck and breast, dark lead-grey ; sides, under tail-coverts and thighs, light yellowish red, with longitudinal narrow dark streaks ; beak blue, lighter towards the base ; cere and feet yellow ; irides brown ; claws black. Female—*upper plumage and tail light red, with transverse spots and bars of dark brown ; lower, paler than in the* male. *Length fifteen inches ; breadth thirty inches. Eggs reddish white, blotched and mottled with dark red-brown. A common resident throughout the British Isles.*

THE Kestrel being the most abundant and by far the most conspicuous in its habits of all the British birds of prey, is probably, in most instances, the bird which has been observed whenever the appearance of ' a Hawk ' has been mentioned. Though rapid in flight whenever it chooses to put forth its full powers, it is more remarkable for the habit which has acquired for it the name of ' Windhover ' ; and there can scarcely be any one, however unobservant, who makes even but an occasional expedition into the country, but has stopped and gazed with delight on its skilful evolutions. Suspended aloft, with its head turned towards the wind, but neither advancing against the breeze, nor moved by it from its position, it agitates its wings as regularly and evenly as if they were turned on a pivot by machinery. Presently, impelled as it were by a spirit of restlessness, it suddenly darts forward, perhaps ascending or descending a few feet, and making a slight turn either to the right or the left. Then it skims on with extended, motionless pinions, and once more anchors itself to the air. But on what object is it intent all this while ? for that some design is present here is indubit-able. Not surely on the capture of birds, for at that slight elevation its keen eye would detect the movement of a bird at a mere glance ; nor has it the dashing flight one would expect to see in a hunter after game furnished with the same organs of motion as itself. But, if intent on the capture of small animals which creep out of holes in the earth and hunt for their food among the grass, surely no method can be conceived of exploring the field so quickly and so completely. The Kestrel, then, though stigmatized by gamekeepers with an evil name, does not merit the reproaches heaped on it ; while to the farmer it is an invaluable ally, destroying countless beetles, the grubs of which would gnaw away the roots of his crops ; caterpillars, which would devour the foliage ; and, above all, mice, which would fatten on the grain. For such food its appetite is enormous, and its stomach capacious, an instance being recorded of a specimen having been shot, the craw of which contained no less than seventy-nine caterpillars, twenty-four beetles, a full-grown field mouse, and a leech. To this varied bill of fare it adds, as occasion offers, slow-worms, lizards, frogs, grasshoppers, and earthworms. In the winter, indeed, when these animals have withdrawn to their retreats, it is compelled by hunger to provide itself with what my readers would consider more palatable food ; for now it preys on any birds which it is swift enough to overtake, and strong enough to master. The skill with which it plucks the feathers from birds before tearing them to pieces, certainly argues in favour of the theory that a bird-diet is not unnatural to it, or, that the habit, if an acquired one, came to an apt learner. But in autumn and winter, game-birds are fully fledged and being quite able to take care of themselves are by no means liable to fall a prey to the Kestrel. Thus, admitting, as we fear we must, that if, while hovering for mice, it detects a young Partridge in the hayfield, it is unable to withstand the temptation of carrying it off as a delicate repast for its young, yet an occasional trespass of this kind far from counterbalances the advantages it confers as a consistent destroyer of vermin.

The Kestrel appears to be generally distributed over the country, showing no marked predilection for upland or lowland, heath or marsh. It is very frequently seen near the sea-coast, to which in winter it habitually resorts, finding there, no doubt, greater facilities for obtaining food. Like others of its tribe, it possesses little architectural skill, placing its nest in a hole in a cliff, in ruins, or on lofty trees, often appropriating the deserted dwelling of some more industrious builder than itself. On the Continent it resorts to buildings in towns and cities, as, for instance, the Louvre in Paris, and the towers of cathedrals. During summer it hawks principally in the gardens and orchards near the town, and when harvest is gathered in, repairs to the cornfields to hunt for mice among the stubble. When taken young from the nest, it is easily tamed, and becomes one of the most amusing of pets. Even after being fully fledged and allowed its liberty, it will remain in the neighbourhood of the place where it was reared, coming regularly to be fed, and recognizing the presence of its master by repeating its wild note, *klee, klee, klee*, and flying to meet him. An anecdote is recorded in the *Zoologist* of a male Kestrel having, in the second year of his domestication, induced a female bird to join him in his half-civilized life, and to assist him in rearing a joint family. 'Billy' still continued to make himself quite at home at the house where he was brought up, coming fearlessly into the nursery and making friends with the children ; but his mate never threw off her wild nature so far as to do this, contenting herself with waiting outside, and asserting her right to her fair share of whatever food he brought out. Tame Kestrels have been observed to have the habit of hiding their food when supplied with more than they can consume at the time. I have often noticed, too, in the case of tame Kestrels, that the Chaffinches and other small birds which frequent gardens show no instinctive dread of them, as if they were their natural enemies, but perch on the same tree with them, fearless and unnoticed.

The Kestrel was formerly trained to hunt small birds, and in the court of Louis XIII was taught to hawk for Bats.

ORDER GALLIFORMES

FAMILY TETRAONIDÆ

THE CAPERCAILLIE TETRÁO UROGÁLLUS (*Plate XIX*)

Feathers of the throat elongated, black ; head and neck dusky ; wings brown, speckled with black ; breast lustrous green ; abdomen black with white spots ; rump and flanks marked with undulating lines of black and ash-colour ; tail black with white spots ; beak horn-white ; eyebrows naked, red, beneath the eye a white spot. Length thirty-six inches. Female—a third smaller, barred and spotted with tawny red, black, and white ; throat tawny red, unspotted ; breast deep red ; tail dark red with black bars, white at the tip ; bill dusky. Eggs dull yellowish white, speckled with yellowish brown. Resident in Scotland from southern Argyll and Lanarkshire north to the Dornoch Firth and occurring sporadically beyond these limits.

THE Capercaillie, Wood Grouse, or Cock of the Woods, was a rare bird in Scotland in Pennant's time (1769), and was found only in the Highlands north of Inverness. It became extinct in the eighteenth century, but was re-introduced in 1837 in Scotland, and it is now common in fir-woods there, especially in Perthshire. In the pine forests of Sweden and Norway it is still indigenous, but, being a large and beautiful bird, is much sought after, and is annually receding from the haunts of men. It is also found in some of the central countries of Europe, as Poland and the Jura mountains, where it is said to be rather common. It is not only an inhabitant of woods, but passes its time for the most part in trees, and feeds in great measure on the young shoots of the Scotch fir. In summer it adds to its dietary berries, seeds, and insects, for which it searches among bushes or on the ground, returning to the woods to roost. The male bird has obtained great celebrity for his marvellous performances when serenading the hens during the morning and evening twilight in spring. ' During his play, the neck of the Capercaillie is stretched out, his tail is raised and spread like a fan, his wings droop, his feathers are ruffled up, and, in short, he much resembles in appearance an angry Turkey Cock. He begins his play with a call something resembling the words *peller, peller, peller* ; these sounds he repeats at first at some little intervals, but, as he proceeds, they increase in rapidity, until, at last, and after perhaps the lapse of a moment or so, he makes a sort of gulp in his throat, and finishes by drawing in his breath. During the continuance of this latter process, which only lasts a few seconds, the head of the Capercaillie is thrown up, his eyes are partially closed, and his whole appearance would denote that he is worked up into an agony of passion.' This performance, however attractive it may be to those for whose benefit it is intended, exercises a fascination over himself which is often dangerous ; for the sportsman, well acquainted with the sound, is thus guided to his perch, and, shy though the bird is at other times, is able to get near him unperceived or unheeded, and summarily closes his performances. The Capercaillie hen makes her nest upon the ground, and lays from six to twelve eggs. She sits for four weeks. The young keep with her until towards the approach of winter. The size of the full-grown bird varies considerably according to the latitude in which it is found. In Lapland the male weighs about nine or ten pounds, but in the southern provinces of Sweden as much as seventeen pounds. The hen usually weighs from five to six pounds.

THE BLACK GROUSE LYRURUS TÉTRIX (*Plate XVIII*)

Throat-feathers not elongated ; plumage black with violet reflections ; a broad white band on the wings ; secondaries tipped with white ; lower tail-coverts white ; tail much forked, the outer feathers curved outwards. Eyebrows naked, vermilion ; beneath the eye a white spot. Length twenty-three inches. Female —smaller ; head and neck rust-red, barred with black ; rump and tail-feathers black, barred with red ; belly dusky brown with red and whitish bars ; tail slightly forked. Eggs dull yellow, spotted and speckled with reddish brown.

Resident in Devon and Somerset, some districts of Wales and adjacent English counties, and from Staffordshire and Lincolnshire northwards throughout the mainland of Scotland, and in some of the Inner Hebrides.

THE Black Grouse is a native of the northern countries of Europe and of the mountainous districts of the central part of the Continent. In the south it is unknown. Of a hardier nature than the Pheasant, and less fastidious in its dietary, it braves the most inclement seasons, and is never stinted in its supply of food. Moreover, as it rarely wanders far from its heath-clad home, it would probably, if it enjoyed the privilege of insignificance, be abundant in all the extensive waste lands of Britain. But its large size, the excellent flavour of its flesh, and the excitement of the sport which it affords, all tend to keep down its numbers, so that a moor well stocked with Black Grouse is a possession not to be thought lightly of by the highest and wealthiest. The male bird is, in sporting phraseology, a Black Cock, the female a Grey Hen ; and it is the etiquette of the field to shoot Cocks only, the Hens being left for breeding. The Black Cock resembles, in one of its most striking peculiarities, its near relative, the Capercaillie. ' During the spring,' says Mr. St. John, ' and also in the autumn, about the time the first hoar frosts are felt, I have often watched the Black Cocks in the early morning when they collect on some rock or height, and strut and crow with their curious note, not unlike that of a Wood Pigeon. On these occasions they often have most desperate battles. I have seen five or six Black Cocks all fighting at once ; and so violent and eager were they, that I approached within a few yards before they rose. Usually there seems to be a master-bird in these assemblages, who takes up his position on the most elevated spot, crowing and strutting round and round with spread-out tail like a Turkey Cock, and his wings trailing on the ground. The hens remain quietly near him, whilst the smaller or younger male birds keep at a respectful distance, neither daring to crow, except in a subdued kind of voice, nor to approach. If they attempt the latter, the master-bird dashes at the intruder, and often a short *mêlée* ensues, several others joining in it, but they soon return to their former respectful distance. I have also seen an old Black Cock crowing on a birch-tree with a dozen hens below it, and the younger Cocks looking on with fear and admiration. It is at these times that numbers fall to the share of the poacher, who knows that the birds resort to the same spot every morning.'

The food of these birds is abundant in quantity, and though simple, yet partakes of an extensive assortment of flavours. Twigs of the fine-leaved heath (*Erica cinerea*), and heather (*Calluna*) ; buds of the willow and birch ; the tender shoots of cotton-grass, sedge, and grass ; and whortleberries, cranberries, and crowberries, are the principal items of their bill of fare, varied according to the season. In the months of February, March, and April, they do much mischief to plantations by destroying the tender shoots of Scotch and silver fir. ' In searching for food, the Black Grouse frequents the lower grounds of the less-cultivated districts, not generally removing far from the shelter of woods or thickets, to which it betakes itself as occasion requires. It sometimes makes an excursion into the stubble-fields in search of the seeds of cereal plants, and in summer and autumn includes those of the grasses and rushes. While thus employed, it walks and runs among the herbage with considerable agility, and, when apprehensive of danger, flies off to a sheltered place, or settles down and remains motionless until the intruder passes by. It perches adroitly, and walks securely on the branches ; but its ordinary station is on the ground, where also it reposes at night. It may often, especially in spring, be seen on the turf-top of the low walls inclosing plantations. Its flight is heavy, direct, and of moderate velocity, and is capable of being protracted to a great distance.' [1]

The Grey Hen constructs a rude nest of withered grass and a few twigs in the shelter of some low bush, and lays from five to ten eggs. The male bird takes no part in the bringing up of the brood, but leaves the duties of incubation and attention to the wants of his family to the hen, who devotes herself wholly to the careful nurture of her little ones. While the poults are in their nonage, she assiduously leads them about where food is most abundant ; and if surprised by an intruder, leaves them to hide among the heath and ferns, creeps rapidly herself to some distance, and then rises in a fluttering manner, so that a stranger to her habits would suppose her to be wounded. By August 20, the young are supposed to be fully fledged, and the sportsman is expected not only to show his skill as a marksman, but his quickness of eye in discriminating between males and females as the covey rises. The former are to be distinguished by their richer colouring, and by the more strongly marked white on the wings. At this season the old Black Cocks club together.

The Black Cock is found in greater or less quantities in the moorland districts of many of the English counties, but is most abundant in the north of England and Wales, and in Scotland.

THE RED GROUSE LAGÓPUS SCÓTICUS (*Plate XVIII*)

Plumage chestnut-brown, marked on the back with black spots and beneath with black lines ; a fringe of small white feathers round the eyes, and a white spot at the base of the lower mandible ; a crimson fringed band above the eyes ; some of the feathers of the abdomen tipped with white ; tail of sixteen feathers, the four middle ones chestnut with black bars, the rest dusky ; feet and toes covered thickly with grey hair-like feathers. Female—the red eyelid less conspicuous ; colours not so dark and tinged with reddish yellow, the black spots and lines more numerous. Length sixteen inches. Eggs reddish ash-colour, nearly covered with blotches and spots of deep red-brown. Resident in the moorland districts of England from Hereford, Salop, Staffordshire, Derbyshire, and Yorkshire, northward, also in Wales, Scotland, the Orkneys, Hebrides, and Ireland.

THE diminution of the number of Pheasants in France, owing to a relaxation of the efforts formerly made to protect them, and the

[1] Macgillivray.

abundance of the same birds, in those parts of England where unceasing
care is taken of them in severe or protracted winters, tend to prove
the great difficulty of preserving a foreign bird in a country which is
not in every respect adapted to its habits and constitution. On the
other hand, the undiminished abundance of Red Grouse in Great
Britain, in spite of the absence of all artificial protection, and notwithstanding the vast quantity which annually fall a prey to vermin,
poachers, and sportsmen, proves as satisfactorily that where a bird
has become abundant, in a country in all respects suited to its constitution and producing an inexhaustible supply of its natural food,
it is impossible to extirpate it. If we ever had occasion to adopt a
bird as a national emblem, the choice might for one reason fall on
the Red Grouse. It is a native of the British Isles, and is found in no
other country. On the moors of Scotland, the hilly parts of the north
of England, the mountains of Wales, and the wastes of Ireland, it is
as wild and free as the Gull on the sea-cliff. It frequents extensive
heaths where man could not protect it if he would, and finds no stint
of food where few living things can exist but insects and some of the
larger rapacious animals which make it their special prey. Eagles,
Falcons, Buzzards, Crows, foxes, martens and polecats, all wage against
it incessant war ; it is wholly without armour, offensive or defensive ;
yet its numbers are undiminished. And we may confidently say that,
as long as there are large tracts of land in Great Britain unreclaimed,
there will be Grouse.

Red Grouse must, occasionally, fall in the way of the wanderer
over the Scottish moors, whatever may be the object of his rambles ;
but a sportsman alone is privileged to make the bird his study at all
seasons. My sketch, therefore, of the Grouse is to be considered as
taken, not from the limited observation which I have been enabled
to make, when I have chanced to start a bird on the hills of Westmor-
land or the Highlands, but to be compiled from the notes of others
who have had more ample means of observing its habits.

' The Brown Ptarmigan, generally known by the name of Red
Grouse, as compared with the Black Grouse, is met with in Scotland
on all kinds of surface, provided it be covered with heath, whether
Calluna vulgaris (ling) or *Erica cinerea* (Common purple heath), from
the level of the sea to the height of about two thousand feet. The
low sandy heaths of the eastern counties of the middle division appear
to be less favourable to it than the more moist peaty tracts of the
western and northern districts, where the shrubs on which it feeds
attain a great size.'

Its food appears to be much the same as that of the Black Grouse,
to which it is similar in many of its habits ; but it never perches on
trees. It has, moreover, a decided predilection for the national grain
of Scotland. Hence the cultivation of small tracts of land with oats
in the neighbourhood of moors where it abounds is an unprofitable
labour.

Its name, *Lagopus* (Hare-footed), is equally appropriate as descriptive of its thickly clothed foot and its fleetness as a runner. On
ordinary occasions it does not fly much, but keeps concealed among

the heath, seldom choosing to rise unless its enemy comes very near. Red Grouse pair early in the season, and build their nests generally on the borders between heath and lea ground, with a view to providing their young with an open nursery-ground, on which to learn the use of their legs, as well as a safe retreat on the approach of danger. The nest is loosely constructed of straws and twigs which may chance to lie about near the selected spot. The number of eggs is usually eight to ten ; the hen sits very closely, allowing the shepherd almost to trample on her before she springs. The period of hatching is a perilous one for the chicks, for, as they break the shell, they utter a small but shrill chirp—a certain signal to some watchful Hooded Crow that a prey is at hand ; he traces up the sound, drives the mother from her nest, and destroys the whole brood.

Once fairly hatched, the danger decreases ; the young birds, while still quite small, show great readiness in concealing themselves. When disturbed they separate in all directions, crouch on the ground, squeeze between objects that seem to defy all passage, work their way through the cover, or, if they fancy that an eye is fixed on them, lie as motionless as stones. When so far grown as to be able to fly, they still prefer the shelter afforded by the cover ; but if hard pressed the old cock usually rises first, with a cry which some compare to the quack of a Duck. The hen and young birds show no hurry in following his example, but take wing singly, and at unequal intervals—not like Partridges, which always rise in a covey. This is the period when they afford the easiest shot to the sportsman, who often puts them up almost beneath his feet, or under the very nose of his dogs. Later in the season a great change takes place, and this, it is said, whether the birds have been much harassed or not. Become cautious and wild, they no longer trust to concealment or swiftness of foot, but, discovering from a great distance the approach of danger, they rise most frequently out of shot, so that it requires skill and patience to get near them. A slight and early snow sometimes makes it more easy to approach them, at least for a few hours ; but ordinarily, not even extreme cold, or a covering of snow a foot thick, appears to tame them at all. Under such circumstances, they collect in enormous ' packs ', and betake themselves to some particular part of the moor from which the snow has been more or less drifted. These packs keep together during winter, and at the beginning of spring separate and pair, not, however, without some previous altercations ; but these are soon over, and they lose much of their shyness, venturing close to the roads, and being little disturbed by the passage of the traveller.

THE PTARMIGAN LAGÓPUS MÚTUS (*Plate XX*)

Winter plumage—*pure white, a black line from the angle of the beak through the eye ; outer tail-feathers black ; above the eyes a scarlet fringed membrane ; bill and claws black ; tarsi and toes thickly clothed with woolly feathers.* Female—*without the black line through the eyes.* Summer plumage—*wings, under tail-coverts, two middle tail-feathers, and legs, white ; outer tail-*

feathers black, some of them tipped with white ; rest of plumage ash-brown, marked with black lines and dusky spots. Length fifteen inches. Eggs reddish yellow, spotted and speckled with deep reddish brown. Resident on the higher mountains of Scotland from Ben Lomond northwards, and in Islay, Jura, Mull, and Skye.

THIS beautiful bird is the Schneehuhn, ' Snow-chick ', of the Germans, the White Partridge of the Alps and Pyrenees, and the Gaelic *Tarmachan*. Whilst most birds shrink from cold, the Ptarmigan, on the contrary, seems to revel in it, and to fear nothing so much as the beams of the sun. Not even when the valleys rejoice in the livery of spring does it desert the snowy regions altogether, and, when the mist-wreaths clear away, it avoids the rays of the sun by seeking the shady sides of the mountains. Only when the northern regions or lofty mountains are so thickly covered with snow as to threaten it with starvation does it repair to districts where the cold is somewhat mitigated, but never lower into the valleys than where it may quench its thirst with snow. ' The male bird ', says a field naturalist, ' has been seen, during a snow-storm in Norway, to perch himself on a rock which overtopped the rest, and to sit there for some time as if enjoying the cold wind and sleet, which was drifting in his face ; just as one might have done on a sultry summer's day on the top of the Wiltshire downs, when a cool air was stirring there.' [1] The same writer observes : ' I have generally found the Ptarmigan concealed among the grey, lichen-coloured rocks on the summits of the fjelds, and so closely do they resemble these rocks in colour that I could scarcely ever see them on the ground ; and sometimes when the practised eye of my guide found them, and he would point out the exact spot, it was not until after a long scrutiny that I could distinguish the bird within a dozen yards of me. Frequently we would find them on the snow itself, and many a time has a large circular depression in the snow been pointed out to me, where the Ptarmigan has been lying and pluming himself in his chilly bed. He is a noble bird, free as air, and for the most part uninterrupted in his wide domain ; he can range over the enormous tracts of fjeld, seldom roused by a human step, and still more seldom hunted by man. When the winter clothes his dwelling in a garb of snow, he arrays himself in the purest and most beautiful white ; when the summer sun melts away the snow, and the grey rocks appear, he, too, puts on his coloured dress, and assimilates himself once more to his beloved rocks. But the young Ptarmigans are my especial favourites : I have caught them of all ages ; some apparently just emerged from the egg, others some weeks older ; they are remarkably pretty little birds, with their short black beaks and their feathered toes ; and so quickly do they run, and so nimble and active are they in escaping from you, that they are soon beneath some projecting stone, far beyond the reach of your arm, where you hear them chirping and calling out in defiance and derision. The call of the old Ptarmigan is singularly loud and hoarse ; it is a prolonged grating, harsh note, and may be heard at a great distance.' This has been compared to

[1] Rev. A. C. Smith, in the *Zoologist*, vol. viii. p. 2977.

the scream of the Missel Thrush ; but Macgillivray says it seems to him more like the croak of a frog.

Ptarmigans pair early in spring, and build their nest of grass, bents, and twigs in a slight hollow behind a stone or bush, and lay from seven to twelve eggs. The young are able to run about as soon as they are hatched, and, as we have seen, are most expert and nimble in concealing themselves. The hen bird when surprised with her young brood counterfeits lameness, and runs about in great anxiety, as if wishing to draw attention from her chicks to herself. Their food consists of the fresh green twigs of heath and other mountain plants, seeds, and berries. While feeding they run about, and are shy in taking flight even when they have acquired the use of their wings, but crouch on the approach of danger, and remain motionless and silent. When at length they do rise, they fly off in a loose party, and mostly in a direct line, for a distant part of the mountain, the movement of their wings resembling that of the Grouse, but being lighter in character. Early in the season, a long time before Grouse, the coveys of Ptarmigans unite and form large packs, and it is while thus congregated that they perform their partial migrations from the high grounds to what they consider a milder climate, the Norwegian valleys. There, while the ground is covered thickly with snow, they, to a certain extent, modify their habits, and perch on trees, sometimes in such numbers that the branches seem to be altogether clothed in white. It does not appear that any of these flocks make long journeys or cross the sea. In Scotland they are no more numerous in winter than in summer, nor have they been observed to take refuge in the woods. In the comparatively mild temperature of Scotland there occurs no lengthened period during which they cannot find their simple food somewhere in the open country ; they consequently do not leave the moors, but only descend lower.

The Ptarmigan is neither so abundant nor so generally diffused in Scotland as the Grouse. It is resident on high mountains. It is said to have existed at one time in the north of England and in Wales ; if so, it has totally disappeared, nor is it known in Ireland.

FAMILY PHASIANIDÆ

THE PHEASANT PHASIÁNUS COLCHICUS (*Plate XIX*)

Head and neck glossy, with metallic reflections of green, blue, and purple ; sides of the head bare, scarlet, minutely speckled with black ; general plumage spotted and banded with orange-red, purple, brown, yellow, green, and black, either positive or reflected ; tail very long, of eighteen feathers, the middle ones longest. Female—light brown, marked with dusky ; sides of the head feathered ; tail much shorter. Length three feet. Eggs olive-brown. Resident throughout the British Isles, except the Shetlands and Outer Hebrides.

THIS climate suits the Pheasant pretty well, and at most seasons of the year it finds abundance of food ; but in hard winters the supply diminishes, or fails altogether ; and were not food specially scattered about for it in its haunts, it would either die off from being unable to withstand cold and hunger together, or become so weak that it would fall a prey to the smaller rapacious animals, who are not a match for it when it is strong and active. A healthy cock Pheasant has been known to beat off a cat ; a sickly one would be unable to compete with a Magpie or Jay. It is, in fact, an exotic running wild, and enabled to do so only by the care of those who help it to surmount the inconveniences of a life spent in a foreign land.

The Pheasant is said to have been brought originally from Colchis, a country on the shores of the Black Sea, and to have derived its name from the river Phasis, the famous scene of the expedition of the Argonauts, bearing date about 1200 years before Christ. From this epoch it is said to have been known to the Athenians, who endeavoured to acclimatize it for the sake of its beauty as well as the delicacy of its flesh. The Romans received it from the Greeks ; but it was little known, except by name, in Germany, France, and England, until the Crusades. The custom was then introduced from Constantinople of sending it to table decorated with its tail-feathers and head, as a dish for kings and emperors—a special honour until that time confined to the Peacock. Willughby, in the seventeenth century, says of it that, from its rarity, delicacy of flavour, and great tenderness, it seems to have been created for the tables of the wealthy. He tells us, too, that the flesh of Pheasants caught by hawking is of a higher flavour, and yet more delicate than when they are taken by snares or any other method.

If the Pheasant should ever, in this country, lose the protection of the Game Laws, it will probably dwindle away. Under existing circumstances, it offers an inducement to poaching too tempting to be resisted. Gamekeepers engage in more affrays with poachers of Pheasants than of all the other game birds taken collectively ; and if the offence of destroying them were made less penal than it is at present, they would doubtless diminish rapidly. Next to Wood Pigeons, they are said to be the most destructive of all British birds ; so that farmers would gladly do their utmost to exterminate them ; their large size and steady onward flight combine to make them an ' easy shot ' for the veriest tyro in gunnery, while the estimation in which they are held for the table would always secure for them a value in the market.

The places best adapted for Pheasants are thick woods in the neighbourhood of water, where there is abundance of shelter on the ground, in the shape of furze-bushes, brambles, tall weeds, rushes, or tussock grass ; for they pass their lives almost exclusively on the ground, even roosting there, except in winter, when they fly up in the evening, and perch on the lower boughs of middling-sized trees. In April or May, the female bird scratches for herself a shallow hole in the ground under the shelter of some bushes or long grass, and lays from ten to fourteen eggs ; but not infrequently she allows might to prevail over right, and appropriates both the nest and eggs belonging to some evicted Partridge. The situation of the nests is generally known to the keepers, and all that are considered safe are left to be attended to by the owner. Such, however, as are exposed to the depredations of vermin or poachers are more frequently taken, and the eggs are placed under a domestic hen.

Pheasant chicks are able to run about and pick up their own food soon after they have escaped from the egg. This consists of grain, seeds, an enormous quantity of wireworms, small insects, especially ants and their eggs, and green herbage. When full grown, they add to this diet beans, peas, acorns, beech-mast, and the tuberous roots of several wild plants. A strip of buck-wheat, of which they are very fond, is sometimes sown for their special benefit along the skirt of a plantation. In seasons of scarcity they will enter the farmyard, and either quietly feed with the poultry, or, less frequently, do battle with the cocks for the sovereignty. A story is told, in the *Zoologist*, of a male Pheasant, which drove from their perch, and killed in succession, three fine cocks. The proprietor, with a view to prevent further loss, furnished a fourth cock with a pair of steel spurs. Armed with these, the lawful occupant was more than a match for the aggressor, who, next morning, was found lying dead on the ground beneath the perch. Another has been known to beat off a cat ; and a third was in the habit of attacking a labouring man. The female is a timid, unoffending bird, as peaceful in her demeanour as quiet in her garb. The tints of her plumage, far less gaudy than in the male, are a protection to her in the nesting season, as being less likely to attract the notice either of poachers or vermin. Indeed, were she always to lie close, her nest would not be easily discovered, for the colour of her feathers so closely resembles that of withered leaves, that she is, when sitting, less conspicuous than her uncovered eggs would be.

Common Pheasants are occasionally found having a large portion, or even the whole, of their plumage white. These, though highly ornamental when mixed with the common sort, are not prized, owing to their being a more conspicuous mark for poachers.

THE COMMON PARTRIDGE PERDIX PERDIX (*Plate XVIII*)

Face, eyebrows, and throat, bright rust-red ; behind the eye a naked red skin ; neck, breast, and flanks, ash-colour with black zigzag lines, and on the feathers of the flanks a large rust-red spot ; low on the breast a chestnut patch shaped like a horseshoe; upper parts ash-brown with black spots and zigzag lines ; scapulars and wing-coverts darker ; quills brown, barred and spotted with yellowish red ; tail of eighteen feathers, the laterals bright rust-red ; beak olive-brown ; feet grey. Female—less red on the face ; head spotted with white ; upper plumage darker, spotted with black ; the horseshoe mark indistinct or wanting. Length thirteen inches. Eggs uniform olive-brown. Resident in the British Isles, except the Orkneys, Shetlands and Outer Hebrides.

VERY few, even of our common birds, are more generally known than the Partridge. From the first of September to the first of February, in large towns, every poulterer's shop is pretty sure to be decorated with a goodly array of these birds ; and there are few rural districts in which a walk through the fields will fail to be enlivened by the sudden rising and whirring away of a covey of Partridges, in autumn and winter ; of a pair in spring. At midsummer they are of less frequent appearance, the female being too busily occupied, either in incubation or the training of her family, to find time for flight ; and at this season, moreover, the uncut fields of hay, clover, and corn afford facilities for the avoiding of danger, by concealment rather than by flight. The habits of the Partridge, as of the Grouse, are especially terrestrial. It never flies, like the Lark, for enjoyment ; and as it does not perch in trees it has no occasion for upward flight. Still, there are occasions when Partridges rise to a considerable distance from the ground, and this seems to be when they meditate a longer flight than usual.

A friend, to whom I am indebted for many valuable notes on various birds, tells me that when a covey of Partridges are disturbed by a pack of hounds, they lie close at first, as if terrified by the noise and bent on concealing themselves ; but when the pack actually comes on them they rise to a great height, and fly to a distance which may be measured by miles—at least, so he supposes, as he has watched them diminish and fade from the sight before they showed any sign of preparing to alight.

The Partridge, though decorated with no brilliant colours, which would tend to thwart it in its habit of concealing itself among vegetation of the same general hue as itself, is a beautiful bird. Its gait is graceful, its feet small and light, its head well raised ; and its plumage, though devoid of striking contrasts, is exquisitely pencilled, each feather on the back and breast being veined like the gauzy wings of a fly. The most conspicuous part of the plumage of the male bird, the horseshoe on its breast, is invisible as it walks or crouches, and the general tone approaches that of the soil.

Partridges pair early in the year ; but the hen does not begin to lay until May, nor to sit until towards the beginning of June. The nest is merely a depression in the ground, into which a few straws or dead leaves have been drawn. It is sometimes placed among brushwood under a hedge, but more frequently in the border of a field of hay, clover, or corn, or in the wide field itself. The mowing season, unfortunately, is not noted in the calendar of Nature ; so the mother-bird, who is a close sitter, is not infrequently destroyed by the scythe, or, at all events, is driven away, and returns to find her eggs carried off to be entrusted to the care of a domestic hen. In unusually wet seasons, nests which have been fixed in low situations are flooded, and the eggs being thus reduced to a low temperature become addled. When this has taken place, the Partridge makes a second laying, and a late brood is reared.

Notwithstanding this, however, Partridges are exceedingly prolific, and are said to be increasing in numbers in proportion as new lands are reclaimed from the waste, although the Red-legged Partridge has lessened its numbers in some districts. It must certainly be admitted that, in bad seasons, they are treated with a consideration that would scarcely be shown towards them if they were simply destroyers of grain and had nothing to recommend them as objects of sport or as delicacies for the table. When abundant, they fall freely before the sportsmans' gun ; but when the coveys are either small or few, they are treated with forbearance, and enough are left to stock the preserves for the ensuing year.

While the hen is sitting, the male bird remains somewhere in the neighbourhood, and gives timely warning of the approach of danger ; when the eggs are hatched, he accompanies his mate, and shares in the work of teaching the young to shift for themselves—a lesson which they begin to learn at once. The food both of old and young birds is, to a great extent, insects. The young are especially fond of ants and their pupæ or larvæ. During the year 1860, in which there were no broods of Partridges, I was much struck by the fact that stubble-fields abounded, to an unusual degree, with ant-hills. In ordinary seasons, these are found torn to pieces and levelled. This year, scarcely one was touched ; and even at the present time, the end of October, winged ants are far more numerous than they usually are at this time of the year. Besides insects, Partridges feed on the seeds of weeds, green leaves, grain spilt in reaping, and on corn which has been sown. This last charge is a serious one ; yet, on the whole, it is most probable that Partridges do far more good than harm on an estate, the insects and weeds which they destroy more than making amends for their consumption of seed-corn.

I might fill many pages with anecdotes of the devotion of Partridges to their maternal duties—their assiduity in hatching their eggs, their disregard of personal danger while thus employed, their loving trickeries to divert the attention of enemies from their broods to themselves, and even the actual removal of their eggs from a suspectedly dangerous position to a place of safety ; but with many of these stories the reader must be already familiar if he has read any of the works devoted to such subjects.

The number of eggs laid before incubation commences varies from ten to fifteen, or more. Yarrell says, ' Twenty-eight eggs in one instance, and thirty-three eggs in two other instances, are recorded as having been found in one nest ; but there is little doubt, in these cases, that more than one bird had laid eggs in the same nest.' This may be ; but I find in a French author an instance in which no less than forty-two eggs were laid by a Partridge in captivity, all of which, being placed under a hen, would have produced chicks, but for the occurrence of a thunder-storm accompanied by a deluge of rain which flooded the nest, when the eggs, which all contained chicks, were on the point of being hatched. The average number of birds in a covey is, I believe, about twelve ; quite enough to supply the sportsmen and to account for the abundance of the bird.

The character of the Partridge's flight is familiar to most people. Simultaneously with the startled cry of alarm from the cock comes a loud whirr-r-r as of a spinning-wheel : away fly the whole party in a body, keeping a horizontal, nearly straight line : in turns each bird ceases to beat its wings and sails on for a few yards with extended pinions ; the impetus exhausted which carried it through this movement, it plies its wings again, and if it has so long escaped the fowler, may, by this time, consider itself out of danger, for its flight, though laboured, is tolerably rapid.

The call of the Partridge is mostly uttered in the evening, as soon as the beetles begin to buzz. The birds are now proceeding to roost, which they always do in the open field, the covey forming a circle with their heads outwards, to be on the watch against their enemies, of whom they have many. They feed for the most part in the morning and middle of the day, and vary in size according to the abundance of their favourite food. In some districts of France, it is said, the weight of the Partridges found on an estate is considered as a fair standard test of the productiveness of the soil and of the state of agricultural skill.

Most people are familiar with the distich :

> If the Partridge had the Woodcock's thigh,
> It would be the best bird that e'er did flie ;

but every one does not know that the saying was in vogue among epicures in the reign of Charles II.

THE RED-LEGGED PARTRIDGE ALECTORIS RUFA
(*Plate XVIII*)

Throat and cheeks white, surrounded by a black band, which spreads itself out over the breast and sides of the neck in the form of numerous spots and lines, with which are intermixed a few white spots ; upper plumage reddish ash ; on the flanks a number of crescent-shaped spots, the convexity towards the tail rust-red, the centre black, bordered by white ; beak, orbits, and feet, bright red. Length thirteen and a half inches. Eggs dull yellow, spotted and speckled with reddish brown and ash-colour. Resident in England, north to Yorkshire and west to Somerset and sparingly in North Wales.

THE Red-legged Partridge, called also the French and Guernsey Partridge, is a stronger and more robust bird than the common species, which it also greatly surpasses in brilliancy of colouring. As some of its names indicate, it is not an indigenous bird, but a native of the south of Europe, whence it was first introduced into England in the reign of Charles II. To Willughby, who lived at that period, it was unknown except as a native of the continent of Europe and the islands of Guernsey and Jersey. Towards the close of the eighteenth century it was re-introduced into Suffolk, where it has become numerous ; so much so, indeed, in some places, as to have gained the better of the common species for a time.

Its flight is rapid, but heavier and more noisy than that of the Common Partridge. It is less patient of cold, and less able to elude the attacks of birds of prey. It is quite a terrestrial bird, very slow in taking flight, and never perching except when hard pressed, when, on rare occasions, it takes refuge among the thick branches of an oak or pinaster ; here it considers itself safe, and watches the movements of the dogs with apparent unconcern. Sometimes, too, when closely hunted, it takes shelter in a rabbit's burrow or the hole of a tree ; but under ordinary circumstances it runs rapidly before the dogs, and frequently disappoints the sportsman by rising out of shot. The Grey or Common Partridge frequents rich cultivated lands ; the Red Partridge prefers uncultivated plains, ' which summer converts into burning causeways, winter into pools of water—monotonous *landes,* where skeletons of sheep pasture without variation on heath and the dwarf prickly genista. It delights, too, in bushy ravines, or the steep sides of rocky hills covered with holly, thorns, and brambles ; and when it resorts to vineyards, it selects those situated on the sides of steep slopes, where marigolds and coltsfoot are the principal weeds, rabbits and vipers the most abundant animals.' [1] Red Partridges are consequently most numerous in the least cultivated districts of France, especially those between the Cher and the Loire, and between the Loire and the Seine. Towards the east they do not extend beyond the hills of Epernay, and do not cross the valley of the Meuse. The flesh of the Red Partridge is considered inferior to that of the Grey, and the bird itself is less esteemed by sportsmen as an object of pursuit. In England it seems to retain its natural taste of preferring bushy heaths to enclosed land. In the mode of incubation and rearing the young the two species are much alike.

THE QUAIL COTÚRNIX COTÚRNIX (*Plate XX*)

Head mottled with black and reddish brown, with three parallel longitudinal yellowish streaks ; upper plumage ash-brown, variegated with black and straw-colour ; neck reddish yellow, with a double crescent of dusky brown ; breast pale reddish brown, streaked with white ; bill and feet yellowish brown. Female—paler, and wanting the double crescent on the neck. Length eight inches. Eggs yellowish white, blotched or speckled with dusky brown. A summer visitor in small numbers, breeding irregularly in most parts of the British Isles, occasionally remaining during winter.

' THIS species ', says a French naturalist, ' is probably the most productive of all winged creatures ; and it could not well be otherwise, or it would be unable to withstand the war of extermination declared against it by human beings and birds of prey. One may get an idea of the prodigious number of victims which the simple crossing of the Mediterranean costs the species by two well-known and often quoted facts. The Bishop of Capri, a wretched islet scarcely a league in length, which lies at the entrance of the Bay of Naples, used to clear a net revenue of 25,000 francs a year (£1,000) by his Quails. This sum represents 160,000 Quails at the lowest computation. In certain islands of the Archipelago, and parts of the coast of the Peloponnese, the inhabitants, men and women, have no other occupation during two months of the year than that of collecting the Quails which are showered on them from heaven, picking and cleaning them, *salting them* (" they spread them all abroad for themselves ") and packing them away in casks for transportation to the principal markets of the

[1] Toussenel.

Levant ; that is to say, the migration of Quails is to this part of Greece what the migration of herrings is to Holland and Scotland. The Quail-catchers arrive at the shore a fortnight in advance, and every man numbers his ground to avoid disputes. The Quail arrives in France from Africa early in May, and takes its departure towards the end of August.'

Another French author says, ' Like Rails, Woodcocks, Snipes, and many of the waders, the Quail, when it travels towards the seashore, flies only in the night. It leaves the lands, where it has passed the day, about the dusk of the evening, and settles again with the dawn of the morning.' Not infrequently, while performing their transit, they become weary, and alight on vessels, or fall into the sea, and are drowned. ' Being at a small town on the coast, in the month of May,' says M. Pellicot, ' I saw some boats come in with ten or a dozen sharks. They were all opened before me, and there was not one which had not from eight to twelve Quails in its body.' ' Enormous flights are annually observed at the spring and fall after crossing an immense surface of sea, to take a brief repose in the islands of Malta, Sicily, Sardinia, Crete, in the kingdom of Naples, and about Constantinople, where, on these occasions, there is a general shooting match, which lasts two or three days. This occurs always in the autumn. The birds, starting from the Crimea about seven at night, and with a northerly wind, before dawn accomplish a passage of above sixty leagues in breadth, and alight on the southern shore to feed and repose. In the vernal season the direction of the flight is reversed, and they arrive in similar condition on the Russian coast. The same phenomena occur in Malta, etc.' [1]

On its arrival, the Quail betakes itself to open plains and rich grassy meadows, especially where the soil is calcareous, and avoids woody countries. During the early part of summer it frequents cornfields, sainfoin, and lucerne. In September it is found in stubble and clover fields, and among the weeds growing in dry ponds, or it finds shelter in any crops which may yet remain standing. In warm countries it resorts to vineyards, attracted, it is said, not so much by the grapes as by the numerous small snails with which the vines are then infested ; for the crops of the late birds are generally found filled with these molluscs. In locomotion it makes more use of its feet than its wings, and when put up is never induced to perch on a tree. Its flight resembles in character that of the Partridge, but it rarely flies far, and when it alights makes awkward attempts to conceal itself, but often fails, and may sometimes be captured with the hand. In June or July, the female lays from eight to fourteen eggs in a hole in the ground, and brings up her young without the assistance of the male. Towards the end of August the old birds migrate southwards, and are followed by the young. Before the end of October all have disappeared, though instances have occurred of their being shot during winter, especially in seasons when the harvest has been a late one.

Quails inhabit the eastern continent, from China—where they are said to be carried about in winter by the natives, to keep their

[1] Colonel C. H. Smith.

hands warm—to the British Isles. With us they are nowhere plentiful, but are occasionally shot by sportsmen in most parts of the country. In Palestine the Quails still come up in the night, as of old, and ' cover the land '.

ORDER GRUIFORMES

FAMILY GRUIDÆ

THE CRANE GRUS GRUS (*Plate V*)

General plumage ash-grey ; throat, part of the neck, and back of the head, dark blackish grey ; forehead and cere covered with black bristly hairs ; crown naked, orange red ; some of the secondaries elongated, arched, and having the barbs of the feathers free ; bill greenish black, reddish at the base, horn-coloured at the tip ; irides reddish brown ; feet black. Young birds *have the crown feathered, and want the dark grey of the neck and head. Length five feet. Eggs pale greenish ash, blotched and spotted with brown and dark green. A rare occasional visitor to the British Isles.*

TURNER, writing in 1544, informs us that Cranes at that time nested in marshy places in England and that he had often seen their ' pipers '.

From the fact of nine Cranes being recorded among the presents received at the wedding of the daughter of Mr. More, of Loseley, in 1567, it would appear that these birds were tolerably common in England at that date.

Willughby, whose *Ornithology* was published about a hundred years later, says that Cranes were regular visitors in England, and that large flocks of them were to be found, in summer, in the fens of Lincolnshire and Cambridgeshire. Whether they still bred in England he could not say on his own personal knowledge.

Sir Thomas Browne, a contemporary of Willughby, writes, in his account of birds found in Norfolk : ' Cranes are often seen here in hard winters, especially about the champaign and fieldy part. It seems they have been more plentiful ; for, in a bill of fare, when the mayor entertained the Duke of Norfolk, I met with Cranes in a dish.'

Pennant, writing towards the close of the eighteenth century, says : ' On the strictest inquiry, we learn that, at present, the inhabitants of those counties are scarcely acquainted with them ; we therefore conclude that these birds have left our land.' The Crane is, however, still of common occurrence in many parts of the Eastern Continent, passing its summer in temperate climates, and retiring southwards at the approach of winter. Its periodical migrations are remarkable for their punctuality, it having been observed that, during a long series of years, it has invariably traversed France southward in the latter half of the month of October, returning during the latter half of the month of March. On these occasions, Cranes fly in large flocks, composed of two lines meeting at an angle, moving with no great rapidity, and alighting mostly during the day to rest and feed. At other seasons, it ceases to be gregarious, and repairs to swamps and boggy morasses, where in spring it builds a rude nest of reeds and rushes on a bank or stump of a tree, and lays two eggs. As a feeder it may be called omnivorous, so extensive is its dietary. Its note is loud and sonorous, but harsh, and is uttered when the birds are performing their flights as well as at other times.

The Crane of the Holy Scriptures is most probably not this species, which is rare in Palestine, but another, *Grus Virgo*, the Crane figured on the Egyptian monuments, which periodically visits the Lake of Tiberias, and whose note is a chatter, and not the trumpet sound of the Cinerous Crane. In the north of Ireland, in Wales and perhaps elsewhere, the Heron is commonly called a Crane.

FAMILY RALLIDÆ

THE LAND RAIL OR CORN CRAKE CREX CREX (*Plate XXI*)

Upper feathers dusky brown bordered with reddish ash ; over the eye and down the side of the head, a streak of ash ; wing-coverts rust-red ; quills reddish brown ; throat, belly, and abdomen, whitish ; breast pale yellowish brown : flanks barred with white and rust-red ; upper mandible brown, lower whitish ; irides brown ; feet reddish brown. Length ten inches. Eggs yellowish brown, spotted and speckled with grey and reddish brown. A summer visitor to the British Isles, formerly widespread, but now only breeding commonly in northern and western Scotland, Wales, and Ireland. In southern and eastern England it is now chiefly a passage migrant.

THIS bird's whole life, while with us, seems to be spent among the long grass and stalks of hay or corn, between which its long legs and slender body give it peculiar facility of moving, and it is only when hard pressed that it rises from the ground. Its flight is low, with its legs hanging down ; and it usually drops into the nearest hedge or cover which presents itself, and from which it is not easily flushed a second time.

The Corn Crake used to be found, during summer, in all the counties of England, but is now very uncommon in those of the south and east, and increases in abundance as we advance northwards. In the north of Ireland it is to be heard in every meadow and cornfield, and here its incessant cry in the evenings is monotonous, if not wearisome ; in many parts of Scotland it is also very common, and here it is much more frequently seen. In waste lands, where it can find no continuous corn, it takes refuge in patches of flags, rushes, or tall weeds, and if watched for, may be seen leaving its place of concealment, and quietly walking along the grass, lifting its feet high, and stooping from time to time to pick up its food, consisting of worms, insects, snails, and seeds.

The Land Rail is considered a delicate article of food, and has long been prized as such. In France it used to be termed, in old sporting phraseology, ' King of the Quails ', the Quail being a bird which it much resembles in colouring.

The Corn Crake places its nest, which is composed of a few straws, in a hollow in the ground, among corn or hay, and lays from eight to ten, or rarely, twelve eggs. The young birds are able to accompany their parents in their mazy travels as soon as they have left the shell. The note of the old bird is heard much later in the season than the song of most other birds, and is probably employed as a call-note to the young, which, but for some such guidance, would be very likely to go astray. In the still evenings of August, I have, while standing on the shore of the island of Islay, distinctly heard its monotonous *crek-crek* proceeding from a cornfield on the opposite shore of Jura, the Sound of Islay which intervened being here upwards of half a mile wide. On ordinary occasions it is not easy to decide on the position and distance of the bird while uttering its note ; for the Corn Crake is a ventriloquist of no mean proficiency.

THE SPOTTED CRAKE PORZANA PORZANA (*Plate XXI*)

Forehead, throat, and a streak over the eye, lead-grey ; upper plumage olive-brown, spotted with black and white ; breast and under plumage olive and ash, spotted with white, the flanks barred with white and brown ; bill greenish yellow, orange at the base ; irides brown ; feet greenish yellow. Length nine inches. Eggs yellowish red, spotted and speckled with brown and ash. A scarce summer visitor to England and Wales, now only occasional in Scotland and Ireland.

THE Spotted Crake is smaller in size than the Corn Crake, and far less common. It is shot from time to time in various parts of Great Britain, especially in the fen countries, to which its habits are best suited. It frequents watery places which abound with reeds, flags, and sedges, and among these it conceals itself, rarely using its wings, but often wading over mud and weeds, and taking freely to the water, in which it swims with facility. The nest, which is a large structure, composed of rushes and reeds, is placed among thick vegetation, near the water's edge, and contains from seven to ten eggs.

THE LITTLE CRAKE PORZANA PARVA (*Plate XXI*)

Head brown ; upper plumage olive-ash, the feathers black in the centre ; middle of the back black, sprinkled with white ; throat, face, and breast, bluish grey, without spots ; abdomen and flanks indistinctly barred with white and brown ; wings without spots, reaching to the extremity of the tail ; bill green, reddish at the base ; irides red ; feet green. Length seven and a half inches. Eggs yellowish, spotted with olive-brown. A very rare straggler to the British Isles.

THIS species appears to be generally diffused throughout the eastern and southern countries of Europe, but is very rare in England, coming now and again from spring to autumn. It is a shy bird, like the last species, confining itself exclusively to reedy marshes, and building its nest close to the water's edge. It lays seven or eight eggs.

THE WATER RAIL RALLUS AQUÁTICUS (*Plate XXI*)

Upper feathers reddish brown, with black centres ; under plumage in front lead-colour, behind and on the flanks barred with black and white ; bill red, tinged with brown above and at the tip ; irides red ; feet flesh-colour. Length ten inches. Eggs yellowish, spotted with ash-grey and red-brown. A resident throughout the British Isles, except the Shetlands ; also a winter visitor.

THE Water Rail is a generally diffused bird, but nowhere very common, haunting bushy and reedy places near the banks of rivers and lakes, and especially the Norfolk Broads, where it feeds on aquatic insects, worms, and snails. Like the Crakes, it makes more use of its legs than of its wings, and places its safety in concealment. Rarely does it take flight, and then only when closely hunted ; still more rarely does it expose itself outside its aquatic jungle. I recollect on one occasion, during an intense frost, when every marsh was as impenetrable to a bird's bill as a sheet of marble, passing in a carriage near a stream which, having just issued from its source, was unfrozen ; I then saw more than one Water Rail hunting for food among the short rushes and grass on the water's edge. Its mode of walking I thought was very like that of the Moor-hen, but it had not the jerking movement of body characteristic of that bird, which alone would have sufficed to distinguish it, even if I had not been near enough to detect the difference of colour. Either the severity of the weather had sharpened its appetite, and made it less shy than usual, or it had not learnt to fear a horse and carriage, for it took no notice of the intrusion on its privacy, but went on with its search without condescending to look up. The Water Rail, then, unlike the Corn Crake, remains with us all the winter. When forced to rise, this bird flies heavily straight forwards, at no great elevation above the rushes, with its legs hanging loose, and drops into the nearest thicket of weeds. A nest and eggs of this bird are thus described in the *Annals of Natural History* : ' The bird had selected for her nest a thick tuft of long grass, hollow at the bottom, on the side of the reed pond ; the nest, about an inch and a half thick, was composed of withered leaves and rushes ; it was so covered by the top of the grass, that neither bird, nest, nor eggs could be seen ; the entrance to the nest was through an aperture of the grass, directly into the reeds, opposite to where any one would stand to see the nest.' The number of eggs is about ten or eleven. Its note during breeding is a loud, groaning *cro-o-o-an.*

THE MOOR-HEN GALLÍNULA CHLÓROPUS (*Plate IV*)

Upper plumage deep olive-brown ; under tail-coverts and edge of the wing white, the former with a few black feathers ; under plumage slate colour, the flanks streaked with white ; base of the bill and a space on the forehead bright red, point of the bill yellow ; irides red ; feet olive-brown ; a red ring round the tibia. In females *the colours are brighter than in the* males. Young birds *have the front of the neck whitish, the belly grey, the base of the beak and legs olive-brown. Length thirteen inches. Eggs buff, spotted and speckled with orange-brown. Resident throughout the British Isles.*

OF the two common names of this bird, ' Moor-hen ' and ' Water-hen ', the former is that which is more generally in use, though the latter is the more appropriate. The bird frequents moors, it must be admitted, but only such as are watery ; while there is scarcely a river, lake, canal, brook, or even pond, of moderate dimensions, which Moor-hens do not either inhabit all the year round or occasionally visit. The name is objectionable on other accounts ; the male bird is called a Moor-hen as well as the female, while the terms Moor-fowl and Moor-cock have long been applied to the Grouse. For these reasons, I suppose, many recent ornithologists Anglicize the systematic name, and call it the Gallinule, which means ' little fowl ', and is suggestive of the half-domestic habits of the bird, under certain circumstances.

The Gallinule being a common bird of some size, conspicuous colours, and active habits, is an interesting appendage of our rivers and pieces of artificial water. Its note, something between a bark and a croak, is as well known in watered districts as the note of the Cuckoo, and is often uttered when the bird has no intention of being seen. Any one who may happen to be walking on the bank of a reedy pond may perhaps hear its strange cry and see the bird itself at some little distance, swimming about with a restless jerky motion, often dipping its head, and with every dip turning slightly to the right or the left. If he wishes for a nearer view, let him advance quietly, concealing himself as much as he can ; for if he proceeds carelessly, and takes off his eyes for any considerable time from the spot where he observed it, when he looks again it will have disappeared, taken wing, he may imagine, for some distant part of the water. Not so ; the cunning bird, as soon as a stranger was perceived within a dangerous proximity, steered quietly for the nearest tuft of reeds, among which it lies ensconced till he has passed on his way. Or it rose out of the water, and, with its feet trailing on the surface, made for a similar place of concealment ; or dived to the bottom, where it still remains clinging to the weeds. Perhaps it lies close to his feet, having sunk beneath the water, and, aided by feet and wings, rowed a subaqueous course to an often-tried thicket of rushes, where, holding on with its feet to the stems of submerged weeds, it remains perfectly still, leaving nothing above the surface of the water but the point of its beak. If the observer suspects the whereabouts of its concealment, he may beat the rushes with his stick and produce no effect ; the bird knows itself to be safe where it is and will make no foolish attempt to better itself. A water spaniel or Newfoundland dog will be more effective. Very often an animal of this kind is an overmatch for its sagacity, and seizes it in his mouth before the poor bird was aware that the water itself was to be invaded ; but more frequently it discovers an onset of this nature in time to clear itself from its moorings, and dashing out with a splashing movement of feet and wings skims across the pond to another lurking-place, and defies further pursuit.

The Gallinule, though an excellent swimmer and diver, belongs to the waders ; it has, consequently, free use of its legs on land, and here it is no less nimble than in the water. When induced to change the scene it steps ashore, and, with a peculiar jerking motion of its tail, showing the white feathers beneath, and very conspicuous by its bright red bill, which harmonizes pleasantly with the green grass, it struts about and picks up worms, insects, snails, or seeds, with un-flagging perseverance, making no stay anywhere, and often running rapidly. If surprised on these occasions, it either makes for the water, or flies off in a line for some thick hedge or patch of brush-wood, from which it is very difficult to dislodge it.

Its mode of life is pretty much the same all the year round ; it is not a traveller from choice. Only in severe weather, when its haunts are bound up with ice, it is perforce compelled to shift its quarters. It then travels by night and searches for unfrozen streams. At such times it appears occasionally in pretty large numbers in places where usually a few only resort. When the south of Europe is visited by severe frosts it is supposed even to cross the Mediterranean, it having been observed in Algeria, feeding in marshes in half-social parties, where a day or two before none had been seen. To the faculties of swimming and running it adds that of perching on trees ; this it does habitually, as it roosts in low bushy trees ; and it has besides the power of walking cleverly along the branches.

In the neighbourhood of houses where it has long been undisturbed, it loses much of its shy nature, and will not only allow itself to be approached within a short distance, but, becoming half-domesticated, will consort with the poultry in the farm-yard, and come with them to be fed. It is fond also of visiting the kitchen-garden, where it is apt to make itself unwelcome, by helping itself to the tenderest and best of the vegetables. Bishop Stanley, in his entertaining *Book on Birds*, gives some highly amusing anecdotes of the Gallinule.

It builds its nest on the stump of a tree, or in a bush among wet places, or in the roots of alders, but often it is placed on the low-lying branch of a tree overhanging the water. The nest is a large structure, made of rushes and dry flags, and is easy of detection. It is very liable, too, to be swept away by any sudden rise in a river. Added to which, the young frequently fall a prey to pike. But as the bird has two, and sometimes three, broods in a year, each consisting of from six to eight, it remains undiminished in numbers. The nest is some-times placed in a tree at a distance from the water. When this is the case, as the habits of the young birds are aquatic, immediately on their breaking the egg, the old birds convey them in their claws to the water.

An instance is recorded in the *Zoologist* of a female Gallinule being seen thus employed carrying a young one in each foot ; it has been observed, too, that in such cases the male bird builds a second nest, near the water's edge, to which the young retire for shelter during the night, until they are sufficiently fledged to accompany their parents to their ordinary roosting-places in trees.

THE COOT FÚLICA ÁTRA (*Plate IV*)

Upper plumage black, tinged on the back with grey ; under parts bluish grey ; frontal disk large, pure white ; bill white, tinged with rose-red ; irides crimson ; feet grey, tinged with green ; part of the tibia orange-yellow. Length sixteen inches. Eggs brownish, speckled with reddish brown. Resident throughout the British Isles ; also a winter visitor.

THE Coot, seen from a distance, either on land or water, might be mistaken for a Gallinule, flirting up its tail when it swims, jerking its head to and fro, and when on land strutting about with a precisely similar movement of all its members. On a nearer examination, it is clearly distinguished by its larger size and the white bare spot above the bill, in front, from which it is often called the Bald-headed Coot. Their note, in summer, is a loud harsh cry, represented by the syllable *krew*, as it would be uttered by a crazy trumpet. In winter they are nearly mute.

When seen on the sea-coast, they are readily distinguished from Ducks by the different position in which they sit on the water, with their heads low, poking forwards, and their tails sticking high above the body. When flying in large coveys, they crowd together into a mass, but when swimming scatter over a wide space.

They have the same power of concealing themselves by diving among weeds that has been already said to be possessed by the Gallinule. I have seen a female Coot and her brood, when disturbed by a party of sportsmen, paddle for a small patch of rushes, and defy a long-continued and minute search conducted by keepers and clever water-dogs. The latter appeared to traverse, again and again, every square foot of the rush bed ; but not a single bird was dislodged.

FAMILY OTIDIDÆ

THE GREAT BUSTARD OTIS TARDA (*Plate XIX*)

Head, neck, breast, and edge of the wing, ash-grey ; on the crown a longitudinal black streak ; bill with a tuft of elongated loose feathers on each side of the lower mandible ; upper plumage reddish yellow, streaked transversely with black ; lower whitish ; tail reddish brown and white, barred with black. Female—smaller, without a moustache, the streak on the crown fainter. Length nearly four feet. Eggs olive-brown, irregularly blotched with dull red and deep brown. Formerly resident in England, now only a very rare straggler to the British Isles.

THE Great Bustard was formerly not infrequent in Britain, but is now only a very rare visitor. Its last fertile eggs were taken in Norfolk and Suffolk about the year 1838.

ORDER CHARADRIIFORMES

FAMILY HÆMATOPODIDÆ

THE OYSTER CATCHER HÆMATOPUS OSTRALEGUS (*Plate XXXI*)

Head, nape, upper part of the breast, back, wings, and extremity of the tail, deep black ; collar, rim, base of tail-feathers and primaries, a transverse band on the wings, and all the lower parts, white ; bill and orbits bright orange-red ; irides crimson ; feet purplish red. In summer the white collar is absent. Length seventeen inches. Eggs olive-brown, blotched and spotted with ash-grey and black. Resident on the coasts of the British Isles, also breeding inland in Scotland and in a few localities in northern England and Ireland ; also a winter visitor to the coasts.

THE first time I came upon a flock of these birds I was able to approach them nearer than on any other occasion. They frequently uttered a harsh note in a high key which, though unmusical, harmonized well with the scenery. I had many other opportunities of observing them on the shores of the Scottish lochs, and I was once induced, on the recommendation of a friend, to have one served up for dinner as an agreeable variation from the bacon and herrings which mainly constitute the dietary of a Scottish fishing-village inn. But I did not repeat the experiment, preferring fish pure and simple to fish served up through the medium of a fowl. The nature of its food sufficiently accounts for its strong flavour. Oyster Catchers frequent rocky promontories or the broad banks of mud, sand, and ooze, which stretch out from low portions of the coast. Here they feed on mussels and other bivalves, limpets, worms, crustacea, and small fish ; mixing freely with other birds while on the ground, but keeping to themselves while performing their flights. In their mode of using their wings they remind the spectator of Ducks rather than of Plovers, and they advance in a line, sometimes in single file, one after another, but more frequently wing by wing. When they alight, too, it is not with a circular sweep, but with a sailing movement. When the mud-banks are covered by the tide they move to a short distance inland, and pick up slugs and insects in the meadows, or betake themselves to salt marshes and rocky headlands. Their nest is generally a slight depression among the shingle above high-water mark ; but on rocky shores they make an attempt at a nest, collecting a few blades of grass and scraps of seaweed. They lay three or four eggs, and the young are able to run soon after breaking the shell.

In high latitudes Oyster Catchers are migratory, leaving their breeding grounds in autumn, and returning in the spring; consequently, those coasts from which they never depart afford an asylum in winter to vast numbers of strangers, in addition to their native population. On the coast of Norfolk, for example, they are to be seen in small parties all through the summer; but in winter, especially if it be a severe one, they may be reckoned by thousands. They here seem to have favourite spots on which to pass the night. One of these is what is called the 'Eastern point' of Brancaster Marsh, a place of perfect security, for it is difficult of access under any circumstances, and cannot be approached at all with any chance of concealment on the part of the intruder. Towards this point I have seen line after line winging their way, all about the same hour, just before sunset, all following the line of the coast, but taking care to keep well out at sea, and all advancing with perfect regularity, every individual in a company being at the same height above the water. They are very wary at this season, insomuch that though I must have seen many thousands, and examined upwards of twenty species of seashore birds, which had been shot in the neighbourhood, not a single Oyster Catcher was brought to me.

A common name for this bird is Sea Pie, another appropriate one is 'Mussel picker'; and it is thought that 'Catcher' comes from the Dutch *aekster* (Magpie). The note is a shrill *keep, keep*. It swims well, and sometimes it will take to the water of its own accord.

FAMILY CHARADRIIDÆ

THE GOLDEN PLOVER PLUVIALIS APRICARIA (*Plate XXII*)

Winter—upper plumage dusky, spotted with yellow; cheeks, neck, and breast, mottled with ash-brown and buff; throat and abdomen white; quills dusky, white along the shafts towards the end; beak dusky; feet deep ash-colour; irides brown. Summer—upper plumage greyish black, spotted with bright yellow; forehead and space above the eyes white; sides of the neck white, mottled with black and yellow; lore, throat, neck, and lower parts, deep black. Length nine inches. Eggs yellowish green, blotched and spotted with black. A resident, breeding in Wales, northern England, Scotland, and Ireland; also a passage migrant and winter visitor.

THE Golden Plover is a common bird in the south of England during the winter months, and in the mountainous parts of Scotland and the north of England during the rest of the year; yet so different are its habits and plumage at the extremes of these two seasons, that the young naturalist who has had no opportunities of observing them in their transition stage, and has had no access to trustworthy books, might be forgiven for setting down the two forms of the bird as distinct species.

In the hilly districts of the north of Europe, Golden Plovers are numerous, sometimes being, with Ptarmigans, the only birds which relieve the solitude of the desolate wastes. Though numerous in the same localities, they are not gregarious during spring and summer, and are remarkable for their fearlessness of man. So tame, indeed, are they that, in little-frequented places, when disturbed by the traveller they will run along the stony ground a few yards in front of him, then fly a few yards, then stand and stare and run along as before. On such occasions they frequently utter their singular cry —the note so often referred to in Sir Walter Scott's poems—which, like the Nightingale's song, is considered simply plaintive or painfully woe-begone, according to the natural temperament or occasional mood of the hearer. This bird builds no nest ; a natural depression in the ground, unprotected by bush, heather or rock, serves its purpose, and here the female lays four eggs, much pointed at one end, and arranges them in accordance with this.

At the approach of autumn, no matter where their summer may have been passed, Plovers migrate southwards in large flights, those from Scotland to the southern counties of England, where they frequent wide moist pastures, heaths, and reclaimed marshland. From the northern parts of the continent of Europe they take their departure in October, either to the European shores of the Mediterranean, or to the plains of Northern Africa. In these migrations they are not infrequently joined by Starlings. They travel in close array, forming large flocks much wider than deep, moving their sharp wings rapidly, and making a whizzing sound which may be heard a long way off. Now and then, as if actuated by a single impulse, they sweep towards the ground, suddenly alter the direction of their flight, then wheel upwards with the regularity of a machine, and either alight or pursue their onward course. This habit of skimming along the ground and announcing their approach beforehand, is turned to good purpose by the bird-catcher, who imitates their note, attracts the whole flight to sweep down into his neighbourhood, and captures them in his net, a hundred at a time, or, when they are within range, has no difficulty in killing from twelve to twenty at a shot. Not infrequently, too, when some members of a flock have been killed or wounded, the remainder, before they remove out of danger, wheel round and sweep just over the heads of their ill-fated companions, as if for the purpose of inquiring the reason why they have deserted the party, or of alluring them to join it once more. This habit is not peculiar to Plovers, but may be noticed in the case of several of the seaside waders, as Dunlins and Sanderlings. In severe winter weather they desert the meadows, in which the worms have descended into the ground beyond the reach of frost, and so of their bills, and resort to the muddy or sandy seashore. In the Hebrides it is said that they do not migrate at all, but simply content themselves with shifting from the moors to the shore and back again, according to the weather. In the northern parts of France, on the other hand, they are only known as passengers on their way to the south. From making their appearance in the rainy season they are there called *pluviers*, whence our name Plover, which, however, is supposed by some to have been given to them for their indicating by their movements coming changes in the weather, in which respect indeed their skill is marvellous.

The Golden Plover, sometimes called also Yellow Plover, and Green Plover, is found at various seasons in most countries of Europe ; but the Golden Plovers of Asia and America are considered to be different species.

THE DOTTEREL EUDROMIAS MORINELLUS (*Plate XXIII*)

Winter—head dusky ash ; over each eye a reddish white band, meeting at the nape ; face whitish, dotted with black ; back dusky ash, tinged with green, the feathers edged with rust-red ; breast and flanks reddish ash ; gorget white ; beak black ; irides brown ; feet greenish ash. Summer—face and a band over the eyes white ; head dusky ; nape and sides of the neck ash ; feathers of the back, wing-coverts, and wing-feathers, edged with deep red ; gorget white, bordered above by a narrow black line ; lower part of the breast and flanks bright rust-red ; middle of the belly black ; abdomen reddish white. Young birds have a reddish tinge on the head, and the tail is tipped with red. Length nine inches and a half. Eggs yellowish olive, blotched and spotted with dusky brown. A summer visitor, breeding on the mountains in Scotland and the English Lake district ; elsewhere in the British Isles a rare passage migrant.

THE Dotterel, Little Dotard, or Morinellus, ' little fool ', received both the one and the other of its names from its alleged stupidity. ' It is a silly bird ', says Willughby, writing in 1676 ; ' but as an article of food a great delicacy. It is caught in the night by lamp-light, in accordance with the movements of the fowler. For if he stretch out his arm, the bird extends a wing ; if he a leg, the bird does the same. In short, whatever the fowler does, the Dotterel does the same. And so intent is it on the movements of its pursuer, that it is unawares entangled in the net.' Such, at least, was the common belief ; and Pennant alludes to it, quoting the following passage from the poet Drayton :

> Most worthy man, with thee 'tis ever thus,
> As men take Dottrels, so hast thou ta'en us
> Which, as a man his arme or leg doth set,
> So this fond bird will likewise counterfeit.

In Pennant's time, Dotterels were not uncommon in Cambridgeshire, Lincolnshire, and Derbyshire, appearing in small flocks of eight or ten only, from the latter end of April to the middle of June ; and I have been informed by a gentleman in Norfolk that, not many years since, they annually resorted also in small flocks to the plains of that county. Of late years, owing most probably to their being much sought after for the table, they have become more rare ; and the same thing has taken place in France.

The Dotterel has been observed in many of the English counties both in spring and autumn, but I may remark that the name is frequently given in Norfolk and elsewhere to the Ringed Plover, to which bird also belong the eggs collected on the sea-coast, and sold as Dotterel's eggs.

THE RINGED PLOVER CHARADRIUS HIATÍCULA (*Plate XXII*)

Forehead, lore, sides of the face, gorget reaching round the neck, black; a band across the forehead and through the eyes, throat, a broad collar, and all the lower parts, white; upper plumage ash-brown; outer tail-feather white, the next nearly so, the other feathers grey at the base, passing into dusky and black, tipped with white, except the two middle ones, which have no white tips; orbits, feet, and beak, orange, the latter tipped with black. Young— colours of the head dull; gorget incomplete, ash-brown; bill dusky, tinged with orange at the base of the lower mandible; feet yellowish. Length seven and a half inches. Eggs olive-yellow, with numerous black and grey spots. A resident, breeding on coasts of the British Isles and in a few localities inland; also a passage migrant and winter visitor.

On almost any part of the sea-coast of Britain, where there is a wide expanse of sand left at low water, a bird may often be noticed, not much larger than a Lark, grey above and white below, a patch of black on the forehead and under the eye, a white ring round the neck, and a black one below. If the wind be high, or rain be falling, the observer will be able to get near enough to see these markings; for sea-birds generally are less acute observers in foul weather than in fair. On a nearer approach, the bird will fly up, uttering a soft, sweet, plaintive whistle of two notes, and, having performed a rapid, semicircular flight, will probably alight at no great distance, and repeat its note. If it has settled on the plain sand or on the water's edge, or near a tidal pool, it runs rapidly, without hopping, stoops its head, picks up a worm, a portion of shellfish, or a sand-hopper, runs, stops, pecks, and runs again, but does not allow any one to come so near as before. The next time that it alights, it may select, perhaps, the beach of shells and pebbles above high-water mark. Then it becomes at once invisible; or, if the observer be very keen-sighted, he may be able to detect it while it is in motion, but then only. Most probably, let him mark ever so accurately with his eye the exact spot on which he saw it alight, and let him walk up to the spot without once averting his eye, he will, on his arrival, find it gone. It has run ahead with a speed marvellous in so small a biped, and is pecking among the stones a hundred yards off. Its name is the Ringed Plover, or Ringed Dotterel. Fishermen on the coast call it a Stone-runner, a most appropriate name; others call it a Sea Lark. In ornithological works it is described under the former of these names.

The Ringed Plover frequents the shores of Great Britain all the year round. It is a social bird, but less so in spring than at any other season; for the females are then employed in the important business of incubation, and the males are too attentive to their mates to engage in picnics on the sands. The nest is a simple hollow in the sand, above high-water mark, or on the shingly beach ; and here the female lays four large, pointed eggs, which are arranged in the nest with all the small ends together. The young are able to run as soon as they break the shell ; but, having no power of flight for a long time, avoid impending danger by scattering and hiding among the stones. The old bird, on such occasions, uses her wings ; but not to desert her charge. She flies up to the intruder, and, like other members of the same family, endeavours to entice him away by counterfeiting lameness or some injury.

The Ringed Plover sometimes goes inland to rear her young, and lays her eggs in a sandy warren, on the bank of a river or the margin of a lake ; but when the young are able to fly, old and young together repair to the seashore, collecting in flocks, and for the most part continuing to congregate until the following spring. Their flight is rapid and sweeping, consisting of a succession of curves, while performing which they show sometimes their upper grey plumage, and at other times the under, which is of a dazzling white. Occasionally, too, as they wheel from one tack to another, every bird is lost sight of, owing to the perfect unanimity with which, at the same instant, they alter their course, and to the incapacity of the human eye to follow the rapid change from a dark hue to a light.

Not infrequently one falls in with a solitary individual which has been left behind by its companions, or has strayed from the flock. Such a bird, when disturbed, utters its whistle more frequently than on ordinary occasions, and, as its note is not difficult of imitation, I have often enticed a stray bird to fly close up to me, answering all the while. But it has rarely happened that I have succeeded in practising the deception on the same bird a second time.

THE LITTLE RINGED PLOVER CHARADRIUS DUBIUS (*Plate LXVI*)

A band reaching from eye to eye across the head, continued above the base of the bill in front, and passing backwards through the eye and gorget, meeting behind, black ; neck, collar, rump, and under plumage, white ; back of the head and rest of the upper plumage ash-grey ; bill black ; orbits yellow ; feet flesh-colour. Length five inches. Eggs yellowish white, blotched with black and brown. A scarce visitor to the British Isles, which has nested a few times in south-eastern England.

THIS bird is smaller and slighter than the Ringed Plover, but is most easily distinguished by the absence of a white bar in the wing when seen in flight and by its distinctive high-pitched call-note. It frequents banks of sand or gravel in river-beds and the shores of lakes or pools.

THE KENTISH PLOVER LEUCOPOLIUS ALEXANDRINUS
(*Plate XXII*)

Forehead, a band over each eye, chin, cheeks, and under parts, white ; upper part of the forehead, a band from the base of the beak extending through the eye, and a large spot on each side of the breast, black ; head and nape light brownish red ; rest of the upper plumage ash-brown ; two outer tail-feathers white, the third whitish, the rest brown ; beak black ; irides brown ; feet dark grey. Female *wants the black spot on the forehead, and the other parts black in the male are replaced by ash-brown. Length six and a half inches. Eggs olive-yellow, spotted and speckled with black. A rare summer visitor, a few pairs breeding in Kent, and a very rare passage migrant elsewhere on the coasts of the British Isles.*

THE Kentish Plover differs from the preceding in its inferior size, in having a narrower stripe of black on the cheeks, and in wanting the black ring round the neck. It is found from time to time in various parts of the country, breeding in Kent and the Channel Islands, but is most abundant on the shores of the Mediterranean. Its habits resemble closely those of the allied species.

THE GREY PLOVER SQUATÁROLA SQUATÁROLA (*Plate XXII*)

Winter—*forehead, throat, and under plumage, white, spotted on the neck and flanks with grey and brown ; upper plumage dusky brown, mottled with white and ash-colour ; long axillary feathers black or dusky ; tail white, barred with brown and tipped with reddish ; bill black ; irides dusky ; feet blackish grey.* Summer—*lore, neck, breast, belly, and flanks, black, bounded by white ; upper plumage and tail black and white. Length eleven and a half inches. Eggs olive, spotted with black. A passage migrant and winter visitor to the coasts of the British Isles, a few remaining during summer.*

MANY of the waders agree in wearing, during winter, plumage in a great measure of a different hue from that which characterizes them in summer ; and, as a general rule, the winter tint is lighter than that of summer. This change is, in fact, but an extension of the law which clothes several of the quadrupeds with a dusky or a snowy fur in accordance with the season. The Grey Plover, as seen in England, well deserves its name, for, as it frequents our shores in the winter alone, it is only known to us as a bird grey above and white below. But in summer the under plumage is decidedly black, and in this respect it bears a close resemblance to the Golden Plover, with which, in spite of the presence of a rudimentary fourth toe, it is closely allied. The occurrence of the bird, however, in this condition, in England, is exceptional ; while in the northern regions, both of the Old and New World, it must be unusual to see an adult bird in any other than the sable plumage of summer.

The Grey Plover is a bird of extensive geographical range, breeding in the arctic regions and almost cosmopolitan in winter. In this country, as I have observed, it occurs from autumn to spring, frequenting the seashore, and picking up worms and other animal productions cast up by the sea. Grey Plovers are less abundant than Golden Plovers ; yet, in severe seasons they assemble in numerous small flocks on the shores of the eastern counties, and, as Meyer well observes, they are disposed to be ' sociable, not only towards their own species,

but to every other coast bird. When a party either go towards the
shore, or leave it for the meadows and flat wastes, they unanimously
keep together ; but when alighting, they mix with every other species,
and thus produce a motley group.' They fly in flocks, varying from
five to twenty or more, keeping in a line, more or less curved, or in
two lines forming an angle. Their flight is strong and rapid, rarely
direct, but sweeping in wide semicircles. As they advance they
alternately show their upper and under plumage, but more frequently
the latter ; for they generally keep at a height of sixty or a hundred
yards from the ground, in this respect differing from Ringed Plovers,
Dunlins, etc. Occasionally one or two of the flock utter a loud
whistle, which seems to be a signal for all to keep close order.   Just as
Starlings habitually alight wherever they see Rooks or Gulls feeding,
so the Grey Plovers join themselves on to any society of birds which
has detected a good hunting-ground.   During a single walk along the
sands I have observed them mixed up with Dunlins, Knots, Gulls,
Redshanks, and Royston Crows ; but in no instance was I able to
approach near enough to note their habit of feeding. They were
always up and away before any other birds saw danger impending.
In autumn they are less shy.

The people on the coast describe the Grey Plover as the shyest
of all the waders, and could give me no information as to its habits ;
but Meyer, whose description of this bird is very accurate in other
respects, states that ' its general appearance is peculiar to itself ; it
walks about on the ground slowly and with grace, and stops every
now and then to pick up its food ; it carries its body in a horizontal
position on straight legs, and its head very close to its body, consequently increasing the thick appearance of the head '.

The Grey Plover breeds in high latitudes, making a slight hollow
in the ground, and employing a few blades of grass. It lays four eggs,
on which it sits so closely that it will almost be trodden on. When
thus disturbed its habits resemble those of the Ringed Plover.

THE LAPWING OR PEEWIT VANELLUS VANELLUS
(Plate XXIII)

*Feathers on the back of the head elongated and curved upwards ; head, crest,
and breast, glossy black ; throat, sides of the neck, belly, and abdomen, white ;
under tail-coverts yellowish red ; upper plumage dark green with purple
reflections ; tail, when expanded, displaying a large semi-circular graduated
black patch on a white disk, outer feather on each side wholly white ; bill dusky ;
feet reddish brown. Young—throat dull white, mottled with dusky and tinged
with red ; upper feathers tipped with dull yellow. Length twelve and a half
inches. Eggs olive-brown to stone buff, blotched and spotted with dusky black.
Resident throughout the British Isles ; also a passage migrant and winter visitor.*

THE Peewit, or Green Plover, as it is sometimes called, is among the
best-known birds indigenous to the British Isles. This notoriety it
owes to several causes. The lengthened feathers on the back of its

head, forming a crest, at once distinguish it from every other British wader. Its peculiar flight, consisting of a series of wide slow flappings with its singularly rounded wings, furnishes a character by which it may be recognized at a great distance ; and its strange note, resembling the word ' peweet ' uttered in a high screaming tone, cannot be mistaken for the note of any other bird. In London and other large towns of England its eggs also are well known to most people ; for ' Plovers' eggs ', as they are called, are considered great delicacies.

Peewits are found in abundance in most parts of Europe and Asia from Ireland to Japan. They are essentially Plovers in all their habits, except, perhaps, that they do not run so rapidly as some others of the tribe. They inhabit the high grounds in open countries, the borders of lakes and marshes and low unenclosed wastes, and may not infrequently be seen in the large meadows, which in some districts extend from the banks of rivers. They are partially migratory ; hence they may appear at a certain season in some particular spot, and be entirely lost sight of for many months. Individuals which have been bred in high latitudes are more precise in their periods of migration than those bred in the south. In Kamchatka, for instance, their southern migration is so regular that the month of October has received the name of the ' Lapwing month '. In Britain their wanderings are both more uncertain and limited ; for, though they assemble in flocks in autumn, they only migrate from exposed localities to spots which, being more sheltered, afford them a better supply of food.

In April and May these birds deposit their eggs, making no further preparation than that of bringing together a few stalks and placing them in a shallow depression in the ground. The number of eggs is always four, and they are placed in the order so common among the Waders, crosswise. Lapwings are to a certain extent social, even in the breeding season, in so far that a considerable number usually frequent the same marsh or common. It is at this season that they utter most frequently their characteristic cry, a note which is never musical, and heard by the lonely traveller (as has happened to myself more than once by night) is particularly wild, harsh, and dispiriting. Now, too, one may approach near enough to them to notice the winnowing movement of their wings, which has given them the name of Lapwing in England and Vanneau in France (from *van*, a fan). The young are able to run as soon as they have burst the shell, and follow their parents to damp ground, where worms, slugs, and insects are most abundant. When the young have acquired the use of their wings, the families of a district unite into flocks. They are then very wary, and can rarely be approached without difficulty ; but as they are considered good eating, many of them fall before the fowler.

THE TURNSTONE ARENARIA INTÉRPRES (*Plate XXXI*)

Crown reddish white, with longitudinal black streaks ; upper part of the back, scapulars, and wing-coverts, rusty brown, spotted with black ; rest of the plumage variegated with black and white ; bill and irides black ; feet orange-yellow.

Length nine inches. Eggs greenish grey, blotched and spotted with slate and brown. A passage migrant and winter visitor to the coasts of the British Isles, uncommon inland.

THE Turnstone is a regular annual visitor to the shores of Great Britain, and indeed of almost every other country, having been observed as far north as Greenland, and as far south as the Straits of Magellan ; but it is rarely inland. It arrives on our coasts about the beginning of August, not in large flocks like the Plovers, but in small parties, each of which, it is conjectured, constitutes a family. It is a bird of elegant form and beautiful parti-coloured plumage, active in its habits, a nimble runner, and an indefatigable hunter after food. In size it is intermediate between the Grey Plover and Sanderling, being about as big as a Thrush. The former of these birds it resembles in its disposition to feed in company with birds of different species, and its impatience of the approach of man. For this latter reason it does not often happen that any one can get near enough to these birds to watch their manœuvres while engaged in the occupation from which they have derived their name, though their industry is often apparent from the number of pebbles and shells found dislodged from their socket on the sands where a family has been feeding. Audubon, who had the good fortune to fall in with a party on a retired sea-coast, where, owing to the rare appearance of human beings, they were less fearful than is their wont, describes their operations with his usual felicity :
' They were not more than fifteen or twenty yards distant, and I was delighted to see the ingenuity with which they turned over the oyster-shells, clods of mud, and other small bodies left exposed by the retiring tide. Whenever the object was not too large, the bird bent its legs to half their length, placed its bill beneath it, and with a sudden quick jerk of the head pushed it off, when it quickly picked up the food which was thus exposed to view, and walked deliberately to the next shell to perform the same operation. In several instances, when the clusters of oyster-shells or clods of mud were too heavy to be removed in the ordinary way, they would not only use the bill and head, but also the breast, pushing the object with all their strength, and reminding me of the labour which I have undergone in turning over a large turtle. Among the seaweeds that had been cast on shore, they used only the bill, tossing the garbage from side to side with a dexterity extremely pleasant to behold.[1] In like manner I saw there four Turnstones examine almost every part of the shore along a space of from thirty to forty yards ; after which I drove them away, that our hunters might not kill them on their return.'

A writer in the *Zoologist* [2] gives an equally interesting account of the successful efforts of two Turnstones to turn over the dead body of a codfish, nearly three and a half feet long, which had been embedded in the sand to about the depth of two inches.

For an account of the habits of the Turnstone during the breeding season—it never breeds with us—we are indebted to Mr. Hewitson,

---

[1] From this habit, the Turnstone is in Norfolk called a ' Tangle-picker '.—C. A. J.
[2] Vol. ix. p. 3077.

who fell in with it on the coast of Norway. He says, ' We had visited numerous islands with little encouragement, and were about to land upon a flat rock, bare, except where here and there grew tufts of grass or stunted juniper clinging to its surface, when our attention was attracted by the singular cry of a Turnstone, which in its eager watch had seen our approach, and perched itself upon an eminence of the rock, assuring us, by its querulous oft-repeated note and anxious motions, that its nest was there. We remained in the boat a short time, until we had watched it behind a tuft of grass near which, after a minute search, we succeeded in finding the nest in a situation in which I should never have expected to meet a bird of this sort breeding ; it was placed against a ledge of the rock, and consisted of nothing more than the dropping leaves of the juniper bush, under a creeping branch of which the eggs, four in number, were snugly concealed, and admirably sheltered from the many storms by which these bleak and exposed rocks are visited.'

FAMILY SCOLOPACIDÆ

THE SANDERLING CROCETHIA ALBA (*Plate XXIV*)

Winter—*upper plumage and sides of the neck whitish ash ; cheeks and all the under plumage, pure white ; bend and edge of the wing and quills blackish grey ; tail deep grey, edged with white ; bill, irides, and feet, black.* Summer —*cheeks and crown black, mottled with rust-red and white ; neck and breast reddish ash, with black and white spots ; back and scapulars deep rust-red, spotted with black, all the feathers edged and tipped with white ; wing-coverts dusky, with reddish lines, and tipped with white ; two middle tail-feathers dusky, with reddish edges.* Young in autumn—*cheeks, head, nape, and back, variously mottled with black, brown, grey, rust-red, and dull white. Length eight inches. Eggs olive, spotted and speckled with black. A passage migrant and winter visitor to the coasts of the British Isles, rare inland.*

THE early flocks of Sanderlings often consist of old as well as young birds, which is not the common rule with waders. They are plentiful on our sandy shores, and they sometimes visit inland waters. By April the return passage begins. The note is a shrill *wick !* They arrive on our shores early in autumn, keeping together in small flocks, or joining the company of Dunlins, or Ringed Plovers. In spring they withdraw to high latitudes, where they breed ; they are not, however, long absent. Yarrell mentions his having obtained specimens as late as April and June, and I have myself obtained them as early as the end of July, having shot at Hunstanton, on the coast of Norfolk, several young birds of the year, on the twenty-third of that month ; and on another occasion I obtained a specimen on the sands of Abergele, in North Wales, in August.

Like many other shore birds, they have an extensive geographical range, and are found in all latitudes, both in the eastern and western hemispheres.

THE CURLEW NUMENIUS ARQUATA (*Plate XXIII*)

General plumage reddish ash, mottled with dusky spots ; belly white, with longitudinal dusky spots ; feathers of the back and scapulars black, bordered with rust-red ; tail white, with dark brown transverse bars ; upper mandible dusky ; lower, flesh-colour ; irides brown ; feet bluish grey. Length varying from twenty-two to twenty-eight inches. Eggs olive-green, blotched and spotted with brown and dark green. A resident, breeding almost throughout the British Isles, except the Outer Hebrides ; also a passage migrant and winter visitor.

DWELLERS by the seaside—especially where the tide retires to a great distance leaving a wide expanse of muddy sand, or on the banks of a tidal river where the receding water lays bare extensive banks of soft ooze—are most probably quite familiar with the note of the Curlew, however ignorant they may be of the form or name of the bird from which it proceeds. A loud whistle of two syllables, which may be heard for more than a mile, bearing a not over-fanciful resemblance to the name of the bird, answered by a similar cry, mellowed by distance into a pleasant sound—wild, but in perfect harmony with the character of the scene—announces the fact that a party of Curlews have discovered that the ebb-tide is well advanced, and that their feeding-ground is uncovered. The stroller, if quietly disposed, may chance to get a sight of the birds themselves as they arrive in small flocks from the inland meadows ; and though they will probably be too cautious to venture within an unsafe distance, they will most likely come quite close enough to be discriminated. Not the merest novice could mistake them for Gulls ; for not only is their flight of a different character, but the bill, which is thick enough to be distinguished at a considerable distance, is disproportionately long, and is curved to a remarkable degree. Curlews are in the habit of selecting as their feeding-ground those portions of the shore which most abound in worms and small crustaceous animals ; these they either pick up and, as it were, coax from the tip to the base of the beak, or, thrusting their long bills into the mud, draw out the worms, which they dispose of in like manner. When the sands or ooze are covered, they withdraw from the shore, and either retire to the adjoining marshes or pools, or pace about the meadows, picking up worms, snails, and insects. Hayfields, before the grass is cut, are favourite resorts, especially in the North ; and, in districts where there are meadows adjoining an estuary, they are in the habit of changing the one for the other at every ebb and flow of the tide. From the middle of autumn till the early spring Curlews are, for the most part, seaside birds, frequenting, more or less, all the coast ; but at the approach of the breeding season they repair inland, and resort to heaths, damp meadows, and barren hills. Here a shallow nest is made on the ground, composed of bents, rushes, and twigs of heath, loosely put together. The eggs, which are very large, are four in number. During the period of incubation the male keeps about the neighbourhood, but is scarcely less wary than at other seasons. The female, if disturbed, endeavours to lure away the intruder from her dwelling by the artifice, common in the tribe, of pretending to be disabled ; and great anxiety is shown by both male and female if any one approaches the spot where the young lie concealed. The latter are able to run almost immediately after they are hatched, but some weeks elapse before they are fledged. It seems probable that an unusually long time elapses before they attain their full size, for the dimensions of different individuals vary to a remarkable degree. Eight or nine specimens were brought to me in Norfolk in the winter of 1861, and among them about half seemed full-grown ; of the others some were so small that, at the first glance, I supposed them to be Whimbrels.

The Curlew is found on the sea-coast over the whole of Europe and Asia, and along the northern coast of Africa.

The flesh of this bird is said by some to be excellent eating. This, perhaps, may be the case with young birds shot early in autumn before they have been long subjected to a marine diet. My own experience of birds shot in winter does not confirm this opinion. I have found them eatable, but not palatable.

THE WHIMBREL NUMENIUS PHÆOPUS (Plate XXIV)

General plumage pale ash-colour, mottled with white and dusky spots ; crown divided by a longitudinal streak of yellowish white ; over each eye a broader brown streak ; belly and abdomen white, with a few dusky spots on the flanks ; feathers on the back, and scapulars, deep brown, in the middle bordered by lighter brown ; rump white ; tail ash-brown, barred obliquely with dark brown ; bill dusky, reddish at the base ; irides brown ; feet lead-colour. Length not exceeding seventeen inches. Eggs dark olive-brown, blotched with dusky. A passage migrant and summer visitor to the British Isles, breeding regularly in the Orkneys and Shetlands and occasionally in the Highlands and some of the western islands of Scotland.

THOUGH by no means a rare bird, the Whimbrel is of far less common occurrence than the Curlew, and in England is seen only at two periods of the year, in May and August, when performing its migrations. It resembles the Curlew both in figure and habits, though much smaller in size ; its note, however, is entirely different, being a rapid tittering whinny. It is gregarious, but unsociable with other birds.

THE SPOTTED OR DUSKY REDSHANK TRINGA ERYTHROPUS
(Plate LXVI)

Winter—Upper plumage ash-grey ; rump and all the lower parts white ; a dusky band between the bill and eye, edged above with white ; sides and front of the neck mottled with white and ash ; tail and coverts barred with white and dusky ; bill black, the base of the lower mandible red ; feet bright red. Summer—upper plumage dusky ; wing-coverts and scapulars spotted with white ; lower plumage dusky ash ; feathers of the breast and belly ending with

*a narrow white crescent ; feet brown, tinged with red.   Length twelve inches.
Eggs greenish buff, blotched with umber-brown.   An uncommon passage migrant
in the British Isles, chiefly in the eastern counties of England.*

THE COMMON REDSHANK TRINGA TOTANUS (*Plate XXV*)

*Winter—upper plumage ash-brown ; throat, sides of the head, streak over
the eye, neck, and breast, greyish white ; rump, belly, and abdomen, white ;
tail marked transversely with black and white zigzag bars, tipped with white ;
feet and lower half of both mandibles red.   Summer—upper feathers ash-
brown, with a broad dusky streak in the centre ; under parts white, spotted and
streaked with dusky ; feet and lower half of both mandibles vermilion red.
Length ten to eleven inches.   Eggs greenish yellow, blotched and spotted with
brown.   A resident in the British Isles ; also a passage migrant and winter
visitor.*

THE Redshank is a bird of frequent occurrence on all such parts of
the coast as are suited to its habits.   Nowhere, I suppose, is it more
abundant than on the coast of Norfolk—at least, on those parts of
the coast where it can have access to muddy marshes.   It does not,
indeed, confine itself to such places, for it is not infrequently to be
seen on the seashore, feeding in the neighbourhood of Dunlins, Knots,
Grey Plovers, and other waders ; or, when its favourite haunts are
covered by the tide, a solitary bird or a party of three or four meet or
overtake the stroller by the seaside, taking care to keep at a respectful
distance from him, either by flying high over his head or sweeping
along, a few feet above the surface of the sea, in the line of the breakers
or in the trough outside them.   They may easily be distinguished
from any other common bird of the same tribe by the predominance
of white in their plumage.   Other waders, such as Dunlins and
Sanderlings, present the dark and light sides of their plumage alternately, but the Redshank shows its dark and white feathers simultaneously, and if seen only on the wing might be supposed to be striped
with black and white.   Keen-sighted observers can also detect its red
legs.   Its flight, as accurately described by Macgillivray, ' is light,
rapid, wavering, and as if undecided, and, being performed by quick
jerks of the wings, bears some resemblance to that of a Pigeon '.
During its flight it frequently utters its cry, which is a wild shrill
whistle of two or three notes, approaching that of the Ringed Plover,
but louder and less mellow.   At low water, it frequents, in preference
to all other places of resort, flat marshes which are intersected by muddy
creeks, and in these it bores for food.   It is very wary, flying off long
before the fowler can come within shot if it happens to be standing
exposed ; and even if it be concealed under a high bank, where it
can neither see nor be seen, it detects his approach by some means,
and in most cases is up and away before any but the most expert shot
can stop its flight.   On these occasions it invariably utters its alarm
note, which both proclaims its own escape and gives warning to all
other birds feeding in the vicinity.   Scattered individuals thus disturbed sometimes unite into flocks, or fly off, still keeping separate, to

some distant part of the marsh.   On one occasion only have I been enabled to approach near enough to a Redshank to watch its peculiar movements while feeding, and this observation I was much pleased in making, as it confirms the account of another observer.   A writer in the *Naturalist*, quoted by Yarrell and Macgillivray, says : ' I was very much struck with the curious manner in which they dart their bill into the sand nearly its whole length, by jumping up and thus giving it a sort of impetus, if I may use the word, by the weight of their bodies pressing it downwards.'   This account Macgillivray, with an unamiable sneer too common in his writings when he refers to statements made by others of facts which have not fallen within his own observation, considers to be so inaccurate that he pronounces the birds to be not Redshanks at all, and calls them ' Irish Redshanks '.   On the occasion to which I have referred, I saw at a distance a largish bird feeding on a bank of mud close to an embankment.   Calculating as nearly as I could how many paces off it was, I cautiously crept along the other side of the embankment ; and when I had reached what I supposed was the right spot, took off my hat and peeped over.   Within a few yards of me was an unmistakable Redshank, pegging with his long beak into the mud, and aiding every blow with an impetus of his whole body.   In my own mind I compared his movements with those of a Nuthatch, with which I was quite familiar, and, the surface of the mud being frozen hard, I imagined that the laborious effort on the part of the bird was necessitated by the hardness of the ground. Perhaps this may have been the case ; but, whether or not, it is clear enough that the bird does, when occasion requires it, lend the weight of his body to the effort of his beak in searching for food.   I should add that I did not know, at the time, that any similar occurrence had been recorded.

The food of the Redshank consists of worms, marine insects, and any other animal matter which abounds on the seashore.   In small communities it builds its nest of a few blades of grass in the marshes, in a tuft of rushes or long grass, never among the shingle where that of the Ringed Plover is placed, but often under a shrub (popularly known on the coast of Norfolk by the name of ' Rosemary '), the *Sudda fruticosa*, shrubby sea blite, of botanists.   It lays four eggs, which are considered delicate eating.

THE GREEN SANDPIPER TRINGA ÓCHROPUS (*Plate XXVI*)

Upper plumage olive-brown, with greenish reflections, spotted with whitish and dusky ; lower plumage white ; tail white, the middle feathers barred with dusky towards the end, the two outer feathers almost entirely white ; bill dusky above, reddish beneath ; feet greenish.   Length nine and a half inches.   Eggs whitish green, spotted with brown.   Chiefly a passage migrant in the British Isles, but individuals frequently remain for the winter and it is occasionally present in summer, having nested on at least one occasion.

THIS bird, which derives its name from the green tinge of its plumage and legs, must be reckoned among the rarer Sandpipers.   In habits

it differs considerably from most of its congeners, in that it is not given
to congregate with others of its kind, and that it resorts to inland
waters rather than to the sea.   It is seen for the most part in spring
and autumn, at which seasons it visits us when on its way to and from
the northern countries in which it breeds.   While migrating it flies
very high, but when scared from its feeding-ground it skims along the
surface of the water for some distance, and then rises high into the air,
uttering its shrill whistle.   In its choice of food, and habits while feeding, it resembles the Common Sandpiper.   It lays its eggs in deserted
nests and old squirrel dreys.

THE WOOD SANDPIPER TRINGA GLÁREOLA (*Plate XXIV*)

*Winter—a narrow dusky streak between the bill and eye ; upper parts deep
brown, spotted with white ; breast and adjacent parts dirty white, mottled with
ash-brown ; under plumage and tail-coverts pure white ; tail-feathers barred
with brown and white ; two outer feathers on each side with the inner web pure
white ; bill and legs greenish.   Summer—head streaked with brown and dull
white ; the white of the breast clearer ; each of the feathers of the back with
two white spots on each side of the centre.   Length seven and a half inches.   A
passage migrant in the British Isles, chiefly in the eastern counties of England,
which has nested on at least one occasion.*

THIS species closely resembles the last both in appearance and habits.
It received its name of Wood Sandpiper from having been observed
occasionally to resort to boggy swamps of birch and alder, and has
been seen even to perch on a tree.   Its most common places of resort
are, however, swamps and wet heaths.   Like the last, it is a bird of
wide geographical range, nowhere very abundant, coming only on
passage in spring and autumn.

THE GREENSHANK TRINGA NEBULARIA (*Plate XXV*)

*Bill strong, compressed at the base, slightly curved upwards.   Winter—fore-
head, all the lower parts, and lower back, white ; head, cheeks, neck, and sides
of the breast, streaked with ash-brown and white ; rest of the upper feathers
mottled with dusky and yellowish white ; tail white, middle feathers barred
with brown, outer white, with a narrow dusky streak on the outer web ; bill
ash-brown ; legs yellowish green, long and slender.   Summer—feathers of
the back edged with white, breast and adjacent parts white, with oval black
spots ; middle tail-feathers ash, barred with brown.   Length fourteen inches.
Eggs olive-brown, spotted all over with dusky.   A passage migrant and summer
visitor to the British Isles, breeding in the Highlands of Scotland ; individuals
frequently remain during winter.*

AN unusual colour and disproportionate length of leg are characters
which sufficiently distinguish the Greenshank and account for its name.
It is far less common than the Redshank, but seems to resemble it in
many of its habits.   It is sociably disposed towards birds of its own kind
and allied species, but utterly averse to any familiarity with man,

insomuch that fowlers rarely come within shot of it. It frequents low muddy or sandy shores and brackish pools, the oozy banks of lakes, ponds, and rivers, preferring such open situations as allow it a clear view of threatening danger while there is plenty of time to decamp. In the course of feeding it wades unconcernedly through pools of shallow water, and, if so minded, hesitates neither to swim nor to dive.

Its visits to England are paid most commonly in spring and autumn, while it is on its way to and from the northern climates in which it breeds. ' In Scotland it is seen ', says Macgillivray, ' in small flocks here and there along the seashore, by the margins of rivers, and in marshy places, but it is nowhere common, and in most districts of very rare occurrence. By the beginning of summer it has disappeared from its winter haunts, and advanced northwards ; individuals or pairs remaining here and there in the more northern parts of Scotland, while the rest extend their migration.' The same author describes a nest, which he found in the island of Harris, as very like those of the Golden and Lapwing Plovers, with four eggs, intermediate in size between the eggs of these two birds.

THE COMMON SANDPIPER ACTITIS HYPOLEUCUS (*Plate XXVI*)

Upper parts ash-brown, glossed with olive ; back and central tail-feathers marked with fine wavy lines of rich dark brown ; a narrow white streak over each eye ; under plumage pure white, streaked at the sides with brown ; outer tail-feathers barred with white and brown ; bill dusky, lighter at the base ; feet greenish ash. Length seven and a half inches. Eggs whitish yellow, spotted with brown and grey. A summer visitor to the British Isles, breeding in western and northern England, Wales, Scotland, and Ireland.

To this bird has been given not inappropriately the name of Summer Snipe. In form and mode of living it resembles the Snipe properly so called, and it is known to us only during summer, when it is a bird of common occurrence. One need only to repair to a retired district abounding in streams and lakes, at any period of the year between April and September, and there, in all probability, this lively bird will be found to have made for itself a temporary home. Arrayed in unattractive plumage, and distinguished by no great power of song—its note being simply a piping, which some people consider the utterance of one of its provincial names, ' Willy Wicket '—it may nevertheless be pronounced an accomplished bird. It flies rapidly and in a tortuous course, likely to puzzle any but the keenest shot ; it runs with remarkable nimbleness, so that if a sportsman has marked it down, it will probably rise many yards away from the spot ; it can swim if so inclined ; and when hard pressed by a Hawk, it has been seen to dive and remain under water until all danger had passed away. It has never been observed to perch on the twigs of trees, but it has been noticed running along the stumps and projecting roots of trees. Its favourite places of resort are withy holts (where it searches for food in the shallow drains), moss-covered stones in rivers, the shallow banks of lakes, and the flat marshy places intersected by drains, which in

Montagu's Harrier ♀
Peregrine Falcon ♀

Kestrel ♀♂
Hen Harrier ♀♂

XVII

Red Grouse ♂
Black Grouse ♂ ♀

Red-legged Partridge
Partridge ♂

XVIII

Great Bustard ♂

Pheasant ♂

Nightjar ♂

Capercaillie ♂

XIX

Quail
Three-toed Sandgrouse ♂ ♀

Pratincole
Ptarmigan (Winter, Summer)

XX

Little Crake   Spotted Crake
Water Rail   Corn Crake or Land Rail ♂

XXI

Kentish Plover ♀ ♂   Grey Plover ♂ (Summer and Winter)

Golden Plover ♂   Ringed Plover, young and adult

XXII

Curlew
Dotterel

Lapwing or Peewit ♀
Stone Curlew

XXIII

Wood Sandpiper

Knot ♂

Whimbrel

Sanderling ♂

XXIV

Greenshank

Redshank
Black-tailed Godwit ♀

Ruff & Reeve

XXV

Green Sandpiper
Common Sandpiper

Purple Sandpiper
Curlew Sandpiper

XXVI

Great Snipe

Common Snipe

Jack Snipe

Woodcock

XXVII

Dunlin

Little Stint

Cream-coloured Courser

Temminck's Stint

XXVIII

Avocet

Red-necked Phalarope (Winter, Summer)

Grey Phalarope (Winter)
Bar-tailed Godwit ♀

Pomarine Skua   Arctic or Richardson's Skua

Great Shearwater   Great Skua

XXX

Common Tern

Turnstone ♂ *imm.*

Little or Lesser Tern

Oyster-catcher

XXXI

Sandwich Tern

Black Tern

Arctic Tern

Roseate Tern

XXXII

low countries often skirt the seashore.   Its food consists of small worms
and the larvæ and pupæ of the countless insects which spend their lives
in such localities.   It may be presumed, too, that many a perfect
winged insect enters into its dietary, for its activity is very great.   Even
when its legs are not in motion, which does not often happen, its body
is in a perpetual state of agitation, the vibration of the tail being most
conspicuous.

Sandpipers do not congregate like many others of the waders ;
they come to us generally in pairs, and do not appear to flock together
even when preparing to migrate.   The nest is a slight depression in the
ground, most frequently well concealed by rushes or other tufted
foliage, and is constructed of a few dry leaves, stalks of grass, and scraps
of moss.   The Sandpiper lays four eggs, which are large, and quite
disproportionate to the size of the bird.   Indeed, but for their peculiar
pear-shaped form, which allows of their being placed so as to occupy
a small space with the pointed ends all together, the bird would
scarcely be able to cover them.   The parent bird exhibits the same
marvellous sagacity in diverting the attention of an intruder from the
young birds to herself, by counterfeiting lameness, which has been
observed in the Plovers.   The young are able to run within a very short
time after exclusion from the egg, there being an instance recorded
in the *Zoologist* of a gentleman having seen some young birds scramble
away from the nest while there yet remained an egg containing an
unhatched chick.   Early, too, in their life they are endowed with the
instinct of self-preservation, for Mr. Selby states that if discovered and
pursued before they have acquired the use of their wings, they boldly
take to the water and dive.

The Sandpiper is found in all parts of Europe and Asia, but not
in America.

THE BAR-TAILED GODWIT LIMÓSA LAPPONICA (*Plate XXIX*)

*Beak slightly curved upwards ; middle claw short, without serratures.   Winter
—upper plumage variously mottled with grey, dusky, and reddish ash ; lower
part of the back white, with dusky spots ;   tail barred with reddish white and
dusky ; lower parts white.   Summer—all the plumage deeply tinged with red.
Young birds have the throat and breast brownish white, streaked with dusky,
and a few dusky lines on the flanks.   Length sixteen inches.   Eggs greenish
brown, spotted with dark brown.   A passage migrant and winter visitor to the
coasts of the British Isles, rare inland.*

On the coast of Norfolk, where I made my first acquaintance with
this bird in the fresh state, it is called a Half-Curlew.   In like manner,
a Wigeon is called a Half-Duck.   In either case the reason for giving
the name is, that the smaller bird possesses half the market value of the
larger.   It resembles the Curlew in its flight and the colour of its
plumage ; but differs in having its long beak slightly curved upwards,
while that of the Curlew is strongly arched downwards ; and it is far
less wary, allowing itself to be approached so closely that it falls an
easy prey to the fowler.   It appears to be most frequently met with in

spring and autumn, when it visits many parts of the coast in small flocks. In Norfolk it is met with from May, the twelfth of that month being called ' Godwit day ' by the gunners, although it is almost unknown up north at that season.

Their habits differ in no material respects from the other seaside waders, with whom they frequently mingle while feeding, not, seemingly, for the sake of good fellowship, but attracted by a motive common to all, that of picking up food wherever an abundance is to be met with. Their note is a loud, shrill cry, often uttered while on the wing. The female is much larger than the male.

This bird is sometimes called the Sea Woodcock. Its flesh is good eating, but is far inferior in flavour to that of the true Woodcock.

THE BLACK-TAILED GODWIT LIMÓSA LIMÓSA (*Plate XXV*)

Beak nearly straight ; middle claw long and serrated ; upper parts ash-brown, the shafts of the feathers somewhat deeper ; breast and adjacent parts greyish white ; tail black, the base, and the tips of the two middle feathers, white ; beak orange at the base, black at the point ; feet dusky. Summer—much of the plumage tinged with red. Length seventeen and a half inches. Eggs deep olive, spotted with light brown. A visitor to the British Isles, chiefly in spring and autumn, which formerly nested in eastern England and has done so on a few occasions in recent years.

This bird is, in outward appearance, mainly distinguished from the preceding by having two-thirds of the tail black, instead of being barred throughout with white and black and by the conspicuous white bar across its wing. Like its congener, it is most frequently seen in autumn and spring, while on the way to and from its breeding-ground in the north. It is by far the less common of the two. Its habits, as far as they have been observed, approach those of the other Scolopacidæ. In its flight it resembles the Redshank. Its note is a wild screaming whistle, which it utters while on the wing. It builds its nest in swamps, among rushes and sedges, simply collecting a few grasses and roots into any convenient hole, and there it lays four eggs.

THE RUFF AND REEVE PHILOMACHUS PUGNAX (*Plate XXV*)

Male in spring—face covered with yellowish warty pimples ; back of the head with a tuft of long feathers on each side ; throat furnished with a ruff of prominent feathers ; general plumage mottled with ash, black, brown, reddish white, and yellowish, but so variously, that scarcely two specimens can be found alike ; bill yellowish orange. Male in winter—face covered with feathers ; ruff absent ; under parts white ; breast reddish, with brown spots ; upper plumage mottled with black, brown, and red ; bill brownish. Length twelve and a half inches. Female, ' The Reeve '—long feathers of the head and ruff absent ; upper plumage ash-brown, mottled with black and reddish brown ; under parts greyish white ; feet yellowish brown. Length ten and a half inches. In both sexes—tail rounded, the two middle feathers barred ; the three lateral feathers uniform in colour. Eggs olive, blotched and spotted with brown. A passage migrant in the British Isles, which formerly bred in many parts of England.

BOTH the systematic names of this bird are descriptive of its quarrelsome propensities : *philomachus* is Greek for ' a warrior ', *pugnax* Latin for ' pugnacious '. Well is the title deserved ; for Ruffs do not merely fight when they meet, but meet in order to fight. The season for the indulgence of their warlike tastes is spring ; the scene, a rising spot of ground contiguous to a marsh ; and here all the male birds of the district assemble at dawn, for many days in succession, and do battle valiantly for the females, called Reeves, till the weakest are vanquished and leave possession of the field to their more powerful adversaries. The attitude during these contests is nearly that of the domestic Cock —the head lowered, the body horizontal, the collar bristling, and the beak extended. But Ruffs will fight to the death on other occasions. A basket containing two or three hundred Ruffs was once put on board a steamer leaving Rotterdam for London. The incessant fighting of the birds proved a grand source of attraction to the passengers during the voyage ; and about half of them were slain before the vessel reached London. Ruffs are gluttonously disposed too, and, if captured by a fowler, will begin to eat the moment they are supplied with food ; but, however voracious they may be, if a basin of bread and milk or boiled wheat be placed before them, it is instantly contended for ; and so pugnacious is their disposition, that even when fellow-captives, they would starve in the midst of plenty if several dishes of food were not placed amongst them at a distance from each other.

Many years have passed since these birds paid annual visits in large numbers to the fen-countries. They were, however, highly prized as delicacies for the table, and their undeviating habit of meeting to fight a pitched battle gave the fowler such an excellent opportunity of capturing all the combatants in his nets, that they have been gradually becoming more and more rare. The fowler, in fact, has been so successful that he has destroyed his own trade.

Another peculiarity of the Ruff is, that the plumage varies greatly in different individuals—so much so, indeed, that Montagu, who had an opportunity of seeing about seven dozen in a room together, could not find two alike. These birds are now become rare, but occasional specimens are still met with in different parts of Great Britain, and at various seasons ; but if they are ever served up at table, they must be consignments from the Continent.

The female builds her nest of coarse grass, among reeds and rushes, and lays four eggs. The brood, when hatched, remain with her until the period of migration ; but the males take no interest in domestic affairs. The few that have not been caught become more amicably disposed during the latter portion of the year. They lose the feathery shields from whence they derive their English name, and, assuming a peaceful garb, withdraw to some southern climate. The Ruff is about one-third larger than the Reeve ; and the latter is, at all seasons, destitute of a prominent collar.

THE WOODCOCK scólopax rustícola (*Plate XXVII*)

Back of the head barred transversely with dusky ; upper plumage mottled with chestnut, yellow, ash, and black ; lower, reddish yellow, with brown zigzag lines ; quills barred on their outer web with rust-red and black ; tail of twelve feathers tipped above with grey, below with silvery white ; bill flesh-colour ; feet livid. Length thirteen inches. Eggs dirty yellow, blotched and spotted with brown and grey. A resident, breeding in most parts of the British Isles ; also a passage migrant and winter visitor.

THE history of the Woodcock as a visitor in the British Isles is briefly as follows : Woodcocks come to us from the north in autumn, the earliest being annually observed about the twentieth of October. On their first arrival, they are generally found to be in bad condition ; so weak, in fact, that I recollect many instances of flights having reached the coasts of Cornwall, only able to gain the land. Their condition at these times is one of extreme exhaustion ; and they become the prey, not only of the sportsman, but are knocked down with a stick, or caught alive. In the course of a very few days they are enabled to recruit their strength, when they make their way inland. They have been known even to settle on the deck of a ship at sea, in order to rest ; or actually to alight for a few moments in the smooth water of the ship's wake. Their usual places of resort by day are woods and coppices in hilly districts, whither they repair for shelter and concealment. Disliking cold, they select, in preference, the side of a valley which is least exposed to the wind ; and though they never perch on a branch, they prefer the concealment afforded by trees to that of any other covert. There, crouching under a holly, or among briers and thorns, they spend the day in inactivity, guarded from molestation by their stillness, and by the rich brown tint of their plumage, which can hardly be distinguished from dead leaves. Their large, prominent bead-like eyes are alone likely to betray them ; and this, it is said, is sometimes the case. So conscious do they seem that their great security lies in concealment, that they will remain motionless until a dog is almost on them or until the beater reaches the very bush under which they are crouching. When at length roused, they start up with a whirr, winding and twisting through the overhanging boughs, and make for the nearest open place ahead ; now, however, flying in almost a straight line, till discovering another convenient lurking-place, they descend suddenly, to be ' marked ' for another shot. About twilight, the Woodcock awakens out of its lethargy, and repairs to its feeding-ground. Observation having shown that on these occasions it does not trouble itself to mount above the trees before it starts, but makes for the nearest clear place in the wood through which it gains the open country, fowlers were formerly in the habit of erecting in glades in the woods, two high poles, from which was suspended a fine net. This was so placed as to hang across the course which the birds were likely to take, and when a cock flew against it, the net was suddenly made to drop by the concealed fowler, and the bird caught, entangled in the meshes. Not many years ago, these nets were commonly employed in the woods, near the coast of the north of Devon, and they are said still to be in use on the Continent. The passages through which the birds flew were known by the name of ' cockroads ', and ' cockshoots '.

The localities which Woodcocks most frequent are places which abound in earthworms, their favourite food. These they obtain either by turning over lumps of decaying vegetable matter and picking up the scattered worms, or by thrusting their bills into the soft earth, where (guided by scent, it is supposed) they speedily find any worm lying hid, and having drawn it out, swallow it whole, with much dexterity. When the earth is frozen hard, they shift their ground, repairing to the neighbourhood of the sea, or of springs ; and now, probably, they are less select in their diet, feeding on any living animal matter that may fall in their way. In March they change their quarters again, preparatory to quitting the country ; hence it often happens that considerable numbers are seen at this season in places where none had been observed during the previous winter. They now have a call-note, though before they have been quite mute ; it is said by some to resemble the syllables *pitt-pitt-coor*, by others to be very like the croak of a frog. The French have invented the verb *croûler*, to express it, and distinguish Woodcock shooting by the name *croûle*. Some sportsmen wisely recommend that no Woodcock should be shot after the middle of February ; for it has been ascertained that increasing numbers of these remain for the purpose of breeding in this country ; and it is conjectured, with reason, that if they were left undisturbed in their spring haunts, they would remain in yet larger numbers. As it is, there are few counties in England in which their nests have not been discovered ; and there are some few localities in which it is one of the pleasant sights of the evening, at all seasons of the year, to watch the Woodcocks repairing from the woods to their accustomed feeding-ground.

The nest is built of dry leaves, principally of fern, and placed among dead grass, in dry, warm situations, and contains four eggs, which, unlike those of the Snipes, are nearly equally rounded at each end.

There have been recorded numerous instances in which a Woodcock has been seen carrying its young through the air to water, holding the nestling between her thighs pressed close to her body.

During its flight, the Woodcock invariably holds its beak pointed in a direction towards the ground. Young birds taken from the nest are easily reared ; and afford much amusement by the skill they display in extracting worms from sods with which they are supplied. The Woodcock is found in all countries of the eastern hemisphere where trees grow ; but it is only met as a straggler on the Atlantic coast of the United States.

THE GREAT SNIPE CAPELLA MEDIA (*Plate XXVII*)

Crown black, divided longitudinally by a yellowish white band ; a streak of the same colour over each eye ; from the beak to the eye a streak of dark brown ; upper plumage mottled with black and chestnut-brown, some of the feathers edged

*with straw-colour; greater wing-coverts tipped with white; under parts
whitish, spotted and barred with black; tail of sixteen feathers; bill brown,
flesh-coloured at the base. Length eleven and a half inches. Eggs brownish
olive, spotted with reddish brown. A scarce passage migrant in the British Isles,
chiefly in autumn and in eastern and southern England.*

THE Great Snipe, Solitary Snipe, or Double Snipe, is intermediate in
size between the Woodcock and Common Snipe. Though not among
the rarest of our visitants, it is far from common. It is, however, an
annual visitor, and is seen most frequently in the eastern counties in
the autumn. Its principal resorts are low damp meadows and grassy
places near marshes, but it does not frequent swamps like its congeners.
This difference in its haunts implies a different diet, and this bird, it
is stated, feeds principally on the larvæ or grubs of *Tipula* (known by
the common name of Father Daddy-Long-legs), which are in summer
such voracious feeders on the roots of grass. It breeds in the northern
countries of Europe, and in some parts of Sweden is so abundant that
as many as fifty have been shot in a day. When disturbed on its
feeding-ground, it rises without uttering any note, and usually drops in
again, at no great distance, after the manner of the Jack Snipe. It
may be distinguished by its larger size, and by carrying its tail spread
like a fan. In the northern countries where it breeds it is found most
commonly in the meadows after hay-harvest, and as it is much prized
for the delicacy of its flesh it is a favourite object of sport. It is remarkable for being always in exceedingly good condition, a remark which
applies to specimens procured in this country as well as those shot in
Sweden. The nest is placed in a tuft of grass, and contains four eggs.

THE COMMON SNIPE CAPELLA GALLINÁGO (*Plate XXVII*)

*Upper plumage very like the last; chin and throat reddish white; lower parts
white, without spots; flanks barred transversely with white and dusky; tail
of fourteen feathers. Length eleven and a half inches. Eggs light greenish
yellow, spotted with brown and ash. A resident, breeding throughout the British
Isles; also a passage migrant and winter visitor.*

THE Common Snipe is a bird of very general distribution, being found
in all parts of the eastern hemisphere, from Ireland to Kamchatka.
In Britain, Snipes are most numerous in the winter, their numbers
being then increased by arrivals from high latitudes, from which they
are driven by the impossibility of boring for food in ground hardened
by frost or buried beneath snow. In September and October large
flocks of these birds arrive in the marshy districts of England, stopping
sometimes for a short time only, and then proceeding onwards; but
being like many other birds, gregarious at no other time than when
making their migrations, when they have arrived at a district where
they intend to take up their residence, they scatter themselves over
marsh land, remaining in each other's neighbourhood perhaps, but
showing no tendency to flock together. Their food consists of the
creeping things which live in mud, and to this, it is said by some,

they add small seeds and fine vegetable fibre ; but it is questionable whether this kind of food is not swallowed by accident, mixed up with more nourishing diet. The end of their beak is furnished with a soft pulpy membrane, which in all probability is highly sensitive, and enables the bird to discover by the touch the worms which, being buried in mud, are concealed from its sight. Snipes when disturbed always fly against the wind, so when suddenly scared from their feeding-ground, and compelled to rise without any previous intention on their part, they seem at first uncertain which course to take, but twist and turn without making much progress in any direction ; but in a few seconds, having decided on their movements, they dart away with great rapidity, uttering at the same time a sharp cry of two notes, which is difficult to describe, but once heard can scarcely be mistaken. When a bird on such an occasion is fired at, it often happens that a number of others, who have been similarly occupied, rise at the report, and after having performed a few mazy evolutions, dart off in the way described. At other times they lie so close that between the sportsman and the bird which he has just killed there may be others concealed, either unconscious of danger, or trusting for security to their powers of lying hid. This tendency to lie close, or the reverse, depends much on the weather, though why it should be so seems not to have been decided. But the movements of Snipes generally are governed by laws of which we know little or nothing. At one season they will be numerous in a certain marsh ; the next year perhaps not one will visit the spot ; to-day, they will swarm in a given locality ; a night's frost will drive them all away, and a change of wind a few days after will bring them all back again. If very severe weather sets in they entirely withdraw, but of this the reason is obvious ; the frozen state of the marsh puts a stop to their feeding. They then retire to milder districts, to springs which are never frozen, to warm nooks near the sea, or to salt marshes. Perhaps the majority perform a second migration southwards ; for, as a rule, they are most numerous at the two periods of autumn and spring—that is, while on their way to and from some distant winter-quarters. After March they become far less frequent, yet there are few extensive marshes, especially in Scotland and the north of England, where some do not remain to breed. At this season a striking change in their habits makes itself perceptible. A nest is built of withered grass, sometimes under the shelter of a tuft of heath or reeds, and here the female sits closely on four eggs. The male, meanwhile, is feeding in some neighbouring swamp, and if disturbed, instead of making off with his zigzag winter's flight, utters his well-remembered note and ascends at a rapid rate into the air, now ascending with a rapid vibration of wing, wheeling, falling like a parachute, mounting again, and once more descending with fluttering wings, uttering repeatedly a note different from his cry of alarm, intermixed with a drumming kind of noise, which has been compared to the bleat of a goat. This last sound is produced by the vibration of the two outer tail-feathers, in his descents. One of its French names is *Chèvre volant*, flying goat, and the Scottish name ' Heather-bleater ', was also given to it as descriptive of its peculiar summer note. The female sits closely on her eggs, and if disturbed while in charge of her yet unfledged brood, endeavours to distract the attention of an intruder from them to herself by the artifice already described as being employed by others of the waders.

THE JACK SNIPE LYNNOCRYPTES MINIMUS (*Plate XXVII*)

Crown divided longitudinally by a black band edged with reddish brown ; beneath this on either side a parallel yellowish band reaching from the bill to the nape ; back beautifully mottled with buff, reddish brown, and black, the latter lustrous with green and purple ; neck and breast spotted ; belly and abdomen pure white ; tail of twelve feathers, dusky edged with reddish grey ; bill dusky, lighter towards the base. Length eight and a half inches. Eggs yellowish olive, spotted with brown. A passage migrant and winter visitor to the British Isles, occasionally found in summer but not known to breed.

As the Great Snipe has been called the Double Snipe, on account of its being superior in size to the common species, so the subject of the present chapter is known as the Half-Snipe, from being contrasted with the same bird, and being considerably smaller. The present species is far less abundant than the Common Snipe ; yet still it is often seen, more frequently, perhaps, than the other, by non-sporting observers, for it frequents not only downright marshes, but the little streams which meander through meadows, the sides of grassy ponds, and the drains by the side of canals, where the ordinary pedestrian, if accompanied by a dog, will be very likely to put one up. Its food and general habits are much the same as those of the Common Snipe ; but it rises and flies off without any note. Its flight is singularly crooked until it has made up its mind which direction it intends to take ; indeed it seems to decide eventually on the one which was at first most unlikely to be its path, and after having made a short round composed of a series of disjointed curves, it either returns close to the spot from which it was started, or suddenly drops, as by a sudden impulse, into a ditch a few gunshots off. I have seen one drop thus within twenty yards of the spot where I stood, and though I threw upwards of a dozen stones into the place where I saw it go down, it took no notice of them. It was only by walking down the side of the ditch, beating the rushes with a stick, that I induced it to rise again. It then flew off in the same way as before, and dropped into the little stream from which I had first started it.

From this habit of lying so close as to rise under the very feet of the passenger, as well as from its silence, it is called in France *la Sourde*, ' deaf '. In the same country it is known also as ' St. Martin's Snipe ', from the time of its arrival in that country, November 11 ; with us it is an earlier visitor, coming about the second week in September.

A few instances are recorded of the Jack Snipe having been seen in this country at a season which would lead to the inference that it occasionally breeds here ; but no instance of its doing so has been ascertained as a fact.

THE CURLEW SANDPIPER CALIDRIS TESTACEA (*Plate XXVI*)

Bill curved downwards, much longer than the head. Winter—*upper tail-coverts and all the under parts white ; upper plumage ash-brown, mottled with darker brown and whitish ; breast the same colours, but much lighter ; bill black ; iris brown ; feet dusky.* Summer—*crown black, mottled with reddish ; under plumage chestnut-red, speckled with brown and white ; much of the upper plumage black, mottled with red and ash. Length seven and a half inches. Eggs yellowish, with brown spots. A passage migrant on the coasts of the British Isles ; uncommon inland.*

THIS bird, called also the Pigmy Curlew, is of about the same size as the far commoner Dunlin, from which it is distinguished not only by the difference in the colour of its plumage, but by the greater length of its beak, which is curved downwards. Pigmy Curlews are observed from time to time in this country at the periods of autumn and spring. In their habits they resemble the Dunlins, from which they may readily be distinguished, even when flying, by their white upper tail-coverts. They are of wide geographical range, but nowhere abundant, and visit us on passage in spring and autumn.

THE KNOT CALIDRIS CANÚTUS (*Plate XXIV*)

Beak straight, a little longer than the head, much dilated towards the tip ; tail even at the extremity ; a small part of the tibia naked. Winter—*throat and abdomen white ; breast and flanks white, barred with ash-brown ; upper plumage ash-grey, mottled with brown ; wing-coverts tipped with white ; rump and upper tail-coverts white, with black crescents ; bill and legs greenish black.* Summer—*streak over the eye, nape, and all the under plumage, rusty red, the nape streaked with black ; back streaked and spotted with black, red, and grey. The upper plumage of young birds is mottled with reddish brown, grey, black, and dull white ; legs dull green. Length ten inches. Eggs greenish buff, spotted with brown. A passage migrant and winter visitor to the coasts of the British Isles, a few remaining during summer. Rare inland.*

THE Knot, Willughby informs us, is so called from having been a favourite dish of King Canutus, or Knute. It is a migratory bird, visiting the coasts of Great Britain early in autumn, and remaining here till spring, when it retires northwards to breed. During the intervening months it keeps exclusively to the sandy or muddy sea-shore, assembling in small flocks, and mixing freely with Dunlins, Sanderlings, and Purple Sandpipers. Some authors state that it feeds principally early and late in the day, and during moonlight nights ; but I have seen it on the coast of Norfolk in winter feeding at all hours of the day in company with the birds mentioned above, and differing little from them in the mode of obtaining its food. But I remarked on several occasions that, when a flock was disturbed, the Knots often remained behind, being less fearful of the presence of man ; in consequence of which tardiness in rising they more than once fell to our guns after their companions had flown off. On their first arrival, they are said to be so indifferent to the vicinity of human beings that it is not difficult to knock them down with stones. Their provincial name in Norfolk is the Green-legged Shank, the latter name, Shank, being applied for shortness to the Redshank. Dr. Richardson states that 'Knots were observed breeding on Melville Peninsula by Captain Lyon, who tells us that they lay four eggs on a tuft of withered grass, without being at the pains of forming any nest.'

Flocks of young make their appearance early in August, the adults arriving a little later.

THE LITTLE STINT CALIDRIS MINUTA (*Plate XXVIII*)

Bill straight, shorter than the head; two middle and two outer feathers of the tail longer than the rest ('tail doubly forked'); tarsus ten lines; upper plumage ash and dusky; a brown streak between the bill and the eye; under plumage white; outer feathers of the tail ash-brown, edged with whitish; middle ones brown; bill and feet black. Length five and a half inches. Eggs buff, spotted with dark red-brown. A passage migrant in the British Isles, chiefly in autumn.

TEMMINCK'S STINT CALIDRIS TEMMINCKII (*Plate XXVIII*)

Bill slightly bent down at the tip, much shorter than the head; tail graduated. Winter—upper plumage brown and dusky; breast reddish; lower plumage and outer tail-feathers white; bill and feet brown. Summer—All the upper feathers black, bordered with rust-red; breast reddish ash, streaked with black. Length five and a half inches. Eggs greenish buff, speckled with brown. A scarce passage migrant in the British Isles, chiefly in eastern and southern England, which has on two occasions attempted to nest in the Highlands of Scotland.

THE DUNLIN CALIDRIS ALPINA (*Plate XXVIII*)

Bill a little longer than the head, slightly bent down at the tip; two middle tail-feathers the longest, dusky and pointed; a small part of the tibia naked. Winter—throat and a streak between the bill and eye white; upper plumage ash-brown, streaked with dusky; upper tail-coverts dusky; lateral tail-feathers ash, edged with white; breast greyish white, mottled with brown; bill black; feet dusky. Summer—most of the upper plumage black, edged with rust-red; belly and abdomen black. Young birds have the upper plumage variously mottled with ash-brown, dusky, and reddish yellow; the bill is shorter and straight. Length eight inches. Eggs greenish white, blotched and spotted with brown. A resident, breeding in Scotland, northern England, Wales, and Ireland; also a plentiful passage migrant and winter visitor.

THE name *variabilis*, changeable, has been applied to this species of Sandpiper on account of the great difference between its summer and winter plumage. It was formerly, indeed, supposed that the two states of the bird were distinct species; of which the former was called Dunlin, the latter Purre. It is now known that the two are identical, the bird being commonly found to assume in spring and autumn colours intermediate between the two.

Except during the three summer months, May, June, and July, the Dunlin is common on all the shores of Great Britain, where there are extensive reaches of sand or mud. I have obtained specimens on the coast of Norfolk as early as the twenty-fifth of July ; but, generally, it is not until the following month that they become numerous. From this time until late in the winter they are reinforced by constant additions ; and in very severe weather the flocks are increased to such an extent that, if it were possible to number them, they would be probably found to contain very many thousands. Such a season was the memorable winter of 1860–61, when, during the coldest part of it, I made an excursion to the coast of Norfolk for the purpose of observing the habits of the seaside Grallatores and Natatores which, in winter, resort to that coast. Numerous as were the species and individuals of these birds which then flocked to the beach and salt-marshes, I have no doubt, in my own mind, that they were all out-numbered by Dunlins alone. Of nearly every flock that I saw feeding on the wet sand or mud, fully half were Dunlins ; many flocks were composed of these birds alone ; while of those which were constantly flying by, without alighting, the proportion of Dunlins to all other birds was, at least, three to one. Added to which, while the parties of other birds were susceptible of being approximately counted, the individuals which composed a flock of Dunlins were often innumerable.

At one time we saw in the distance, several miles off, a light cloud, as of smoke from a factory chimney : it moved rapidly, suddenly disappeared, and as suddenly again became visible. This was an enormous flock of Dunlins, consisting of many thousands at least. They did not come very near us ; but smaller flocks which flew about in our immediate vicinity presented a similar appearance. As the upper surface of their bodies was turned towards us, they were of a dark hue ; suddenly they wheeled in their flight as if the swarm was steered by a single will, when they disappeared ; but instantaneously revealed themselves again flying in a different direction, and reflected glittering snowy white.

Dunlins, while feeding, show a devoted attention to their occupa-tion, which is not often to be observed in land birds. They run rapidly, looking intently on the ground, now stopping to pick up some scrap of animal matter which lies on the surface of the sand, now boring for living prey where they detect indications of such prey lying hid. Occasionally an individual bird appears to suffer from lameness, and halts in its progress as if its legs were gouty. Frequently they chase a receding wave for the sake of recovering a prize which has been swept from the beach : never venturing to swim, but showing no fear of wetting either feet or feathers. While engaged in these various ways, they often keep up a short conversational twitter, in a tone, however, so low that it can only be heard at a very short distance. While flying, they frequently utter a much louder piping note, which can readily be distinguished from the call of the other seaside birds. I observed that a small detached flock, when disturbed, generally flew off to a great distance ; but if other birds were feeding in the neighbourhood, they more frequently alighted near them, as if assured by their presence that no danger was to be apprehended.

Dunlins have bred in Cornwall and Devon ; but in many parts of Scotland, in the Hebrides and Orkneys ' they frequent the haunts selected by the Golden Plovers, with which they are so frequently seen in company, that they have popularly obtained the name of Plover's Pages. Sometimes before the middle of April, but always before that of May, they are seen dispersed over the moors in pairs like the birds just named, which, at this season, they greatly resemble in habits. The nest, which is composed of some bits of withered grass, or sedge, and small twigs of heath, is placed in a slight hollow, generally on a bare spot, and usually in a dry place, like that selected by the Golden Plover. The female lays four eggs, and sits very assiduously, often allowing a person to come quite close to her before removing, which she does in a fluttering and cowering manner.' [1]

In a few specimens which I obtained, the bill was considerably curved downwards throughout its whole length, thus approaching in form that of the Pigmy Curlew ; but the dusky upper tail-coverts sufficiently distinguished it from its rarer congener.

THE PURPLE SANDPIPER CALIDRIS MARITIMA (*Plate XXVI*)

Bill longer than the head, slightly bent down at the tip, dusky, the base reddish orange ; head and neck dusky brown, tinged with grey ; back and scapulars black, with purple and violet reflections, the feathers edged with deep ash ; breast grey and white ; under plumage white, streaked on the flanks with grey ; feet ochre-yellow. Length eight and a quarter inches. Eggs yellowish olive, spotted and speckled with reddish brown. A passage migrant and winter visitor to the coasts of the British Isles, a few remaining during summer.

THE Purple Sandpiper is described as being far less common than the Dunlin, and differing from it in habits, inasmuch as it resorts to the rocky coast in preference to sandy flats. The few specimens of it which I have seen were associated with Dunlins, flying in the same flocks with them, feeding with them, and so closely resembling them in size and movements, that a description of the one equally characterizes the other. It was only, in fact, by the difference of colour that I could discriminate between them ; and this I did, on several occasions, with great ease, having obtained my specimens singly while they were surrounded by other birds. According to Mr. Dunn, ' The Purple Sandpiper is very numerous in Orkney and Shetland, appearing early in spring, and leaving again at the latter end of April ; about which time it collects in large flocks, and may be found on the rocks at ebb-tide, watching each retiring wave, running down as the water falls back, picking small shellfish off the stones, and displaying great activity in escaping the advancing sea. It does not breed there.'

This species has a wide geographical range. It has been often

---

[1] Macgillivray.

observed in the Arctic regions, where it breeds. It is well known in North America, and is found in various parts of the continent of Europe.

FAMILY RECURVIROSTRIDÆ

THE AVOCET RECURVIROSTRA AVOSÉTTA (*Plate XXIX*)

General plumage white ; crown, nape, scapulars, lesser wing-coverts, and primaries, black ; bill black ; irides reddish brown ; feet bluish ash. Length eighteen inches. Eggs olive-brown, blotched and spotted with dusky. An uncommon visitor to the British Isles, chiefly to the east and south-east coasts of England in spring. It formerly nested in England and in 1938 two pairs bred in Ireland.

IN Ray's time this bird was not infrequent on the eastern maritime coasts. Small flocks still arrive in May and now and again in the autumn, but collectors never allow them to breed. Sir Thomas Browne says of it : ' *Avoseta*, called shoeing horn, a tall black and white bird, with a bill semicircularly reclining or bowed upward ; so that it is not easy to conceive how it can feed ; a summer marsh bird, and not unfrequent in marsh land.' Pennant, writing of the same bird, says : ' These birds are frequent in the winter on the shores of this kingdom ; in Gloucestershire, at the Severn's mouth ; and sometimes on the lakes of Shropshire. We have seen them in considerable numbers in the breeding season near Fossdike Wash, in Lincolnshire. Like the Lapwing, when disturbed, they flew over our heads, carrying their necks and long legs quite extended, and made a shrill noise (*twit*) twice repeated, during the whole time. The country people for this reason call them *Yelpers*, and sometimes distinguish them by the name of *Picarini*. They feed on worms and insects, which they suck with their bills out of the sand ; their search after food is frequently to be discovered on our shores by alternate semicircular marks in the sand, which show their progress.[1] They lay three or four eggs, about the size of those of a Pigeon, white, tinged with green and marked with large black spots.'

The Avocet is met with throughout a great part of the Old World, and is not infrequent in Holland and France. A writer of the latter country says that ' by aid of its webbed feet it is enabled to traverse, without sinking, the softest and wettest mud ; this it searches with its curved bill, and when it has discovered any prey, a worm for instance, it throws it adroitly into the air, and catches it with its beak '.

[1] It is not a little singular that the Spoonbill, a bird which strongly contrasts with the Avocet in the form of its bill, ploughs the sand from one side to another, while hunting for its food.

FAMILY PHALAROPODIDÆ

THE GREY PHALAROPE PHALÁROPUS FULICARIUS (*Plate XXIX*)

Winter—plumage in front and beneath white ; back of the head, ear-coverts, and a streak down the nape, dusky ; back pearl-grey, the feathers dusky in the centre, a white transverse bar on the wings ; tail-feathers brown, edged with ash ; bill brown, yellowish red at the base ; irides reddish yellow ; feet greenish ash. Summer—head dusky ; face and nape white ; feathers of the back dusky, bordered with orange-brown ; front and lower plumage brick-red. Length eight inches and a half. Eggs greenish stone-colour, blotched and spotted with dusky. A passage migrant, chiefly occurring in autumn on the coasts of England and Ireland.

THE Grey Phalarope, without being one of our rarest birds, is not of common occurrence. Its proper home is in the Arctic regions, from whence it migrates southward in winter. It is a bird of varied accomplishments, flying rapidly like the Snipes, running after the fashion of the Sandpipers, and swimming with the facility of the Ducks. In all these respects it does not belie its appearance, its structure being such that a naturalist would expect, *a priori*, that these were its habits. During the breeding season, the Phalarope quits the sea, its usual haunt, and repairs to marshes, pools, and the shores of fjords, where it builds a neat nest, in a hollow of the ground, with grass and other weeds, and lays four eggs. The usual time of its appearance in Great Britain is autumn ; sometimes it comes then in numbers ; but specimens have been obtained in winter. On all these occasions it has shown itself singularly fearless of man.

THE RED-NECKED PHALAROPE PHALÁROPUS LOBATUS
(*Plate XXIX*)

Head deep ash-grey ; throat white ; neck bright rust-red ; under plumage white, blotched on the flanks with ash ; back black, the feathers bordered with rust-red ; a white bar across the wing ; two middle tail-feathers black, the rest ash, edged with white ; bill black ; irides brown ; feet greenish ash. Length seven inches. Eggs dark olive, closely spotted with black. A summer visitor, breeding in the Shetlands, Orkneys, Hebrides, and north-western Ireland, elsewhere in the British Isles a rare visitor, chiefly in autumn.

THE Red-necked Phalarope, or Lobefoot, is, like the preceding species, an inhabitant of the Arctic regions, but extends its circle of residence so far as to include the extreme north and north-western fringe of the British Isles. It builds its nest of grass, in the marshes or on the islands in the lakes, and lays four eggs. The most marked habit of these birds seems to be that of alighting at sea on beds of floating seaweed, and indifferently swimming about in search of food, or running, with light and nimble pace, after the manner of a Wagtail. They are often met with thus employed at the distance of a hundred miles from land. They are described as being exceedingly tame, taking little notice of the vicinity of men, and unaffected by the report of a gun.

FAMILY BURHINIDÆ

THE THICK-KNEE OR STONE CURLEW

BURHINUS ŒDICNEMUS (*Plate XXIII*)

Upper parts reddish ash with a white spot in the middle of each feather ; space between the eye and beak, throat, belly, and thighs, white ; neck and breast tinged with red, and marked with fine longitudinal brown streaks ; a white longitudinal bar on the wing ; first primary with a large white spot in the middle ; second, with a small one on the inner web ; lower tail-coverts reddish, the feathers, except those in the middle, tipped with black ; beak black, yellowish at the base ; irides, orbits, and feet, yellow. Length seventeen inches. Eggs yellowish brown clouded with greenish, blotched and spotted with dusky and olive. A summer visitor, breeding in south-eastern England, some wintering in south-western England.

THOUGH a citizen of the world, or at least of the eastern hemisphere, this bird is commonly known under the name of Norfolk Plover, from its being more abundant in that county than in any other. It is also called Thick-knee, from the robust conformation of this joint ; and Stone Curlew, from its frequenting waste stony places and uttering a note which has been compared to the sound of the syllables *curlui* or *turlui*. Like the Cuckoo, it is more frequently heard than seen, but that only by night. In some of its habits it resembles the Bustard, and is said even to associate, in northern Africa, with the Lesser Bustard. Its favourite places of resort are extensive plains ; it runs rapidly when disturbed, and when it does take wing, flies for a considerable distance near the ground before mounting into the air.

By day the Thick-knee confines itself to the ground, either crouching or hunting for food, which consists of worms, slugs, and beetles, under stones, which it is taught by its instinct to turn over. After sunset, it takes flight, and probably rises to a great height, as its plaintive whistle, which somewhat resembles the wail of a human being, is often heard overhead when the bird is invisible. It is singularly shy, and carefully avoids the presence of human beings, whether sportsmen or labourers. Yet it is not destitute of courage, as it has been seen to defend its nest with vigour against the approach of sheep or even of dogs. Nest, properly speaking, it has none, for it contents itself with scratching a hole in the ground and depositing two eggs. The males assist in the office of incubation. The young inherit the faculty of running at an early age, being able to leave their birth-place with facility soon after they are hatched ; but the development of their wings is a work of time, for their body has attained its full size long before they are able to rise from the ground. Before taking their departure southwards in autumn, they assemble in parties, of considerable flocks, when they are somewhat more easy of approach than in spring. In the chalky plains of La Marne in France they are very numerous ; and here, by the aid of a light cart, fowlers in quest of them have little difficulty in shooting large numbers, the birds being less afraid of the approach of a horse than of a human being. But when obtained they are of little value, as their flesh is barely eatable.

The Thick-knee is migratory, visiting the eastern and southern counties of England in the beginning of April to stay till October. His flights are made by night.

FAMILY GLAREOLIDÆ

THE CREAM-COLOURED COURSER CURSORIUS CURSOR
(Plate XXVIII)

Plumage reddish cream-colour ; wing-coverts bordered with ash-grey ; throat whitish ; behind the eyes a double black bar ; lateral tail-feathers black towards the tip, with a white spot in the centre of the black ; abdomen whitish. Length nine inches. Eggs light brown, closely marked all over with streaks and spots of brown. A very rare visitor to the British Isles.

IT is a native of the arid regions and deserts of northern Africa and western Asia from Morocco to north-western India. It is singularly fearless of man, and when disturbed prefers to run, which it does very swiftly, rather than to take flight.

THE PRATINCOLE GLAREOLA PRATINCOLA (Plate XX)

Crown, nape, back, scapulars, and wing-coverts, greyish brown ; throat and front of the neck white, tinged with red, and bounded by a narrow black collar, which ascends to the base of the beak ; lore black ; breast whitish brown ; lower wing-coverts chestnut ; under parts white, tinged with brownish red ; tail-coverts, and base of tail-feathers, white ; the rest of the tail dusky, much forked ; beak black, red at the base ; irides reddish brown ; orbits naked, bright red ; feet reddish ash. Length nine inches and a half. Eggs pale stone-colour, spotted with grey and dusky. A very rare straggler to the British Isles.

IN some of its habits the Pratincole resembles the Plovers, as it frequents open plains and runs with great rapidity. In nidification, also, and in the shape, colour, and markings of its eggs it is associated with the same tribe ; while in its mode of flight and habit of catching flies while on the wing, it approaches the Swallows. It inhabits plains and barren localities in southern Europe, western Asia, Arabia, and Africa.

FAMILY STERCORARIIDÆ

THE GREAT SKUA STERCORARIUS SKUA (*Plate XXX*)

Upper plumage brown, of several shades ; shafts of the quills, basal half of the primaries, and shafts of the tail-feathers, white ; under, reddish grey, tinged with brown ; two central tail-feathers but slightly elongated, not tapering ; tarsus two and a half inches long, somewhat rough at the back. Length twenty-five inches. Eggs olive-brown, blotched with brown. A summer visitor, breeding in the Shetlands and Orkneys, elsewhere in the British Isles an occasional visitor to the coasts.

THE Skuas, called also Skua Gulls, are sufficiently distinguished from the true Gulls by their strong hooked bills and talons, and by the habits of daring and voracity founded on these characters. The present species, though called common, is only to be so considered in high latitudes ; for it is very rarely seen on the coasts of England. During the breeding season it is highly courageous ; and will strike furiously at, and will even pursue, any one who may happen to approach its nest, which is constructed among the heath or moss ; the female laying two eggs.

The voice of the Great Skua is said to resemble that of a young Gull, being sharp and shrill ; and it is from the resemblance of its cry to that of the word Skua, or Skui, that it obtains its popular name. Its northern name is Bonxie.

THE POMARINE SKUA STERCORARIUS POMARINUS (*Plate XXX*)

Upper plumage uniform dark brown ; feathers of the nape long, tapering lustrous ; sides of the face and under plumage white ; a collar of brown spots on the breast, and similar spots on the flanks ; shafts of the quills and tail-feathers white, except at the tip ; two central tail-feathers projecting three inches, not tapering but twisted vertically ; tarsus two inches long, rough at the back, with projecting scales. Length twenty-one inches. Young birds— upper plumage dusky brown, mottled with reddish yellow ; under, yellowish white, thickly set with brown spots and bars. Eggs ash-green, spotted with dusky. A passage migrant and winter visitor to the coasts of the British Isles.

THE habits of this bird vary but little from those of the other species. Its home is in the Arctic seas, from which it strays southwards in winter, and is occasionally seen on our coasts. The following account of the capture of one of these birds, in 1844, indicates a bird of unusual daring and voracity : ' About the beginning of last October, a Pomarine Skua was taken in the adjoining village of Ovingdean. It had struck down a White Gull, which it would not quit : it was kept alive above a fortnight, and then died. The very first day of its captivity it (is said to have) devoured twenty-five Sparrows.

Once it escaped, and immediately attacked a Duck, which it held till recaptured.' [1]

THE ARCTIC OR RICHARDSON'S SKUA
STERCORARIUS PARASITICUS (*Plate XXX*)

Crown dusky; cheeks, neck, and under plumage, white, tinged with yellow or brown; rest of the plumage dusky, the wings and tail the darkest. Two central tail-feathers tapering from the base, pointed, and projecting six inches; tarsus less than two inches. Length twenty-one inches. Eggs olive, with a circle of brown spots near the larger extremity, the rest speckled with the same colour. A summer visitor to the British Isles, breeding in northern Scotland, the Hebrides, Orkneys, and Shetlands; also a passage migrant on the coasts.

THIS species of Skua, most familiarly known, perhaps, as the Arctic Gull, received its distinctive name, ' Richardson's ', in honour of the eminent Arctic naturalist. It is distinguished from the species already described by its longer tail, but the habits of all are much alike; indeed, the names of ' Arctic Gull ', ' Boatswain ', ' and Man-of-War ', appear to be sometimes employed indiscriminately. Richardson's Skua, like the rest, inhabits the Arctic seas, but extends its wanderings southwards in far greater numbers than either of the other species, so that its occurrence on the east coast of England is not unusual. According to Mr. Dunn, ' numbers of this bird breed in Orkney and Shetland, appearing regularly in May and leaving in August. It constructs its nest on low, not mossy, heaths in exposed situations. The female lays two eggs, and has recourse to the same stratagems that the Plover employs to decoy you from the nest; but when a person approaches near to the place where the nest is built, becomes bold and fierce, and strikes severely with the feet and bill.' The following account is taken from Mr. St. John's *Wild Sports of the Highlands* : ' I was much amused the other day by the proceedings of a pair of the Black-toed Gull or Boatswain. These two birds were sitting quietly on an elevated ridge of sand, near which a number of other Gulls of different kinds were fishing, and hovering about in search of what the waves might cast up. Every bird, indeed, was busy and employed, excepting these two black robbers, who seemed to be quietly resting, quite unconcerned. When, however, a Gull had picked up a prize, these birds seemed instinctively to know it, and darting off with the rapidity of a Hawk (which bird they much resemble in their manner of flight), they attacked the unfortunate Gull in the air, and in spite of his screams and attempts to escape, they pursued and beat him till he disgorged the fish or whatever he had swallowed, when one of them darted down and caught the substance before it could reach the water. The two then quietly returned to their sandbank, where they waited patiently to renew the robbery, should an opportunity occur. As the flock of Gulls moved on with the flow of the tide, the Boatswains moved on also, hovering on their flank like a pair of plundering freebooters. I

[1] *Zoologist*, vol. iii. p. 880.

observed that, in chasing a Gull, they seemed perfectly to understand each other as to who should get the spoil ; and in their attacks on the largest Gulls (against whom they waged the most fearless warfare), they evidently acted so as to aid each other. If another pair of Boatswains intruded on their hunting-ground they immediately seemed to send them farther off ; not so much by actual battle, as by a noisy and screaming argument, which they continued most vigorously till the new-comers left the neighbourhood.

' I never saw these birds hunt for their own living in any other way than by robbing the other Gulls. Though not nearly so large as some of the birds which they attack, their Hawk-like swoops and great courage seem to enable them to fight their way most successfully. They are neatly and powerfully made, their colour a kind of sooty dull black, with very little gloss or shining tints on their feathers.'

THE LONG-TAILED SKUA STERCORARIUS LONGICAUDUS
(Plate LXVII)

Principally distinguished from the last by its inferior size. Two central tail-feathers tapering, pointed and projecting nine inches. Length, exclusive of the two central tail-feathers, thirteen and a half inches. Eggs olivebrown, with dark brown spots. An irregular visitor to the coasts of the British Isles, chiefly in autumn.

FAMILY LARIDÆ

THE SANDWICH TERN STERNA SANDVICENSIS (Plate XXXII)

Bill long, black, the tip yellowish ; tarsus short (one inch) ; tail long ; head and crest black ; nape, upper part of the back, and all the lower parts, brilliant white, tinged on the breast with rose ; back and wings pale ash-grey ; quills deeper grey ; tail white ; feet black, yellowish beneath. Young birds—head mottled with black and white ; back, wing-coverts, and tail-feathers, varied with irregular lines of black ; bill and feet dark brown. Length eighteen inches. Eggs greyish green, blotched with brown and black. A summer visitor to the British Isles.

THE Sandwich Tern, which takes its name from the place where it was first seen in England, is not uncommon on many parts of the coast during the summer months. In some places it seems to be abundant. A large colony inhabits the Farne Islands. They breed as far north as the Orkneys. Upon the Northumberland coast it is called *par excellence* ' The Tern ', all the other species passing under the general name of ' Sea Swallows '. Its habits are so like those of the Common Tern, to be described hereafter, that, to avoid repetition, I purposely omit all accounts of its mode of fishing, and content myself with quoting, on the authority of Audubon and Meyer, incidents in its biography which I have not noticed in the Common Tern. The former author says : ' Its cries are sharp, grating, and loud enough to be heard at the distance of half a mile. They are repeated at intervals while it is travelling, and kept up incessantly when one intrudes upon it in its breeding-ground, on which occasion it sails and dashes over your head, chiding you with angry notes, more disagreeable than pleasant to your ear.' Meyer, writing of the same bird, says : ' The Sandwich Tern is observed to be particularly fond of settling on sunken rocks where the waves run high, and the surf is heavy : this being a peculiar fancy belonging to this species, it is sometimes called by the name of Surf Tern.'

THE ROSEATE TERN STERNA DOUGALLI (*Plate XXXII*)

Bill black, red at the base ; feet orange, claws small, black ; tarsus three-quarters of an inch long ; tail much forked, much longer than the wings ; upper part of the head and nape black ; rest of the upper plumage pale ash-grey ; tail white, the outer feathers very long and pointed ; cheeks and under plumage white, tinged on the breast and belly with rose. Length fifteen to seventeen inches. Eggs yellowish stone-colour, spotted and speckled with ash-grey and brown. A summer visitor to the British Isles.

OF this Tern Dr. M'Dougall, its discoverer, says, ' It is of light and very elegant figure, differing from the Common Tern in the size, length, colour, and curvature of the bill ; in the comparative shortness of the wing in proportion to the tail, in the purity of the whiteness of the tail, and the peculiar conformation and extraordinary length of the lateral feathers. It also differs from that bird in the hazel-colour and size of the legs and feet.'

Roseate Terns have been discovered on several parts of the coast, principally in the north, as in the mouth of the Clyde, Lancashire, and the Farne Islands. They associate with the Common Terns, but are far less numerous. Selby says, ' the old birds are easily recognized amidst hundreds of the other species by their peculiar and buoyant flight, long tail, and note, which may be expressed by the word *crake*, uttered in a hoarse grating key '.

THE COMMON TERN STERNA HIRUNDO (*Plate XXXI*)

Bill moderate, red with a black tip ; head and long feathers on the back of the head black ; upper parts bluish ash ; quills ash-grey, brown at the tips ; tail much forked, not longer than the wings, white, the two outer feathers on each side dusky on the outer webs ; under parts white, tinged with grey on the breast ; irides reddish brown ; feet coral-red. Young birds have a good deal of white about the head, and the feathers on the back are tipped with white ; tail ash-grey, whitish at the tip. Length fourteen inches. Eggs olive-brown, blotched and spotted with ash and dusky. A summer visitor to the British Isles.

ON those parts of the coast where the Common Tern is abundant, no sea-bird is more likely to attract the notice of the visitor. It is less in size than any of the common species of Gull, with which, however, it is often confounded by the unobservant. It is more lively and active in its motions, not ordinarily flying in circles, but, if I may use the expression, ' rambling ' through the air, frequently diverging to the right or left, and raising or depressing itself at frequent intervals. These characters alone are sufficient to distinguish the Tern from any of the Gulls ; but it presents yet more striking features. Its tail is elongated and forked like that of the Swallow, and from this character rather than from its flight it is commonly known as the Sea Swallow. Its mode of taking its prey is totally different from that of the Gulls. Very frequently a single Tern may be observed pursuing its course in a line with the breakers on a sandy shore at the distance perhaps of from fifty to a hundred yards from the beach. Its beak is pointed downwards, and the bird is evidently on the look-out for prey. Suddenly it descends perpendicularly into the water, making a perceptible splash, but scarcely disappearing. In an instant it has recovered the use of its wings and ascends again, swallowing some small fish meanwhile if it has been successful, but in any case continuing its course as before. I do not recollect ever to have seen a Tern sit on the water to devour its prey when fishing among the breakers. Often, too, as one is walking along the shore, or sailing in a boat, when the sea is calm, a cruising party of Terns comes in sight. Their flight now is less direct than in the instance just mentioned, as they ' beat ' the fishing-ground after the fashion of spaniels, still, however, making way ahead. Suddenly one of the party arrests its flight, hovers for a few seconds like a Hawk, and descends as if shot, making a splash as before. If unsuccessful it rises at once, but if it has captured the object on which it swooped, it remains floating on the water until it has relieved itself of its incumbrance by the summary process of swallowing it. I do not know a prettier sight than a party of Terns thus occupied. They are by no means shy, frequently flying quite over the boat, and uttering from time to time a short scream, which, though not melodious, is more in keeping with the scene than a mellow song would be.

In rough weather they repair to sheltered bays, ascend estuaries, or follow the course of a river until they have advanced far inland. They are harbingers of summer quite as much as the Swallow itself, coming to us in May and leaving in September for some warmer coast. They usually breed on flat shores, laying two or three eggs on the ground, in marshes, or on sandy shingle. The eggs in my collection were procured on the coast of Norfolk, but I have seen the birds themselves in the greatest numbers in Belfast Lough and in Loch Crinan.

THE ARCTIC TERN STERNA MACRURA (*Plate XXXII*)

Bill slender, red throughout ; under plumage ash-grey ; tail much forked, longer than the wings ; legs orange-red, in other respects very like the last.

Length fifteen inches. Eggs as in the last. A summer visitor to the British Isles, also a passage migrant.

THIS bird, as its name indicates, frequents high northern latitudes, to which, however, it is not confined ; since in the Orkneys and Hebrides it is the common species. It breeds also on the coast of some of the northern English counties, though several instances are recorded of large flocks making their appearance in different places at the season when they were probably on their way from their winter quarters—far away to the south—to their breeding-ground. In the rocky islands, which they frequent from May to September, they form colonies and lay their eggs, generally apart from the allied species. The eggs closely resemble those of the Common Tern, but are somewhat smaller. In its habits and general appearance the Arctic Tern comes so close to the last-named species, that the birds, even when flying together, can only be distinguished by the most practised eye.

THE LITTLE (OR LESSER) TERN STERNA ALBIFRONS
(*Plate XXXI*)

Bill orange, with a black tip ; feet orange ; forehead, and a streak above the eye, white ; crown black ; upper parts pearl-grey ; under white ; tail much forked, shorter than the wings. Young birds have the head brownish, with darker streaks ; upper plumage yellowish white and dusky ; bill pale yellow, with a dark tip ; legs dull yellow. Length eight and a half inches. Eggs stone-colour, spotted and speckled with grey and brown. A summer visitor to the British Isles except the Shetlands.

ON the sandy and marshy shores of Norfolk, the Lesser Tern is a bird of common occurrence in summer, either single, or in small parties of three or four. Not infrequently, as the seaside visitor is sauntering about on the sands, one of these birds seems to take offence at its dominion being invaded. With repeated harsh cries it flies round and round the intruder, coming quite close enough to allow its black head and yellow beak to be distinguished. Its flight is swift, something like that of a Swallow, but more laboured, and not so rapid. If fired at, it takes little notice of the noise ; and, knowing nothing of the danger, continues its screams [1] and circling till its pertinacity becomes annoying. When feeding it presents a far pleasanter appearance. Then, altogether heedless of intrusion, it skims along the surface of the drains in the marshes, profiting by

---

[1] I have been beset in this manner by a Lesser Tern, so far on in the summer that I could not attribute its actions to any anxiety about either eggs or young. I am inclined to think it is, on such occasions, taught by its instinct to accompany a traveller for the sake of the insects disturbed by his movements. During the summer months, the shingle, on a sunny beach, is haunted by myriads of sluggish flies, which rarely take wing unless thus disturbed. That the Chimney Swallow often accompanies the traveller for this object, I have no doubt ; as I have seen them fly to and fro before me, darting in among the swarming flies, and so intent in their chase, as to pass within a few yards of my feet every time they crossed my path.

its length of wing and facility of wheeling, to capture flying insects. At least, if this be not its object, I can in no other way account for the peculiar character of its flight. At other times, either alone or in company with a few other individuals of the same species, it is seen flying slowly along, some fifteen or twenty feet above the surface of a shallow tidal pool, or pond, in a salt-marsh. Suddenly it arrests its onward progress, soars like a Kestrel for a second or two, with its beak pointed downwards. It has descried a shrimp, or small fish, and this is its way of taking aim. Employing the mechanism with which its Creator has provided it, it throws out of gear its apparatus of feathers and air-tubes, and falls like a plummet into the water, with a splash which sends circle after circle to the shore ; and, in an instant, having captured and swallowed its petty booty, returns to its aerial watch-post. A social little party of three or four birds, who have thus taken possession of a pond, will remain fishing as long as the tide is high enough to keep it full. They take little notice of passengers ; and if startled by the report of a gun, remove to a short distance only, and there resume their occupation. Sometimes they may be seen floating about in the open sea, resting their wings, perhaps, after a long flight, or simply idling, certainly not fishing ; for although they plunge from a height, with great ease and elegance, diving proper is not one of their accomplishments.

To the stranger who visits the coast of Norfolk, the Lesser Tern will, perhaps, be pointed out under the name of ' Sea Swallow ', or, more probably, as a ' Shrimp-catcher '. Either of these names is appropriate. Its mode of progress through the air is more like a Swallow's than that of the Common Tern, and in size it does not so very much exceed the Swift as to make the comparison outrageous. A shrimp it can undoubtedly catch ; and it exercises its vocation in shallow water, such as shrimps alone inhabit or small fish no larger than shrimps.

Like the other Terns it is migratory, repairing year after year to low flat shores on various parts of the coast, arriving in May, and departing in September for some climate subject to no cold severe enough to banish small marine animals to deep water. The Lesser Tern makes no nest, but lays its eggs, generally two, among the shingle.

THE BLACK TERN CHLIDONIAS NIGER (*Plate XXXII*)

Bill black ; feet purple-brown, the membrane short ; head and neck black ; upper parts lead-colour ; under parts dark ash-grey ; under tail-coverts white ; tail not much forked, shorter than the wings ; irides brown. In winter, the lore, throat, and breast, are white. Length ten and a quarter inches. Eggs dark olive-brown, blotched and spotted with black. A passage migrant in the British Isles, chiefly in southern and eastern England, where it formerly nested.

THE Black Tern is a common bird in most temperate countries which abound in extensive marshes. In its habits it is scarcely less aquatic than the preceding species, but differs from them all in preferring fresh water to salt. It was formerly of frequent occurrence in England ; but draining and reclaiming have given over many of its haunts to the Partridge and Wood Pigeon. A few, however, are not infrequently seen in spring and autumn, when on their way from and to their winter quarters, which are the warmer regions of the globe. In Norfolk its name still lingers as the ' Blue Darr ', a corruption, probably, of Dorr-Hawk (another name of the Nightjar), a bird which it closely resembles in its mode of flight. Like the Dorr-Hawk, the Black Tern feeds on beetles and other insects, which it catches on the wing, but adds to its dietary small fresh-water fish, which it catches by dipping for them. While in pursuit of its winged prey, it does not confine itself to the water, but skims over the marsh and adjoining meadows, sometimes even alighting for an instant to pick up a worm. Black Terns are sociable birds among themselves, but do not consort with other species. They lay their eggs in the most inaccessible swamps, on masses of decayed reeds and flags, but little elevated above the level of the water. The nests are merely depressions in the lumps of vegetable substance, and usually contain three or sometimes four eggs. They are placed near enough to each other to form colonies ; and the birds continue to flock together during their absence in warmer climates.

SABINE'S GULL xema sabini (*Plate LXVI*)

Head and neck dark grey, terminating in a narrow black collar ; lower part of the neck, all the under parts, and tail, white ; upper plumage grey ; wings black and white, longer than the tail ; bill yellow, black at the base ; irides dark ; orbits vermilion ; feet black. Young birds *and adults in winter want the dark head. Length thirteen inches. Eggs olive, blotched with brown. A scarce autumn and winter visitor to the coasts of the British Isles.*

THE LITTLE GULL larus minutus (*Plate XXXIII*)

Summer—*head and neck black ; lower part of the neck, tail, all the under plumage, white ; upper plumage pale ash-grey ; primaries white at the end ; bill reddish brown ; irides dark ; legs vermilion.* Winter—*forehead, front and sides of the neck, white ; nape and cheeks white, streaked with greyish black. Length eleven inches. Eggs yellowish buff to olive-brown, spotted and blotched with dark brown. An autumn and winter visitor to the British Isles, chiefly to the east coast of England.*

This, the smallest of the Gulls, comes sometimes in numbers to the British coast. It is said to be remarkably active and graceful in its movements through the air, and to associate with Terns. Its food consists of marine insects and small fish. It breeds in the Baltic countries of Europe and in Russia and Siberia.

THE BLACK-HEADED GULL LARUS RIDIBUNDUS
(*Plate XXXIII*)

Summer—head and upper part of the neck deep brown ; lower part of the neck and all the under plumage white, slightly tinged with rose ; upper plumage bluish ash ; primaries white, edged with ash, and broadly tipped with black ; irides brown ; bill and feet red, with a purple tinge. In winter the head and neck are white ; bill and feet bright vermilion. In young birds the hood is pale brown ; the upper plumage dark brown, mottled at the edges of the feathers with yellowish ; bill livid at the base, the tip black ; feet yellowish. Length seventeen inches. Eggs olive, spotted with brown and dusky. A resident, breeding in most parts of the British Isles, also a winter visitor.

BLACK-HEADED, Black-Cap, Brown-headed, Red-Legged, and Pewit, are all common distinctive names of this Gull, to which may be added that of Laughing Gull. The latter name might with equal propriety be applied to several other species, whose harsh cry resembles a laugh.

Brown-headed Gull is the most appropriate of all the above names, at least in summer, for at this period both male and female are best distinguished by the deep brown colour of the head and upper part of the neck.

This is one of the most frequent of the Gulls, to be sought for in the breeding season not on the rocky shore among cliffs, but on low flat salt marshes on the coast and in fresh-water marshes far inland. Early in spring large numbers of Brown-headed Gulls repair to their traditional breeding-grounds and wander over the adjoining country in search of food, which consists of worms and grubs. From the assiduity with which they resort to arable land and follow the plough, they have been called Sea Crows. In April and May they make their simple preparations for laying their eggs by trampling down the broken tops of reeds and sedges, and so forming a slight concavity. The number of eggs in each nest is generally three, and as a large number of birds often resort to the same spot, the collecting of these eggs becomes an occupation of importance. By some persons they are considered a delicacy, and, with the eggs of the Redshank, are substituted for Plovers' eggs ; but to a fastidious palate they are not acceptable, and far inferior to an egg from the poultry yard. Willughby describes a colony of Black-Caps on a small island in a marsh or fish pond, in the county of Stafford, distant at least thirty miles from the sea. He says that when the young birds had attained their full size, it was the custom to drive them from the island into nets disposed along the shore of the lake. The captured birds were fattened on meat and garbage, and sold for about fourpence or five-pence each (a goodly price in those days, 1676). The average number captured every year was 1200, returning to the proprietor an income of about £15. In *The Catalogue of Norfolk and Suffolk Birds*, it is stated that precisely the same sum is paid for the privilege of collecting the eggs from Scoulton Mere, in Norfolk. Towards the end of July, when the young are fully fledged, all the birds, old and young, repair to the sea, and scatter themselves in small flocks to all parts of the coast, preferring a low sandy shore, or the mouth of a tidal river, as the Thames and the Clyde, where they are of common occurrence. They also accompany shoals of herrings and other small fish, often congregating with other species in countless numbers.

Before winter the distinctive character afforded by the brown plumage of the head and neck has entirely disappeared. These parts are now of a pure white, and the red legs afford the best distinguishing feature.

THE COMMON GULL LARUS CÁNUS (*Plate XXXIV*)

In spring the head and neck of this species are white and the mantle is a pale grey, a little darker in summer, the rump, tail, and under parts, white ; primaries comparatively long, and the three outer pairs dull black on the lower portions, with large white ' mirrors ' near the tips in mature birds—in the rest the predominant tone is a pale grey, the black only forming a bar, and all but the first primary broadly tipped with white ; bill a rich yellow towards the point ; legs and feet greenish yellow in summer, darker in winter. In winter the head and neck are streaked and spotted with ash-brown. Length eighteen inches. Eggs olive-brown, spotted with dark brown and dusky. A resident, breeding in Scotland and northern and western Ireland, but in very few localities in England ; also a passage migrant and winter visitor.

THE ' Blue Maa ', as this species is called in the north, breeds in abundance in Scotland, including the Hebrides, Orkneys, and Shetlands, as well as in the west of Ireland ; grassy sides and islands of lochs or slopes that face the sea, often not far above high water, are its favourite resorts, where it breeds in colonies, the nest of seaweeds, heather, and dry grass being fairly large and usually containing three eggs.

During winter this species is found on coasts and estuaries with other gulls, but flocks often travel far inland to feed on arable fields or grassland both in lowland districts and hilly regions.

THE LESSER BLACK-BACKED GULL LARUS FUSCUS
(*Plate XXXIV*)

Wings reaching two inches beyond the tail ; head and neck white, streaked (in winter) with brown ; lower parts pure white ; rest of the upper plumage blackish grey ; primaries black, the first two with an oval white spot near the tip ; secondaries and scapulars tipped with white ; bill, irides, and feet, yellow ; tarsus two and a quarter inches long ; orbits red. In young birds the white plumage is mostly replaced by grey mottled with brown, and the black by dusky edged with yellowish ; the primaries have no white spots, and the bill is dusky. Length twenty-three inches. Eggs brownish grey, spotted with brown and black. A summer visitor to the British Isles, some remaining during winter ; also a passage migrant.

THIS is a generally diffused species, occurring in considerable numbers, not only on various parts of our coast, but in the Baltic, the Mediterranean, the Black Sea, the Red Sea, and African lakes.   It repairs in spring either to rocky islands, steep cliffs, or sometimes to inland lakes, where it builds a rather large nest of tufts of grass, and lays two or three eggs.   When the young are hatched it is very impatient of having its stronghold invaded, and resents molestation by darting at the head of the intruder.

THE HERRING GULL LARUS ARGENTÁTUS (*Plate XXXIII*)

Head and neck white, streaked in winter with light brown ; tail and lower parts white ; back and wings bluish ash ; primaries dusky, passing into black, the shafts black and extremities white ; secondaries edged and tipped with white ; bill, orbits, and irides, yellow ; feet flesh-colour. In young birds *the white is mostly replaced by dark grey, mottled with brown ; wings and tail brown, the latter reddish yellow towards the end ; bill dusky ; irides, orbits, and feet, brown. Length twenty-three inches. Eggs olive-brown, spotted with dark brown and dusky. A resident in the British Isles ; also a winter visitor.*

THE Herring Gull is a large and powerful bird, thoroughly competent to dispose of a herring or even a more bulky fish.   It is common on most parts of the British coast, and remains with us all the year, building its nest on steep cliffs, or rocky islands.   Like the other Gulls, it may easily be tamed if taken young ; and, when kept in a garden, earns its maintenance by keeping down slugs and other vermin.

Gulls are, moreover, of material service, for they perform for the surface of the sea the same office which crustaceous animals do for its depths.   Most of their time is spent in either flying or swimming about (they are no divers) in quest of food, which is of that nature that, if suffered to accumulate, more than one of our senses would be offended. All animal matter which, when life is extinct, rises to the surface, it is their especial province to clear away.   To perform this necessary work, they have need of a quick eye and a voracious appetite.   That they have the former in an eminent degree, any one may convince himself who, when taking a sea voyage, sees the vessel followed, as he often will, by a flock of Gulls.   Let him fling overboard, into the foaming track of the ship, where his own eye can distinguish nothing, ever so small a portion of bread or other kind of food.   That some one individual at least among the flock will have seen it fall and be able to descry it is certain ; now, probably, a general scramble will ensue, and the prize will be secured by the swiftest.   Having tried this several times with the same result, let him throw over, instead of meat or bread, a bit of wood.   Not a bird will come near even to examine it. I have often tried this experiment, and have met with but one result. To prove that the Gull is capable of consuming a large quantity of food, as well as quick-sighted, a single anecdote will suffice : ' A man who was shooting on the banks of the river Yare, seeing something, which had the appearance of an eel half-swallowed, hanging from the mouth of a Gull which was flying overhead, fired at the bird, and on taking it up, found, not an eel, but—five tallow candles attached to a piece of thread, to the other end of which was fastened a sixth, the latter having been *almost entirely swallowed*. The candles were about twelve inches in length, with cotton wicks, such as are used on board the fishing boats, from the deck of which he had probably taken them.' The Gull, then, is not choice in its diet ; it is, in fact, omnivorous. It skims the deep for dead animal matter, follows the ship for offal thrown overboard, paces the shore in quest of molluscs and marine insects, flies inland in stormy weather in winter and spring, and follows the plough along with Rooks and Jackdaws, alights on fields which have been manured with decomposed fish, resorts to marshes for frogs and worms, and after an inundation repairs to the lately submerged ground, and picks up the small quadrupeds which have been drowned. It usually flies at no great elevation above the water, but when repairing inland and returning it frequently rises to a very great height.

THE GREATER BLACK-BACKED GULL LARUS MARÍNUS
(*Plate XXXIV*)

Wings extending but little beyond the tail ; legs pale flesh-colour. Length thirty inches ; breadth about five feet nine inches. In most other respects resembling the Lesser Black-backed Gull. Eggs stone-buff, blotched and spotted with dusky brown. A resident on the coasts of the British Isles ; also a winter visitor.

OF the two Black-backed Gulls, the Greater, or ' Cobb ', is by far the less frequent on our coasts. It remains with us all the year, but is most frequent in the south during winter. In spring, Greater Black-backed Gulls for the most part withdraw to cliffs and rocky islands far north, as, for instance, the Orkneys and Hebrides, where they are numerous, a few only nesting southwards. They are exceedingly wary, and give notice of the approach of danger to other animals. Consequently, they are held in dislike by the gunner, whether in pursuit of sea-birds or seals. Like the rest of the Gulls, they are omnivorous, but are, more than any others, addicted to carrion, in quest of which they often wander inland ; hence they are sometimes called Carrion Gulls. ' If a floating prize presents itself,' says Mr. St. John, ' such as the remains of a large fish or dead bird, it is soon discovered by one of the large Gulls, who is not, however, allowed to enjoy his prize alone, for every one of his fellows within sight joins in tearing it to pieces. When I have winged a Duck, and it has escaped and gone out to sea, I have frequently seen it attacked, and devoured almost alive, by these birds.'

THE GLAUCOUS GULL OR BURGOMASTER
LARUS HYPERBOREUS (*Plate XXXIV*)

General plumage white ; back and wings bluish grey ; tail and terminal portion of the quills white ; bill strong, yellow ; legs livid flesh-colour. Young mottled with white, grey, and light brown ; shafts of the quills white ; in other respects like the last, but the bill is longer and stouter. Length about twenty-nine

*inches ; breadth five feet two inches.   Eggs as in the last, but of a greener hue.
A winter visitor to the coasts of the British Isles.*

THE Glaucous Gull, a large, handsome, and powerful bird, resembles
in many of its habits the species last described, but it has not been
known to breed in even the most northerly of the British Isles.   It
pays occasional visits to our shores in winter.   A few specimens only
have been shot in the southern portion of the island, and no large
number in Scotland ; but in the neighbourhood of the whale fishery
it is common enough.   It is very voracious, and not only eats fish,
whether dead or alive, and shares with the whale-fisher in his booty,
but pursues other sea-fowl, compels them to disgorge their prey, robs
them of their eggs, and, if they resist, kills and devours them.[1]   In
short, it is the very tyrant of the Arctic Ocean.   Its predatory habits
were noticed by the early navigators in these waters, who gave it the
name of Burgomaster ; but as no accurate description of the bird was
brought home, and as some of our other large Gulls are open to a
charge of similar rapacity, the name was naturally transferred by
Willughby to another species, which he calls the Wagel (probably the
Great Black-backed Gull in immature plumage).   This was in 1676.
A hundred years later Brunnich gave it the name of Glaucous Gull ;
but it is still called Burgomaster by the Dutch, and by Arctic voyagers
generally.

THE ICELAND GULL LARUS GLAUCOIDES (*Plate LXVII*)

*Wings reaching a little beyond the tail ; back and upper wing-coverts pale blue ;
rest of the plumage white, in winter head streaked with grey ; bill yellow ;
irides pale yellow ; feet deep flesh-colour.   Young birds pale yellowish grey,
barred and mottled with brown ; bill pale flesh-colour, having dark horn-colour
towards the tip ; feet pale flesh-colour.   Length twenty-two inches.   A scarce
winter visitor to the coasts of the British Isles.*

THE KITTIWAKE GULL RISSA TRIDACTYLA (*Plate XXXIII*)

*Hind toe represented by a small knob without a claw.   Winter plumage—
head and neck pale bluish ash, a few fine dusky streaks before the eyes ; forehead,
region of the eyes, and all the under parts, pure white ; upper plumage bluish
ash ; first primary with the outer web black, four first tipped with black, two
or three of them ending in a small white spot, fifth having the tip white bordered
with black ; bill greenish yellow ; orbits red ; irides brown ; feet dark olive-
brown.   In summer, the whole of the head and neck is white.   Young birds
have the head white, mottled with grey and dusky ; upper feathers tipped with
brown ; bend and upper edge of the wing black ; primaries black ; tail white,
towards the end tipped with black ; bill, orbits, and irides, black ; feet pale
brown.   Length fifteen and a half inches.   Eggs stone-colour, spotted with grey
and two shades of brown.   A resident on the coasts of the British Isles.*

THE Kittiwake Gull takes its name from the cry with which in the
breeding season it assails any intruder on its domain.   It is a beautiful

[1] A specimen shot in Norfolk was found to contain a full-grown Golden Plover
entire.

bird, especially in its variegated immature plumage, remarkable for its delicacy of colouring and the easy grace of its flight, frequenting high cliffs in summer, while engaged in the duties of incubation, and at all other times preferring the open sea to estuaries, and feeding on such small fish as swim near the surface. It is very abundant in the Arctic regions of both hemispheres during summer, and extends its southern limits so far as to include the British Isles, but is most numerous in the north. Its nest, built of seaweed or bents, is placed high up in the face of a precipitous cliff, generally on a narrow ledge, and in close proximity with others belonging to birds of the same species. It contains three eggs, and the young birds remain in their airy nest until fully fledged, when, as well as their parents, they disperse over the neighbouring seas, rarely venturing either to perch on land or fly over it. The young of the Kittiwake, previous to its first moult, is sometimes called the Tarrock.

FAMILY ALCIDÆ

THE COMMON GUILLEMOT ÚRIA AALGE (*Plate XXXV*)

Bill much compressed, longer than the head, greyish black ; upper plumage brownish black ; the secondaries tipped with white ; a whitish patch behind the eye on each side ; under plumage white ; feet dusky ; iris brown. Length nearly eighteen inches. Eggs greenish or bluish, blotched and streaked with black. A resident on the coasts of the British Isles.

THIS is one of our common sea-birds during a great portion of the year, though little known to ordinary seaside visitors, owing to its habit of keeping well out to sea and having nothing ostentatious in its habits. Yet, during a cruise in a yacht, on almost any part of the coast, a practised eye will often discover a few stragglers, distinguished among other sea-birds by their black and white colours, short neck, and sharp beak. They swim low in the water ; and when disturbed do not invariably dive like the Grebes and Divers, but readily take wing. They are essentially marine birds, never resorting to fresh water, and living exclusively on fish, which they capture by diving, an art in which they are scarcely less skilful than the true Divers, and which they practise in the same way—by the means, namely, of both wings and feet. Occasionally, a small party may be observed, flying in single file near the surface of the water. On the eastern coast of England, the Guillemot is best known by the name of Willock. It is also called Tinker's Hue, or, as Yarrell gives it, ' Tinkershere ' ; and in the west of England it is often called a Murr. Tinker's Hue is, I presume, the sobriquet of a white bird with a smutty back ; Murr is clearly a corruption of Mergus, or ' diver '. Yet more commonly it is known as the ' Foolish Guillemot ', a term of reproach analogous to that of ' Booby ', given to it from the indifference which it evinces, in the breeding season, to one of its few, but that one the most formidable of its enemies, man. Early in spring Guillemots throng together from all parts of the open sea, and repair to some lofty cliff, where, on a narrow ledge of rock, which in their folly they deem inaccessible, they lay each a single egg. As the bird holds the egg between her legs, she could not well cover more than one ; and though a concave nest is very needful to keep eggs together when there are several, no such contrivance is necessary when there is one only ; so the Foolish Guillemot builds no nest, but lays a solitary egg on the bare rock. The egg, which is large, is thick-shelled and rough, so that it receives no detriment from the rock ; and it is not likely to roll off, for at one end it is thick, and at the other tapers almost to a point ; consequently, if accidentally moved by the parent bird when taking flight, it turns as if on a pivot, but does not fall off. At this season, the cliffs to which Guillemots resort are frequented also by myriads of other sea-birds, such as Razor-bills, Puffins, and Gulls, each congregating with its own species, but never consorting with another. In Iceland, the Faroe Islands, St. Kilda, the Orkneys, and many parts of the coast of Scotland, the breeding season of these birds is the harvest-time of the natives. Either by climbing from below, or by being let down with ropes from above, the egg-collectors invade the dominions of these literally feathered ' tribes '. The Foolish Guillemots, rather than leave their charge, suffer themselves to be knocked on the head, to be netted, or noosed. Although stationed so close to each other that a Foolish Guillemot alone could know its own egg, they learn no wisdom from the fate of their nearest neighbours. They are captured in detail for the sake of their feathers ; and their eggs are taken for food. Such as escape this systematic slaughter flounder, as well as they are able, into the sea when nearly fledged, or are carried thither by their foolish mothers. There they learn to swim, to dive, and to fish, and about the middle of August old and young disperse.

Huge baskets of their eggs are sometimes brought to the markets of seaport towns (I have seen them so far south as Devonport), and sold for a price exceeding that of domestic fowls, for they are much larger, and are said to afford good eating. Wilson, in his *Voyage round the Coasts of Scotland*, says that the natives of St. Kilda prefer the eggs of these and other sea-fowl, ' when *sour* ; that is, when about ten or twelve days old, and just as the incipient bird, when boiled, forms in the centre into a thickish flaky matter, like milk '.[1] Great quantities are used in the neighbourhood of Flamborough Head early in the nesting season.

THE BLACK GUILLEMOT ÚRIA GRYLLE (*Plate XXXV*)

Upper and under plumage black ; middle of the wings white ; iris brown ; feet red. Length thirteen and a half inches. Eggs whitish grey, blotched and speckled with grey and two shades of brown. A resident in the British Isles,

[1] Vol. ii. p. 45.

breeding on the coasts of Ireland, the Isle of Man, and Cumberland, on the west and north coasts of Scotland and in the Hebrides, Orkneys, and Shetlands.

THE Black Guillemot is a resident species breeding on the Isle of Man and on the Irish coasts. In Scotland it is common. Its mode of life, as described by Macgillivray, who was familiarly acquainted with it, differs in no material respect from that of the species already described. It is, however, much smaller, and lays two or sometimes three eggs. In summer, these birds may be readily distinguished from other sea-fowl, by their black and white plumage and red feet : the predominant tint of the plumage in winter is white, with a tinge of grey.

THE LITTLE AUK ÁLLE ÁLLE (*Plate I*)

Head and upper parts black ; two bands across the wings, a spot above the eye, and all the under parts, white. In summer the throat and front of the neck are also black. Length about seven inches. Eggs uniform pale blue. A winter visitor to the coasts of the British Isles.

THE Little Auk is essentially a northern sea-bird, coming to us in winter, and is described by Arctic voyagers under the name of Rotche. It is an indefatigable swimmer, and has considerable powers of flight ; but it does not possess the faculty of diving to the same degree as the Divers and Grebes, as it generally stays but a short time under water. Hence it must find its food near the surface ; and this is supposed to consist of the small crustaceous animals which are so abundant in the Arctic waters. Little Auks are eminently social birds, and have been observed occasionally in such numbers on the water and floating masses of ice as almost to hide their resting-place. They rarely travel far south ; and when they visit our shores, which is in winter, and after tempestuous weather, they are supposed to have been driven hither against their will. Instances are recorded of specimens having been found far inland, disabled or dead. It lays only a single egg.

THE PUFFIN FRATÉRCULA ÁRCTICA (*Plate XXXV*)

Crown, collar, and upper parts, black ; cheeks, region of the eyes, and throat, greyish white ; under parts pure white ; bill bluish grey at the base, yellow in the middle, bright red at the tip ; upper mandible with three transverse furrows, lower, with two ; iris whitish ; orbits red ; feet orange-red. Length twelve and a half inches. Eggs whitish, with indistinct ash-coloured spots. A resident, breeding on the coasts of the British Isles.

UNLIKE the majority of sea-birds which have been passing under our notice, Puffins visit the shores of the British Isles in summer, and even in winter they are not absent. They make their appearance about April or May, not scattering themselves indiscriminately along the coast, but resorting in vast numbers to various selected breeding-places, from the Scilly Islands to the Orkneys. Their home being the sea, and their diet small fish, they possess the faculties of swimming and diving to a degree of perfection. They have, moreover, considerable powers of flight ; but on land their gait is only a shuffling attempt at progress. Their vocation on shore is, however, but a temporary one, and requires no great amount of locomotion. Soon after their arrival they set to work about their nests. Fanciful people who class birds according to their constructive faculty as weavers, basket-makers, plasterers, and so on, would rank Puffins among miners. Building is an art of which they are wholly ignorant, yet few birds are lodged more securely. With their strong beaks, they excavate for themselves holes in the face of the cliff to the depth of about three feet, and at the extremity the female lays a solitary egg—solitary, that is to say, unless another bird takes shelter in the same hole, which is not infrequently the case. Puffins generally show no overweening partiality for their own workmanship ; sloping cliffs which have been perforated by rabbits are favourite places of resort ; and here they do not at all scruple to avail themselves of another's labour, or, if necessary, to eject by force of beak the lawful tenant. If the soil be unsuited for boring, they lay their eggs under large stones or in crevices in the rock. The old bird sits most assiduously, and suffers herself to be taken rather than desert her charge, but not without wounding, with her powerful beak, and to the best of her ability, the hand which ventures into her stronghold. Hundreds burrow on Lundy Island. *Lunde* means Puffin, and *ey* Island, the name being given by the old Scandinavian rovers who settled there.

The young are fed by both parents, at first on half-digested fish, and when older on pieces of fresh fish. At this period they suffer their colonies to be invaded without showing much alarm, and are either shot, knocked down with a stick, or noosed without difficulty. As soon as the young are fully fledged, all the Puffins withdraw to the open seas, where they pass the winter, and do not approach land until the return of the breeding season. ' A small island near Skye, named Fladda-huna, is a great breeding haunt of Puffins, a species which arrives in the earlier part of May, literally covering the rocks and ledgy cliffs with its feathered thousands. Although these have no concern with our Grouse-shooting season, they almost totally disappear on the twelfth of August.' [1] It was just about this period (August 7) in the present year (1861) that I observed several large flocks of Puffins, floating with the tide through the Sound of Islay, and was told by an intelligent gamekeeper that ' these birds habitually *swim* through the sound at this season, but always *fly* when returning '. In Scotland there are many large colonies, also in the cliffs by Flamborough Head, and on the Farne Islands.

Puffins and some other sea-birds appear to be either liable to a fatal epidemic or to be surprised by some atmospheric disturbance, being unable to resist which, they perish in large numbers. I have seen a portion of the seashore in Cornwall strewn for the distance of more than a mile with hundreds of their remains. All the softer parts had been apparently devoured by fishes and crustaceous animals, and nothing was left but the unmistakable parrot-like beaks. A friend

[1] Wilson's *Voyage round the Coasts of Scotland.*

informs me that he witnessed a similar phenomenon in Norfolk, in September, 1858 ; but in this instance the carcases of the birds were not devoured, and the birds were of different kinds. He estimated that about ninety per cent. were Guillemots, and the remainder Puffins, Razor-bills, Scoters, and a sprinkling of Black-throated Divers. A similar mortality among sea-birds is recorded in the *Zoologist* as having taken place on the coast of Norfolk, in May, 1856. On this occasion they were so numerous as to be thought worth collecting for manure.

Other names by which the Puffin is known are Sea Parrot, Coulterneb, Mullet, Bottlenose ; and, in Scotland, Ailsa Parrot, Tammie-Norie, and Tammas.

THE RAZOR-BILL ALCA TORDA (*Plate XXXV*)

Wings reaching to the origin of the tail ; head and upper parts black ; a band across the wing ; an interrupted line from the eye to the base of the bill, and all the under parts white ; bill black, with three or four furrows, of which the middle one is white ; irides hazel ; legs dusky. In summer the line from the eye to the bill is pure white, and the whole of the throat and neck is black, tinged with red. Length seventeen inches. Eggs white, blotched and spotted with two shades of brown. A resident on the coasts of the British Isles.

IN general habits, the Razor-bill closely resembles the Guillemot and Puffin. Indeed, in some parts of the coast, the Razor-bill is called a Puffin, and the latter a Sea Parrot ; and in Cornwall both Guillemots and Razor-bills are known by the common name of Murre. At a distance the birds can only be distinguished by a practised eye ; but on a close inspection they cannot possibly be confounded.

Razor-bills are common on many parts of our coast during the later summer months. They are more frequently seen swimming than flying, and if pursued by a boat are little disposed to take alarm until they are approached to within twenty or thirty yards, when they dive, but soon reappear not very far off. If two birds be in company and one be killed by a shot from a gun, its companion, instead of taking measures to ensure its own safety, seems to lose the power of self-preservation. It paddles round its companion as if unable to comprehend the reason why it neither dives nor flies, and if pursued suffers itself to be overtaken and knocked down by an oar. This sympathetic feeling is not confined to birds which have paired, or to members of the same family ; for in an instance which came under my own notice, both birds were only a few months old, and, as the Razor-bill lays but one egg, the birds could not possibly have grown up together. Towards winter, Razor-bills migrate southwards, either to avoid cold or to find waters where their prey swims nearer to the surface than in our climate. In spring they return northwards, and repair, like Puffins, to places of habitual resort for the purpose of breeding. At this season, also, they are eminently social, laying each an egg in close proximity on a ledge in the rocks, lower down than the Puffins, but above the Guillemots, all of which birds flock to the same portion of coast, often in countless multitudes. The egg differs from that of the Guillemot not only in colour but in shape, being less decidedly pear-shaped. It is much sought after as an article of food, and is said to be very palatable.

ORDER COLUMBIFORMES

FAMILY PTEROCLIDÆ

THE THREE-TOED, OR PALLAS'S, SAND-GROUSE
SYRRHAPTES PARADOXUS (*Plate XX*)

Head yellowish grey ; upper parts buff, barred with black ; quills and long, pointed central tail-feathers, bluish-grey ; chin, vent, and feathers of legs, whitish ; neck and breast greyish buff crossed by a mottled black gorget ; belly banded with black. Legs and toes feathered to the claws ; no hind toe. Length sixteen to twenty inches. Eggs greyish buff to yellowish brown spotted with purplish brown. A rare occasional visitor to the British Isles, sometimes in large flocks.

THIS species was not known with us till 1859. Great flights visited this country in 1863, in 1888, and in 1889 when a few pair nested. During the succeeding twenty years small parties appeared on several occasions. In 1908 there was another considerable invasion, but since 1909, when some appeared in Yorkshire, there has been no authentic record of occurrence. Pallas's Sand-grouse is an inhabitant of the steppes of central Asia and south-eastern Russia, and the reasons for its occasional invasions of western Europe are unknown.

FAMILY COLUMBIDÆ

THE WOOD PIGEON OR RING DOVE COLUMBA PALUMBUS
(*Plate XXXVI*)

Head, cheeks, neck, and upper part of the tail, bluish grey ; back and wing-coverts darker ; a white crescent-shaped spot on each side of the neck surrounded by scale-like feathers with green and purple reflections ; primaries grey towards the base, white in the middle, and dusky towards the extremity, with the outer web white ; tail barred with black at the end ; abdomen whitish ; bill orange, powdered with white at the base ; iris light yellow ; feet blood-red ; claws brown. Length sixteen and a half inches. Eggs pure white. A resident in the British Isles, except the Shetlands ; also a winter visitor.

Two hundred and fifty years ago the taste for keeping different sorts of Pigeons was as strong as it is in the present day, and the popular

names of Runts, Croppers, Shakers, Carriers, Jacobins, Turbits, Bar-
baries, Tumblers, Horsemen, Spots, etc., modern though they may
sound, were then applied to the very same varieties which are described
under these names in recent *Guides to the Poultry-yard*.   Many of these
were of foreign origin, and were known at a remote period in various
eastern countries, so that there can be no doubt that the custom of
keeping tame Pigeons is of very ancient date.

The Pigeons in some of their habits approach the gallinaceous
birds.   They are furnished with long and powerful wings, by help of
which they can sustain a rapid and continuous flight.   They seek their
food mostly on the ground, but do not scratch with their feet, and are
more given to bathe in water than to flutter in a bath of dust, though
in this habit also they not infrequently indulge.   They are furnished,
moreover, with a large crop, in which the food supplied to their young
is partially macerated and reduced to a kind of pulp before the latter
are fed.   This process is carried on more by the agency of the receiver
than of the giver, as the young birds, instead of opening their mouths
and allowing the food to be dropped in, help themselves by inserting
their bills into the sides of the old bird's mouth.   Their mode of
drinking differs from that of the true gallinaceous birds ; they do not
take short sips, lifting the head after every draught, but satisfy their
thirst by one continuous immersion of the whole bill.   They build
their nests of a few sticks, and lay two white eggs.

Some of the foreign species are distinguished by their brilliant
plumage.   Those inhabiting Britain are unmarked by gaudy tints,
but redeemed from plainness by the metallic glossy lustre of their
neck feathers.

The Wood Dove, called also Wood Pigeon and Ring Dove, is the
largest British species, exceeding in dimensions most varieties of the
domestic Pigeon.   The summer wanderer through a wood in almost
any part of the country can scarcely fail to have been disturbed in
his meditations by the sudden flapping of wings of some large bird,
which, without uttering any note, dashes through the foliage of a
neighbouring tree, and makes off with hurried flight for some distant
part of the wood.   Seen through the openings of the trees, its predominant tint is blue-grey, but a large patch of white is distinctly
perceptible on each wing.   It might be mistaken for a hawk, so rapidly
does it cleave its way through the air ; but birds of prey are too wary
to betray their movements by the sound of their wings ; they, too,
rather launch into the air, than start with a violent clapping of their
pinions.   A Jay might make a similar noise ; but when alarmed it
always utters its harsh scream, and, if it comes in sight, may at once
be distinguished by the striking contrast of its white and black feathers.
The bird just disturbed can scarcely, then, be anything but a Wood
Dove, perhaps frightened from its nest, perhaps attending on its mate,
or it may have been simply digesting its last meal, or waiting until sent
forth by the cravings of hunger in quest of a new one ; for the bird,
though exemplary as a spouse and parent, has a large crop which
is never allowed to remain long empty.   The food and habits of Wood
Pigeons vary with the season.   In spring and summer they are most

frequently seen alone or in pairs. They then feed principally on the tender leaves of growing plants, and often commit great ravage in fields of beans and peas. Spring-sown corn is attacked by them both in the grain and the blade, and as soon as young turnips have put forth their second pair of leaves, they, too, come in for their share of devastation. As the season advances, they visit the cornfields, especially those in the vicinity of their native woods, preferring, above all, those parts where the corn has been laid, and where a neighbouring grove or thicket will afford them a ready retreat if disturbed. They are very partial also to oily seeds of all kinds, and it is said that since colza has been extensively grown in the south of France, Wood Pigeons have become a scourge of agriculture, and that consequently war is waged on them unsparingly. It has been remarked also, that they have become much more abundant in Scotland in consequence of ' the great increase in the cultivation of turnips and clover, which afford them a constant supply of food during winter, and the great increase of fir woods, which are their delight both for roosting and rearing their young '. At the approach of autumn they assemble in small flocks, and resort to oak and beech woods, especially the last, where acorns and beech-mast, swallowed whole, afford them an abundant and generous diet. They are now in great demand for the table, but, being very cautious and shy, are difficult of approach. A good many, however, are shot by men and boys, who discover beforehand in what particular trees they roost, and, lying in ambush to await their arrival, fire at them as they drop in in small parties. In winter, the small flocks unite and form large ones. So large, indeed, are these sometimes in severe seasons, that it is fair to suppose that their numbers are considerably augmented by subsidies from colder climates, driven southwards perhaps by scarcity of food. In districts abounding in oak and beech woods, they find abundance of food during the greater part of the winter ; but when this supply is exhausted, or the ground is covered with snow, they repair once more to the turnip-fields, and feed on the green leaves. Hunger, however, does not rob them of their shyness, or make them confiding ; for let a human figure appear in ever so large a field where a flock is feeding, the alarm is at once caught and communicated to the whole party, who lose no time in displaying the white bar on the wing, and are soon beyond the reach of fowler and gun.

Among the first woodland sounds of spring and the last of autumn is the note of the Ring Dove, often continued for a long time together, always monotonous, but never wearisome. It is generally considered to be tinged with melancholy, and on this account the bird itself is supposed to have been named the Queest or Cushat.

> Deep toned
> The Cushat plains ; nor is her changeless plaint
> Unmusical, when with the general quire
> Of woodland harmony it softly blends.
>
> GRAHAME.

Wordsworth celebrates it under a name generally given to the next species.

> I heard a Stock Dove sing or say
> His homely tale, this very day ;
> His voice was buried among trees,
> Yet to be come at by the breeze.
> It did not cease ; but cooed and cooed,
> And somewhat pensively he wooed ;
> He sang of love with quiet blending,
> Slow to begin, and never ending ;
> Of sorrows, faith, and inward glee ;
> That was the song, the song for me.

And again, still more happily :

> Over his own sweet voice the Stock Dove broods.

The note may be imitated by attempting to whistle, in a very deep tone, the syllables ' cooe-coo-roo-o-o-o ' ; or still more closely by clasping the hands together, so as to form a hollow, open only between the second joints of the thumbs, and blowing the same words over the orifice. With a little practice so close an imitation may be produced, that a genuine cooer may be beguiled into giving an answer. I may add, too, that with the same natural instrument and with a greater expenditure of breath the hoot of the Owl may be imitated ; with a gentler effort and a quiver of the tongue the coo of the Turtle Dove may be nearly approached.

The Wood Dove has never been considered to be the origin of the domestic Pigeon, nor will it breed in captivity. There is no difficulty, however, in rearing birds taken young from the nest ; and birds so brought up will alight with perfect confidence on the person of their foster nurse, and feed from his hand or mouth. The nest of the Wood Dove is an unsubstantial structure, composed of sticks so loosely put together that the eggs or young birds are sometimes visible from below. It is placed in a fork or among the branches of a tree ; a thick fir is preferred ; but nests are to be met with in ivy and thorn bushes either in a wood, coppice, or, more rarely, in a hedgerow. The number of eggs is always two. The male bird assists in the office of incubation.

THE STOCK DOVE COLUMBA ŒNAS (*Plate XXXVI*)

Head, throat, wings, and lower parts, bluish grey ; the lower parts of the neck with metallic reflections, no white spots ; breast wine-red ; a black spot on the two last secondaries and some of the wing-coverts ; primaries grey at the base, passing into dusky ; tail grey, barred with black at the extremity, the outer feather with a white spot on the outer web near the base ; irides reddish brown ; bill yellow, red at the base ; feet red ; claws dusky. Length twelve and a half inches. Eggs white. A resident in the British Isles, except the Outer Hebrides, Orkneys, and Shetlands.

THE Stock Dove is by some persons supposed to be so called from its having been believed at one time to be the origin of the domestic Pigeon ; but as it bore the name before the above question was mooted, it is more reasonable to suppose that it derived its name from its habit

of nestling in the *stocks* of trees, and not on the branches like the Ring
Dove, nor in caves like the Rock Dove. Ray and Willughby, who
treat the domestic Dove as a distinct species, gave it the name of
Œnas (from the Greek *oinos*, wine), and Vinago (from the Latin
vinum), from the purpled or wine-red hue of its breast and wings.
Temminck does not hesitate to identify the domestic Pigeon with the
Rock Dove, without even hinting the possibility of its having derived
its origin from the Stock Dove. Since, therefore, the two birds have
no marked resemblance, it may be reasonably supposed that the
relationship between them rests solely on the narrow foundation that
there exists a wild Pigeon, popularly called a Stock Dove, and that
the word ' stock ' has among other meanings that of ' parentage ' or
' origin '. Thus the name gave rise to a theory which, having a
plausible show, was hastily assumed, and was then employed to prove
a fact which will not bear the test of examination. The Stock Dove
in its habits closely resembles the Ring Dove, from which it cannot
easily be distinguished at a distance. When tolerably near, a sharp
eye can detect the absence of the white patch on the wings and of the
ring round the neck. Its flight is more rapid, and it rarely perches
on a slender bough, preferring to alight on a main branch or stump.
Its note is softer, and approaches that of the tame Pigeon. But the
great mark of distinction is that on which I have supposed its name
to be founded ; that it does not build its nest among the branches of
trees, but in the side of a stump, or other locality, where no one would
even think of looking for a Ring Dove's nest. It also frequently makes
its nest in holes in the ground, generally selecting a rabbit's burrow.
It has greatly increased in the south of England of late, and it nests
along the Moray and Dornoch Firths.

THE ROCK DOVE COLUMBA LIVIA (*Plate XXXVI*)

*Plumage bluish ash, lighter on the wings ; rump white ; neck and breast
lustrous with green and purple reflections, without a white spot ; two transverse
black bands on the wings ; primaries and tail tipped with black ; rump white ;
outer tail-feather white on the outer web ; irides pale orange ; bill black ; feet
red. Length twelve and a half inches. Eggs white. Resident on the coasts
of Ireland and Scotland and in the Hebrides, Orkneys, and Shetlands.*

THE Rock Dove, though a bird of extensive range, is less generally
known in its natural condition than either of the other British species.
As its name imports, its favourite place of resort is the rocky coast ;
but this it frequents, not because it has any predilection for the seashore and its productions, but that its instincts teach it to make lofty
rocks its stronghold, just as the natural impulse of the Ring Dove is
to find safety in the forests. If this species is the original of all the
numerous varieties of tame Pigeon, it must inhabit most countries of
the eastern hemisphere ; for a pigeon-fancier's dove-cot, to be complete, must contain several sorts which were first brought from remote
regions ; and we know that in Egypt, Phœnicia, and Persia, Pigeons
had a mythological importance at an early date. It is said that the

Pigeons which have established themselves in various public buildings of continental cities, as Saint Mark's at Venice, and Pont Neuf at Paris, are exclusively Rock Pigeons ; and I have seen it stated that they frequent the towers of Canterbury Cathedral ; but it is possible that these may be in all cases derived from tame birds escaped from domestication, and resuming, to a certain extent, their wild habits and original plumage. That they resort to ruinous edifices near the sea in retired districts is beyond question, as I have seen them flying about and alighting on the walls of an old castle in the island of Kerrera, near Oban, in the Western Highlands, indifferent, seemingly, whether they nestled in the lofty cliffs on the mainland, where they are numerous, or on the equally secure ruins of masonry in the opposite island. That they are truly wild here there can be no doubt. Indeed, the precipitous shores of Scotland, the Hebrides, and Orkneys, afford them exactly the kind of retreat that suits their habits ; and here among inaccessible rocks they build their nests and on their return from their inland marauding expeditions, pass their nights. Their attitudes, mode of flight, progression when on the ground, note, and manner of feeding, are the same as those of the common tame Pigeon ; and, as might be expected, both wild and tame birds agree in declining to perch on trees.

Macgillivray, who had opportunities of watching them in their native haunts at all seasons, informs us that they leave their caves in the crags at early dawn, and, proceeding along the shore, unite with other parties on their way till they reach the cultivated grounds, where they settle in large flocks, diligently seeking for grains of barley and oats, seeds of wild mustard and other weeds, picking up also the small snails [1] which abound in sandy pastures near the sea. In summer they make frequent short visits of this kind, returning at intervals to feed their young. In winter they form much larger flocks, and, making the best use of their short day, feed more intently, thus holding out a temptation to the fowler, who, if sufficiently wary, can sometimes approach near enough to kill a large number at a shot. They are supposed to pair for life ; and this, I believe, is generally the case with tame Pigeons. They lay two eggs, and sit for three weeks. The male and the female sit, alternately relieving each other. They breed twice a year, but the number of eggs never exceeds two. Hence the old Scottish saying, ' a doo's cleckin', for a family of only two children— a boy and a girl. They may be distinguished from the other common species while flying, by showing a large patch of white between the back and the tail.

THE TURTLE DOVE STREPTOPELIA TURTUR (*Plate XXXVI*)

Head and nape ash, tinged with wine-red ; a space on the sides of the neck composed of black feathers tipped with white ; neck and breast pale wine-red ; back ash-brown ; primaries dusky ; secondaries bluish ash ; scapulars and

---

[1] *Helix ericetorum,* a flattish, striped shell ; and *Bulimus acutus,* an oblong, conical hell, mottled with grey and black.

wing-coverts rust-red with a black spot in the centre of each feather ; abdomen and lower tail-coverts white ; tail dusky, all but the two middle feathers tipped with white, the outer feather edged with white externally ; irides yellowish red ; feet red ; bill brown. Eggs white. A summer visitor to England and Wales, breeding chiefly in the south, east, and midlands and only rarely in the extreme west and north. In Scotland and Ireland a rare summer and autumn visitor.

NEARLY three thousand years ago the Turtle Dove had the distinction of being enumerated among the pleasant things of spring : ' Lo, the winter is past, the rain is over and gone ; the flowers appear on the earth ; the time of the singing of birds is come, and the voice of the Turtle is heard in our land.' [1] Less sweetly, but to the same effect, sings a poet of the last century :

> The cuckoo calls aloud his wand'ring love,
> The Turtle's moan is heard in ev'ry grove ;
> The pastures change, the warbling linnets sing.
> Prepare to welcome in the gaudy spring !
>
> PHILIPS.

There is no melody in the song of the Turtle, as it consists of a single note, a soft, sweet, agitated murmur, continued without pause for a long time, called a ' moan ' [2] both by Latin and English poets, not from its being suggestive of pain, but because there is no other word which describes it so nearly. I have already had occasion to remark how unsatisfactory are most of the attempts which have been made to represent the songs of birds by combinations of letters, but the Latin name of the Turtle-dove, *Turtur*, is a notable exception. Pronounced ' tur-r-r tur-r-r ', it will instantly recall the note to any one who has once heard it. The French name also, *Tourterelle*, can belong to this bird alone.

The Turtle Dove is found in all the southern countries of Europe, in Palestine, and other parts of south-western Asia and in northern Africa. In England it is a visitor in the southern and midland counties only, arriving in spring and remaining with us until the end of September. Its favourite places of resort are groves, belts of trees, and tall hedgerows in cultivated districts. Here it builds its unsubstantial nest of a few sticks, and lays two eggs. Its food consists of seeds of various kinds, and it has the discredit of resorting to fields of green wheat for the sake of feeding on the milky grain. I am doubtful whether this charge can be sustained. Often enough when walking through a cornfield one may see two or three Turtle Doves rise suddenly from the thick corn with a rustle and low cry of alarm, rapidly dart away in the direction of the nearest grove, disappearing in the shade, all but a white segment of a circle, formed by the tips of their tail-feathers ; but on examining the spot from which they rose, I have been unable to detect any ears of corn rifled of their contents, though the ground was thickly matted with weeds, which might have furnished them food. I am informed by a young friend that he has often shot

[1] Cant. ii. 11, 12.
[2] ' Nec gemere aëriâ cessabit Turtur ab ulmo.'—VIRGIL.
Nor shall from lofty elm the Turtle cease to moan.

them while in the act of rising from such situations and has invariably found their crops distended with the green seed-vessels of a weed common in cornfields, the corn-spurrey (*Spérgula arvensis*). This being the case, the Turtle Dove is more a friend than an enemy to the farmer, even if it sometimes regales on ripe grain or interferes with the occupation of the gleaner. It is also very partial to vetches. I have met with an instance where a Turtle Dove paid daily visits to one particular spot, under a hedge in a field, and though fired at by the owner of the field many times under the idea that it was a rare bird, it soon returned ; and when at last shot, its crop was found to be full of vetch seeds which had been accidentally spilled from a bag.

The Turtle Dove is smaller than any of the other British Doves. When flying, it seems scarcely larger than a Missel Thrush ; but it is more slender in shape, and its wings are much longer. It beats its wings, too, more rapidly, and moves through the air with greater velocity. The tints of its plumage are more varied than in the other British species, but far inferior in brilliancy to many foreign ones.

The Turtle Dove so frequently kept in a cage is the Collared Turtle Dove (*Streptopelia risoria*), a native of India and China. This species is distinguished by a black crescent on the back of the neck, the horns of which nearly meet in front. Turtle Doves are much kept in Germany, owing to a strange popular superstition that they are more predisposed than the human species to nervous disorders and rheumatism, and that when any of these complaints visit a house, they fall on the birds rather than on their owners.

ORDER CUCULIFORMES

FAMILY CUCULIDÆ

THE CUCKOO cúculus canórus (*Plate LXIV*)

Upper plumage bluish ash-colour, darker on the wings, lighter on the neck and chest ; under parts whitish with transverse dusky streaks ; quills barred on the inner webs with oval white spots ; tail-feathers blackish, tipped and spotted with white ; bill dusky, edged with yellow ; orbits and inside of the mouth orange-yellow ; iris and feet yellow. Young—ash-brown, barred with reddish brown ; tips of the feathers white ; a white spot on the back of the head. Length thirteen inches and a half, breadth twenty-three inches. Eggs varying in colour and markings. A summer visitor to the British Isles, breeding throughout except in the Shetlands.

No bird in a state of nature utters a note approaching so closely the sound of the human voice as the Cuckoo ; on this account, perhaps, partially at least, it has at all times been regarded with especial interest. Its habits have been much investigated, and they are found to be unlike those of any other bird. The Cuckoo was a puzzle to the earlier naturalists, and there are points in its biography which are controverted still. From the days of Aristotle to those of Pliny, it was supposed to undergo a metamorphosis twice a year, appearing during the summer months as a Cuckoo, ' a bird of the hawk kind, though destitute of curved talons and hooked beak, and having the bill of a Pigeon ; should it chance to appear simultaneously with a Hawk it was devoured, being the sole example of a bird being killed by one of its own kind. In winter it actually changed into a Merlin, but reappeared in spring in its own form, but with an altered voice, laid a single egg, or rarely two, in the nest of some other bird, generally a Pigeon, declining to rear its own young, because it knew itself to be a common object of hostility among all birds, and that its brood would be in consequence unsafe, unless it practised a deception. The young Cuckoo being naturally greedy, monopolized the food brought to the nest by its foster-parents ; it thus grew fat and sleek, and so excited its dam with admiration of her lovely offspring, that she first neglected her own chicks, then suffered them to be devoured before her eyes, and finally fell a victim herself to his voracious appetite.' [1] A strange fiction, yet not more strange than the truth, a glimmering of which appears throughout. We know well enough now that the Cuckoo does not change into a Merlin, but migrates in autumn to the southern regions of Africa ; but this neither Aristotle nor Pliny could have known, for the common belief in their days was, that a continued progress southwards would bring the traveller to a climate too fierce for the maintenance of animal life. Now the Merlin visits the south of Europe, just at the season when the Cuckoo disappears, and returns northwards to breed in spring, a fact in its history as little known as the migration of the Cuckoo. It bears a certain resemblance to the Cuckoo, particularly in its barred plumage, certainly a greater one than exists between a caterpillar and a butterfly, so that there were some grounds for the belief in a metamorphosis, strengthened not a little by the fact that the habits of the bird were peculiar in other respects. Even so late as the time of our own countrymen, Willughby and Ray (1676), it was a matter of doubt whether the Cuckoo lay torpid in a hollow tree, or migrated during winter. These authors, though they do not admit their belief of a story told by Aldrovandus of a certain Swiss peasant having heard the note of a Cuckoo proceed from a log of wood which he had thrown into a furnace, thought it highly probable that the Cuckoo did become torpid during winter, and were acquainted with instances of persons who had heard its note during unusually mild winter weather. A Cuckoo which had probably been hatched off too late to go away with the rest remained about the tennis ground of a relative of the present editor until the middle of November, getting very tame. Then, unfortunately, a cat got it. The assertion again of the older naturalists, that the Cuckoo is the object of hatred among birds generally, seems credible, though I should be inclined to consider its habit of laying its eggs in the nests of other birds as the cause rather than the consequence of its

[1] Plin. *Nat. Hist.* lib. x. cap. ix.

unpopularity. The contrary, however, is the fact, numerous anecdotes of the Cuckoo showing that it is regarded by many other birds with a respect which amounts to infatuation, rather than with apprehension. The statement that it lays but one egg is erroneous, so also is the assertion of Willughby that it invariably destroys the eggs found in a nest previously to depositing its own. Pliny's assertion that the young bird devours its foster brothers and sisters is nearer the truth, but his account of its crowning act of impiety in swallowing its nurse, is, I need not say, altogether unfounded in fact. Having disposed of these errors, some of which are entertained by the credulous or ill-informed at the present day, I will proceed to sketch in outline the biography of this singular bird, as the facts are now pretty generally admitted.

The Cuckoo arrives in this country about the middle of April; the time of its coming to different countries is adapted to the time of the foster-parents' breeding. During the whole of its stay it leads a wandering life, building no nest, and attaching itself to no particular locality. It shows no hostility towards birds of another kind, and little affection for those of its own. If two males meet in the course of their wandering they frequently fight with intense animosity. I was once witness of an encounter between two birds who chanced to meet in mid-air. Without alighting they attacked each other with fury, pecking at each other and changing places just as one sees two barn-door cocks fight for the supremacy of the dunghill. Feathers flew in profusion, and in their passion the angry birds heeded my presence so little that they came almost within arm's length of me. These single combats account for the belief formerly entertained that the Cuckoo was the only sort of Hawk that preyed on its own kind. The female does not pair or keep to one mate.

The Cuckoo hunts for its food both in trees and on the ground. On its first arrival it lives principally on beetles, but when caterpillars become abundant it prefers them, especially the hairy sorts. In the months of May and June, the female Cuckoo lays her eggs (the number of which is variously estimated from five to twelve), choosing a separate locality for each, and that invariably the nest of some other bird. The nests in which the egg of a Cuckoo has been found in this country include those of the Hedge Sparrow, Robin, Redstart, Whitethroat, Willow-warbler, Sedge Warbler, Wagtail, Pipit, Skylark, Yellow Bunting, Chaffinch, Greenfinch, Linnet, Blackbird, and Wren; the Pipit being the most frequent. The hen Cuckoo watches from the bough of a tree the building of nests by the fostering species. When she knows that they are completed and laying has begun she glides down to the nest, removes one of the fosterer's eggs in her bill and lays one of her own in its place. In the case of domed nests, such as those of the Wren, or nests in holes, such as those of the Redstart or Wagtail, she clings to the outside of the nest and ejects her egg into it, not always successfully. The egg is relatively very small. If it were very much larger than the rest, it might excite suspicion, and be either turned out, or be the cause of the nest being deserted; it would require, moreover, a longer incubation than the rest, and would either fail to be hatched, or produce a young Cuckoo at a time when his foster-brothers had grown strong enough to thwart his evil designs. As it is, after twelve or thirteen days' incubation, the eggs are hatched simultaneously, or nearly so, the Cuckoo being generally the first. No sooner does the young bird see the day, than he proceeds to secure for himself the whole space of the nest and the sole attention of his foster-parents, by insinuating himself under the other young birds and any eggs which may remain unhatched, and hurling them over the edge of the nest, where they are left to perish. 'The singularity of its shape', says Dr. Jenner, 'is well adapted for these purposes ; for, different from other newly-hatched birds, its back from the shoulders downwards is very broad, with a considerable depression in the middle.' To the question which naturally suggests itself, 'Why does the young Cuckoo thus monopolize the nest and the attentions of its foster-parents ?' the solution is plain. The newly hatched bird must of necessity be less in size than the egg from which it proceeded, but a full-grown Cuckoo exceeds the dimensions of a whole brood of Pipits ; its growth therefore must be rapid and cannot be maintained without a large supply of food. But the old birds could not possibly with their utmost exertions feed a brood of their own kind and satisfy the demands made by the appetite of the voracious stranger as well. The latter consequently saves them from this impossible task, and, by appropriating to his single use the nourishment intended for a brood of four or five, not only makes provision for his own well-being, but helps them out of a difficulty. So assiduously is he taken care of that he soon becomes a portly bird and fills his nest ; in about three weeks he is able to fly, but for a period of four or five weeks more his foster-parents continue to feed him. It is probable that the young Cuckoo actually exercises some fascination over other birds. There is a case on record in which a pair of Meadow Pipits were seen to throw out their own young ones to make room for the intruder. In another instance, a young Cuckoo which had been taken from the nest and was being reared by hand escaped from confinement. Having one of its wings cut, it could not fly, but was found again at the expiration of a month, within a few fields of the house where it was reared, and several little wild birds were in the act of feeding it. The Bishop of Norwich [1] mentions two instances in which a young Cuckoo in captivity was fed by a young Thrush which had only just learnt to feed itself.

In the days when omens were observed, it was considered a matter of high import to hear the song of the Nightingale before that of the Cuckoo. Thus Chaucer says :

> it was a commone tale
> That it were gode to here the Nightingale,
> Moche rathir [2] than the lewde [3] Cuckowe singe.

So, when on a certain occasion he heard the Cuckoo first, and was troubled in consequence, he represents the Nightingale as thus addressing him :

[1] *Familiar History of Birds.*   [2] Earlier.   [3] Unskilful.

be thou not dismaied
For thou have herd the Cuckow erst than me,
For if I live it shall amendid be
The nexte Maie, if I be not afraied.

More recently Milton thus addresses the Nightingale :

Thy liquid notes that close the eye of day,
First heard before the shallow Cuccoo's bill,
Portend success in love.

Whether any traces of this popular belief yet linger in our rural districts, I do not know ; but I can recall my childish days in the west of England (where there are no Nightingales), when I looked forward with implicit faith to the coming of the Cuckoo, to ' eat up the dirt ', and make the Devonshire lanes passable for children's spring wanderings.

The song of the Cuckoo, I need scarcely remark, consists of but two notes, of which the upper is, I believe, invariably, E flat, the lower most frequently C natural, forming, however, not a perfect musical interval, but something between a minor and a major third. Occasionally two birds may be heard singing at once, one seemingly aiming at a minor, the other a major third ; the effect is, of course, discordant. Sometimes the first note is pronounced two or three times, thus ' cuck-cuck-cuckoo ', and I have heard it repeated rapidly many times in succession, so as to resemble the trilling note of the Nightingale, but in a lower key. The note of the nestling is a shrill plaintive chirp, which may best be imitated by twisting a glass stopper in a bottle. Even the human ear has no difficulty in understanding it as a cry for food, of which it is insatiable. Towards the end of June the Cuckoo, according to the old adage, ' alters its tune ', which at first loses its musical character and soon ceases altogether. In July the old birds leave us, the males by themselves first, and the females not many days after ; but the young birds remain until October.

ORDER STRIGIFORMES

FAMILY TYTONIDÆ

THE BARN OWL TYTO ALBA (*Plate XXXVII*)

Beak yellowish white ; upper parts light tawny yellow, minutely variegated with brown, grey, and white ; face and lower plumage white, the feathers of the margin tipped with brown. Length fourteen inches ; breadth nearly three feet. Eggs white. A resident in the British Isles, except the Outer Hebrides, Orkneys, and Shetlands.

RETURNING from our summer evening's walk at the pleasant time when twilight is deepening into night, when the Thrush has piped its last roundelay, and the Nightingale is gathering strength for a fresh flood of melody, a sudden exclamation from our companion ' What was that ? ' compels us to look in the direction pointed at just in time to catch a glimpse of a phantom-like body disappearing behind the hedgerow. But that the air is still, we might have imagined it to be a sheet of silver paper wafted along by the wind, so lightly and noiselessly did it pass on. We know, however, that a pair of Barn Owls have appropriated these hunting-grounds, and that this is their time of sallying forth ; we are aware, too, how stealthily they fly along the lanes, dipping behind the trees, searching round the haystacks, skimming over the stubble, and all with an absence of sound that scarcely belongs to moving life. Yet, though by no means slow of flight, the Barn Owl can scarcely be said to *cleave* the air ; rather, it *fans* its way onwards with its down-fringed wings, and the air, thus softly treated, quietly yields to the gentle force, and retires without murmur to allow it a passage. Not without meaning is this silence preserved. The nimble little animals that constitute the chase, are quick-sighted and sharp of hearing, but the pursuer gives no notice of his approach, and they know not their doom till they feel the inevitable talons in their sides. The victim secured, silence is no longer necessary. The successful hunter lifts up his voice in a sound of triumph, repairs to the nearest tree to regale himself on his prize, and, for a few minutes—that is, until the chase is resumed—utters his loud weird shriek again and again. In the morning, the Owl will retire to his private cell and will spend the day perched on end, dozing and digesting as long as the sunlight is too powerful for his large and sensitive eyes. Peep in on him in his privacy, and he will stretch out or move from side to side his grotesque head, ruffling his feathers, and hissing as though your performance were worthy of all condemnation. Yet he is a very handsome and most amusing bird, more worthy of being domesticated as a pet than many others held in high repute. Taken young from the nest, he is soon on familiar terms with his owner, recognizes him by a flapping of wings and a hiss whenever he approaches, clearing his premises of mice, and showing no signs of pining at the restriction placed on his liberty. Give him a bird, and he will soon show that, though contented with mice, he quite appreciates more refined fare. Grasping the body with his talons, he deliberately plucks off all the large feathers with his beak, tears off the head, and swallows it at one gulp, and then proceeds to devour the rest piecemeal. In a wild state his food consists mainly of mice, which he swallows whole, beetles, and sometimes fish, which he catches by pouncing on them in the water.

The service which the Barn Owl renders to the agriculturist, by its consumption of rats and mice, must be exceedingly great, yet it is little appreciated. ' When it has young,' says Mr. Waterton, ' it will bring a mouse to the nest every twelve or fifteen minutes. But in order to have a proper idea of the enormous quantity of mice which this bird destroys, we must examine the pellets which it ejects from its stomach in the place of its retreat. Every pellet contains from four to seven skeletons of mice. In sixteen months from the time that the apartment of the Owl on the old gateway was cleared out, there has been a deposit of above a bushel of pellets.'

The plumage of the Barn Owl is remarkable for its softness, its delicacy of pencilling on the upper parts and its snowy whiteness below. Its face is perfectly heart-shaped during life, but when the animal is dead becomes circular. The female is slightly larger than her mate, and her colours are somewhat darker. The nest of the Barn Owl is a rude structure placed in the bird's daily haunt. The eggs vary in number, and the bird lays them at different periods, each egg after the first being hatched (partially at least) by the heat of the young birds already in being. That this is always the case it would not be safe to assert, but that it is so sometimes there can be no doubt. The young birds are ravenous eaters and proverbially ugly ; when craving food they make a noise resembling a snore. The Barn or White Owl is said to be the most generally diffused of all the tribe, being found in almost all latitudes of both hemispheres, and it appears to be everywhere an object of terror to the ignorant. A bird of the night, the time when evil deeds are done, it bespeaks for itself an evil reputation ; making ruins and hollow trees its resort, it becomes associated with the gloomiest legends ; uttering its discordant note during the hours of darkness, it is rarely heard save by the benighted traveller, or by the weary watcher at the bed of the sick and dying ; and who more susceptible of alarming impressions than these ? It is therefore scarcely surprising that the common incident of a Screech-Owl being attracted by a solitary midnight taper to flutter against the window of a sick room, and there to utter its melancholy wail, should for a time shake the faith of the watcher, and, when repeated with the customary exaggerations, should obtain for the poor harmless mouser the unmerited title of ' harbinger of death '.

FAMILY STRIGIDÆ

THE LONG-EARED OWL ASIO ÓTUS (*Plate XXXVII*)

Beak black ; iris orange-yellow ; egrets very long, composed of eight or ten black feathers, edged with yellow and white ; upper parts reddish yellow, mottled with brown and grey ; lower parts lighter, with oblong streaks of deep brown. Length fifteen inches ; breadth thirty-eight inches. Eggs white. Resident in the British Isles except the Outer Hebrides, Orkneys, and Shetlands ; also a winter visitor.

THOUGH not among the most frequent of the English Owls, this species occurs in most of the wooded parts of England and Ireland. It is more common than is usually supposed in France where it unites in its own person all the malpractices which have been popularly ascribed to the whole tribe of Owls. It is there said to be held in great detestation by all the rest of the feathered tribe ; a fact which is turned to good account by the bird-catcher, who, having set his traps and limed twigs, conceals himself in the neighbourhood and imitates the note of this Owl. The little birds, impelled by rage or fear, or a silly combination of both, assemble for the purpose of mobbing the common enemy. In their anxiety to discern the object of their abhorrence, they fall one after another into the snare, and become the prey of the fowler. The Long-eared Owl is not altogether undeserving of the persecution which is thus intended for her, her principal food being field-mice, but also such little birds as she can surprise when asleep. In fact, she respects neither the person nor the property of her neighbours, making her home in the old nests of large birds and squirrels, and appropriating, as food for herself and her voracious young, the carcases of any that she finds herself strong enough to master and kill.

The cry of this bird is only occasionally uttered—a sort of barking noise. The note of the young bird is a loud mewing and seems to be intended as a petition to its parents for a supply of food. A writer in the *Zoologist*,[1] who has had many opportunities of observing this species in its native haunts, says that it does not confine its flight entirely to the darker hours, as he has met with it in the woods sailing quickly along, as if hawking, on a bright summer day. It is curious to observe, he says, how flat they invariably make their nests, so much so, that it is difficult to conceive how the eggs retain their position, even in a slight wind, when the parent bird leaves them. The eggs are four to six in number, and there are grounds for supposing that the female bird begins to sit as soon as she has laid her first egg.

THE SHORT-EARED OWL ASIO FLAMMEUS (*Plate XXXVII*)

Face whitish ; beak black ; iris yellow ; egrets inconspicuous, of a few black feathers ; eyes encircled by brownish black ; upper plumage dusky brown, edged with yellow ; lower pale orange, streaked with brown. Length sixteen inches ; breadth thirty-eight. Eggs white. A winter visitor to all parts of the British Isles ; also a resident, breeding in most parts of Scotland and in some districts of England.

FROM the name, Hawk-Owl, sometimes given to this species, we should expect to find this bird not so decidedly nocturnal in its habits as the preceding ; and such is the case ; for, though it does not habitually hunt by day, it has been known to catch up chickens from the farmyard, and has been seen in chase of pigeons. If attacked during daylight, it does not evince the powerless dismay of the last species, but effects a masterly retreat by soaring in a spiral direction until it has attained an elevation to which its adversary does not care to follow it. Unlike its allies, it frequents neither mountains nor forests, but is found breeding in a few marshy or moorland districts ; later in the year it is met with in turnip-fields and stubbles. As many as twenty-eight were once seen in a single turnip-field in England ; from whence it has been inferred that in autumn the Short-eared Owls are gregarious, and establish themselves for a time in any place they fall in with, where field-mice or other small quadrupeds are abundant. In England this

[1] Vol. ii. p. 652.

bird is not uncommonly started by sportsmen when in pursuit of game. It then flies with a quick zigzag motion for about a hundred yards, and alights on the ground, never on a tree. By some, it is called the Woodcock-Owl, from its arriving and departing at about the same time with that bird ; it is not, however, invariably a bird of passage, since many instances are on record of its breeding in this country, making a rude nest in a thick bush, either on the ground, or close to it, and feeding its young on mice, small birds, and even the larger game, as Moor-fowl, a bird more than double its own weight. The Short-eared Owl affords a beautiful illustration of a fact not generally known, that the nocturnal birds of prey have the right and left ear differently formed, one ear being so made as to hear sounds from above, and the other from below. The opening into the channel for conveying sound is, in the *right* ear, placed *beneath* the transverse fold, and directed *upwards*, while in the *left* ear the same opening is placed *above* the channel for conveying sound, and is directed *downwards*.

In the severe weather of January, 1861, I had the gratification of seeing three or four of these Owls among the sand-hills of the coast of Norfolk, near Holkham. I imagined them to be in pursuit of the Redwings and other small birds which had been driven by the intense cold to the sea-coast, since they flew about as Hawks do when hunting for prey, and occasionally alighted among the sandhills. I even fell in with several heaps of feathers, showing where some unhappy bird had been picked and eaten. A few days afterwards, however, I inquired at another part of the coast whether there were any Owls there, and received for an answer, ' No, because there are no rabbits ' ; from which I inferred that these birds have the reputation of hunting larger game than Thrushes, a charge which the size and power of their hooked talons seems to justify.

THE TAWNY OWL STRIX ALÚCO (*Plate XXXVII*)

Beak greyish yellow ; irides bluish dusky ; upper parts reddish brown, variously marked and spotted with dark brown, black, and grey ; large white spots on the scapulars and wing coverts ; primaries and tail feathers barred alternatively with dark and reddish brown ; lower parts reddish white, with transverse brown bars and longitudinal dusky streaks ; legs feathered to the claws. Length sixteen inches ; breadth three feet. Eggs dull white. A resident in wooded districts of England and Wales and the mainland of Scotland.

THIS bird, the Ulula of the ancients, took its name from the Latin *ululare* ; the word used to denote, and partially to imitate, the cry of the wolf ; it enjoys also the doubtful honour of giving name to the whole tribe of ' Owls ', whether they howl, hoot, or screech. This species is much more common than the Barn Owl in many districts, although it is decreasing in others. Owing to its nocturnal habits, and dusky colour, it is not so often seen as heard. It has many a time been my amusement to repair, towards the close of a summer evening, to a wood which I knew to be the resort of these birds, and to challenge them to an exchange of greetings, and I rarely failed to succeed. Their note may be imitated so exactly as to deceive even the birds themselves, by forming a hollow with the fingers and palms of the two hands, leaving an opening only between the second joints of the two thumbs, and then by blowing with considerable force down upon the opening thus made, so as to produce the sound hoo-hoo-hoo-o-o-o. I have thus induced a bird to follow me for some distance, echoing my defiance or greeting, or whatever he may have deemed it ; but I do not recollect that I ever caught sight of the bird.

Squirrels, rats, mice, moles, shrews, and any small birds that he can surprise asleep, with insects, form his principal food. These he hunts by night, and retires for concealment by day to some thick tree or shrubbery, either in the hill country or the plains. The nest, composed principally of the dried pellets of undigested bones and fur, which all the Owls are in the habit of disgorging, is usually placed in a hollow tree : here the female lays about four eggs, from which emerge, in due time, as many grotesque bodies enveloped in a soft plush of grey yarn ; destined, in due time, to become Tawny Owls. The full-grown females are larger than the males, and, being of a redder tinge, were formerly considered a distinct species. The old birds utter their loud *hoo-hou !* or *to-whit, tu-who !* chiefly in the evening.

THE LITTLE OWL ATHENE NOCTUA (*Plate LXVIII*)

Upper plumage greyish brown, spotted with white ; under, yellowish white with longitudinal brown marks, a broad dull white band across the throat ; beak brownish white ; irides very small, yellow ; tarsi feathered, toes sprinkled with a few white hairs. Length nine inches. Eggs white. A naturalized resident, breeding almost throughout England and Wales.

THIS small species is less nocturnal than most of its allies and may frequently be observed in the daytime perched on a telegraph post or fence-post by the roadside. It frequents by preference more or less open country, breeding in holes in hedgerow trees, pollard willows, buildings or cliffs, and hunts chiefly at dusk and dawn. Almost all its food is captured on the ground and consists principally of large beetles and other insects, earthworms and small rodents.

ORDER CAPRIMULGIFORMES

FAMILY CAPRIMULGIDÆ

THE NIGHTJAR CAPRIMÚLGUS EUROPÆUS (*Plate XIX*)

General plumage ash-grey, spotted and barred with black, brown, and reddish brown ; first three primaries with a large white patch, on the inner web ; two outer tail-feathers on each side tipped with white. Length ten inches and a

*quarter ; breadth twenty-two inches.   Eggs whitish, beautifully marbled with
brown and ash.   A summer visitor breeding throughout the British Isles, except
the Outer Hebrides, Orkneys, and Shetlands.*

THIS bird used to be described as a nocturnal robber who finds his
way into the goat-pens, sucks the dugs of the goats, poisoning them
to such an extent that the animals themselves are blinded, and their
udders waste away.   This fable we notice in order to account for the
strange name Goatsucker, by which it was formerly so well known.
The bird has, indeed, strangely enough, been known all over Europe
by an equivalent for this name from the earliest times.   The bird itself
is perfectly inoffensive, singular in form and habits, though rarely seen
alive near enough for its peculiarities of form and colour to be observed.
Its note, however, is familiar enough to persons who are in the habit
of being out late at night in such parts of the country as it frequents.
The silence of the evening or midnight walk in June is occasionally
broken by a deep *churr-churr-err* which seemingly proceeds from the
lower bough of a tree, a hedge, or paling.   And a whirring of the
wings comes often from their being brought in contact as the birds twist
in insect-hunting.[1]   The churring is nearly monotonous but not quite
so, as it occasionally rises or falls about a quarter of a note, and appears
to increase and diminish in loudness.   Nor does it seem to proceed
continuously from exactly the same spot, but to vary its position, as
if the performer were either a ventriloquist or were actually shifting
his ground.   The bird perches with its feet resting lengthwise on a
branch, its claws not being adapted for grasping, and turns its head
from side to side, thus throwing the sound as it were in various directions, and producing the same effect as if it proceeded from different
places.   I have repeatedly worked my way close up to the bird, but
as I labour under the disadvantage of being short-sighted, and derive
little assistance from glasses at night, I have always failed to observe
it actually perched and singing.   In the summer of 1859 a Nightjar
frequented the immediate neighbourhood of my own house, and I
had many opportunities of listening to its note.   One evening especially
it perched on a railing within fifty yards of the house, and I made sure
of seeing it, but when I had approached within a few yards of the
spot from whence the sound proceeded the humming suddenly stopped,
but was presently again audible at the other end of the railing which
ran across my meadow.   I cautiously crept on, but with no better
success than before.   As I drew near, the bird quitted its perch,
flew round me, coming within a few feet of my person, and, on my
remaining still, made itself heard from another part of the railing
only a few yards behind me.   Again and again I dodged it, but always
with the same result ; I saw it, indeed, several times, but always on
the wing.   At last a longer interval of silence ensued, and when I
heard the sound again it proceeded from a distant hedge which
separated the meadow from a common.   Here probably its mate was
performing the domestic duty of incubation cheered by the dismal

[1] Mr. Bell informs me that it is so like the croak of the Natter-Jack Toad, that
he has more than once doubted from which of the two the sound proceeded.

ditty of her partner ; but I never saw her, though I undertook another nocturnal chase of the musician, hunting him from tree to tree, but never being able to discover his exact position, until the cessation of the sound and the sudden rustling of leaves announced the fact of his having taken his departure.

In the dusk of the evening the Nightjar may commonly be seen hawking for moths and beetles after the manner of the Swallow tribe, only that the flight is less rapid and more tortuous. I once saw one on the common mentioned above, hawking seemingly in company with Swifts and Swallows during the bright glare of a summer afternoon ; but most frequently it spends the day either resting on the ground among heath or ferns or on the branch of a tree, always (according to Yarrell and others) crouching close down upon it, in the line of the limb, and not across it. When perched on the ground it lies very close, ' not rising (a French author says) until the dogs are almost on it, but worth shooting in September '. The poet Wordsworth, whose opportunities of watching the Nightjar in its haunts must have been numerous, knew that the whirring note is an accompaniment of the chase :

> The busy Dor-Hawk chases the white moth
> With burring note——

> The burring Dor-Hawk round and round is wheeling :
> That solitary bird
> Is all that can be heard
> In silence, deeper far than deepest noon.

One point in the economy of the Nightjar is still disputed, the use which it makes of its serrated middle claw. White, and another observer, quoted by Yarrell, have seen the bird while on the wing capture insects with the claw and transfer them to the mouth. Wilson, on the other hand, states that the use of this singular structure is to enable the bird to rid itself of vermin, to which it is much exposed by its habit of remaining at rest during the heat of the day. As he has actually observed a bird in captivity thus employing its claw, it would follow that the same organ is used for a twofold purpose.

The Nightjar is a migratory bird and the last to arrive in this country, appearing not before the middle of May. It is found more or less sparingly in all parts of England, especially those which abound most in woods interspersed with heaths and brakes. In the wooded valleys of Devonshire it is of frequent occurrence, and here it has been known to remain so late in the season as November, whereas from most other localities it migrates southwards about the middle or end of September. It builds no nest, but lays its singularly beautiful eggs, two in number, on the ground among the dry herbage of the common.

Other names by which it is locally known are Fern Owl, Wheeler, and Nightchurr.

ORDER APODIFORMES

FAMILY APODIDÆ

THE SWIFT Ápus Ápus (*Plate XLI*)

General plumage sooty brown ; chin greyish white ; tarsi feathered ; bill, feet, and claws, shining black. Length eight inches ; width seventeen inches. Eggs pure white. A summer visitor, breeding throughout the British Isles, except north-western Scotland, the Hebrides, Orkneys, and Shetlands.

THE Swift is, perhaps, the strongest and swiftest of all birds ; hence a voyage from southern Africa to England is performed without over-taxing its strength. It stands in need of no rest after this prodigious flight, but immediately on its arrival starts with a right good will on its pursuit of food, as if its journey had been but a pleasant course of training for its daily vocation. With respect to temperature, however, its powers of endurance are limited ; it never proceeds far northwards, and occasionally even suffers from unseasonably severe weather in the temperate climates where it fixes its summer residence. Mr. F. Smith, of the British Museum, related in the *Zoologist*,[1] that, at Deal, on the eighth of July, 1856, after a mild but wet day, the temperature suddenly fell till it became disagreeably cold. The Swifts were sensibly affected by the atmospheric change ; they flew unsteadily, fluttered against the walls of the houses, and some even flew into open windows. ' Whilst observing these occurrences,' he says, ' a girl came to the door to ask me if I wanted to buy a bat ; she had heard, she told me, that I bought all kinds of bugs, and her mother thought I might want a bat. On her producing it, I was astonished to find it was a poor benumbed Swift. The girl told me they were dropping down in the streets, and the boys were killing all the bats ; the church, she said, was covered with them. Off I started to witness this strange sight and slaughter. True enough ; the children were charging them everywhere, and on arriving at the church in Lower Street I was astonished to see the poor birds hanging in clusters from the eaves and cornices ; some clusters were at least two feet in length, and, at intervals, benumbed individuals dropped from the outside of the clusters. Many hundreds of the poor birds fell victims to the ruthless ignorance of the children.' Being so susceptible of cold, the Swift does not visit us until summer may be considered to have completely set in. In the south it is generally seen towards the end of April, but it generally brings up the rear of the migratory birds by making its first appearance in the first or second week in May, in the north.

Early in August it makes itself, for a few days, more than ever conspicuous by its wheeling flights around the buildings which contain

[1] September, 1856, p. 5249.

its nest, and then suddenly disappears. At this period, too, its note is more frequently heard than during any other part of its visit, and in this respect it is peculiar. As a general rule, birds cease their song partially, if not entirely, when their eggs are hatched. The new care of providing for the wants of a brood occupies their time too much to allow leisure for musical performance, so that with the exception of their call-notes, and their cries of alarm or defiance, they are for a season mute. An early riser, and late in retiring to roost, the Swift is always on the wing. Thus, whether hunting on his own account or on behalf of his mate and nestlings, his employment is unvaried, and the same amount of time is always at his disposal for exercising his vocal powers. These are not great ; he has no roundelay ; he neither warbles nor carols ; he does not even twitter. His whole melody is a scream, unmusical but most joyous ; a squeak would be a better name, but that, instead of conveying a notion that it results from pain, it is full of rollicking delight. Some compare it to the noise made by the sharpening of a saw ; to me it seems such an expression of pent-up joy as little children would make if unexpectedly released from school, furnished with wings, and flung up into the air for a game of hide-and-seek among the clouds. Such soarings aloft, such chasings round the pinnacles of the church-tower and the gables of the farm-houses, no wonder that they cannot contain themselves for joy. Every day brings its picnic or village feast, with no weariness or depression on the morrow.

The nest of the Swift is constructed of any scraps that the bird may chance to find floating in the air, or brought to it by the wind, for it literally never perches on the ground, whence it rises with difficulty. These are rudely pressed together in any convenient aperture or moulding in a building, and cemented together by some glutinous secretion from the bird's mouth. Two eggs are laid, and the young, as a matter of necessity, remain in the nest until quite fledged.

Another name for the Swift is Black Martin, and in heraldry it is familiarly known as the Martlet, the figure of which is a device of frequent occurrence in heraldic coats of arms, and denotes that the original wearer of the distinction served as a crusader pilgrim. In Arabia it is still known by the name of Hadji, or Pilgrim, to denote its migratory habits.

ORDER CORACIIFORMES

FAMILY ALCEDINIDÆ

THE KINGFISHER ALCEDO ATTHIS (*Plate XXXVIII*)

Back azure-blue ; head and wing-coverts bluish green, spotted with azure-blue ; under and behind the eye a reddish band passing into white, and beneath this a band of azure-green ; wings and tail greenish blue ; throat white ; under plumage rusty orange-red. Length seven inches and a quarter ; width ten inches. Eggs glossy white, nearly round. A resident in England, Wales, Ireland, and southern Scotland.

HALCYON days, every one knows, are days of peace and tranquillity, when all goes smoothly, and nothing occurs to ruffle the equanimity of the most irascible member of a household ; but it may not be known to all my younger readers that a bird is said to be in any way concerned in bringing about this happy state of things. According to the ancient naturalists the Halcyon, our Kingfisher, being especially fond of the water and its products, chooses to have even a floating nest. Now the surface of the sea is an unfit place whereon to construct a vessel of any kind, so the Halcyon, as any other skilful artisan would, puts together on land first the framework, and then the supplementary portion of its nest, the materials being shelly matter and spines, whence derived is unknown ; but the principal substance employed is fish-bones. During the progress of the work the careful bird several times tests its buoyancy by actual experiment, and when satisfied that all is safe, launches its future nursery on the ocean. However turbulent might have been the condition of the water previously to this event, thenceforth a calm ensued, which lasted during the period of incuba-tion ; and these were ' Halcyon days ' (*Halcyonides dies*), which set in seven days before the winter solstice, and lasted as many days after. What became of the young after the lapse of this period is not stated, but the deserted nest itself, called halcyoneum, identical, perhaps, with what we consider the shell of the echinus, or sea-urchin, was deemed a valuable medicine.[1]

The real nest of the Kingfisher is a collection of small fish-bones, which have evidently been disgorged by the old birds. A portion of one which I have in my possession, and which was taken about twenty years since from a deep hole in an embankment at Deepdale, Norfolk, consists exclusively of small fish-bones and scraps of the shells of shrimps. A precisely similar one is preserved in the British Museum, which is well worthy the inspection of the curious. It was found by Mr. Gould in a hole three feet deep on the banks of the Thames ; it was half an inch thick and about the size of a tea saucer, and weighed 700 grains. Mr. Gould was enabled to prove that this mass was deposited, as well as eight eggs laid, in the short space of twenty-one days. In neither case was there any attempt made by the bird to employ the bones as materials for a structure ; they were simply spread on the soil in such a way as to protect the eggs from damp, possessing probably no properties which made them superior to bents or dry leaves, but serving the purpose as well as anything else, and being more readily available, by a bird that does not peck on the ground, than materials of any other kind.

The wanderer by the river's side on a bright sunny day, at any season, may have his attention suddenly arrested by the sight of a bird shooting past him, either up or down the stream, at so slight an

[1] Plin. *Nat. Hist.* lib. x. cap. 32 ; xxxii. cap. 8.

elevation above the water that he can look down on its back. Its flight is rapid, and the colour of the plumage so brilliant, that he can compare it to nothing less dazzlingly bright than the richest feathers of the peacock, or a newly dug specimen of copper ore. After an interval of a few seconds it will perhaps be followed by a second, its mate, arrayed in attire equally gorgeous with emerald, azure, and gold. Following the course of the bird, let him approach cautiously any pools where small fish are likely to abound, and he may chance to descry, perched motionless on the lower branch of an alder overhanging the stream, on some bending willow, or lichen-covered rail, the bird which but now glanced by him like a meteor. If exposed to the rays of the sun, the metallic green of its upper plumage is still most conspicuous ; if in the shade, or surrounded by leaves, its chestnut-red breast betrays its position. Not a step farther in advance, or the fisherman, intent as he is on his sport, will take alarm and be off to another station. With beak pointed downwards it is watching until one among a shoal of minnows or bleaks comes within a fair aim ; then with a twinkle of the wing it dashes head foremost from its post, plunges into the stream, disappears for a second, and emerges still head foremost with its struggling booty. A few pinches with its powerful beak, or a blow against its perch, deprives its prey of life, and the morsel is swallowed entire, head foremost. Occasionally, where convenient perches are rare, as is the case with the little pools left by the tide on the seashore (for the Kingfisher is common on the banks of tidal rivers as well as on inland streams and lakes), it hovers like a Kestrel, and plunges after small fish, shrimps, and marine insects. It once happened to me that I was angling by a river's side, quite concealed from view by a willow on either side of me, when a Kingfisher flew down the stream, and perched on my rod. I remained perfectly still, but was detected before an opportunity had been afforded me of taking a lesson from my brother sportsman.

The Kingfisher is a permanent resident in this country, and may be observed, at any season, wherever there is a river, canal, or lake, those streams being preferred the banks of which are lined with trees or bushes. Like most other birds of brilliant plumage, it is no vocalist ; its only note being a wild piping cry, which it utters while on the wing. Happily the Kingfishers are again on the increase in our country.

FAMILY MEROPIDÆ

THE BEE-EATER MÉROPS APIÁSTER (*Plate XXXVIII*)

Forehead white, passing into bluish green ; upper plumage chestnut ; throa, golden yellow, bounded by a black line ; wings variegated with blue, brownt and green ; tail greenish blue. Length eleven inches. Eggs glossy white A very rare visitor to the British Isles in summer, chiefly to the eastern and southern counties of England. In 1920 a pair attempted to nest near Edinburgh.

THIS bird, which in brilliancy of plumage vies with the Humming-birds, possesses little claim to be ranked among soberly clad British birds. Stray instances are indeed met with from time to time, but at distant intervals. In the islands of the Mediterranean, and in the southern countries of Europe, they are common summer visitors, and in Asia Minor and the south of Russia they are yet more frequent. They are gregarious in habits, having been observed, both in Europe, their summer, and in Africa, their winter residence, to perch together on the branches of trees in small flocks. They also build their nests near each other. These are excavations in the banks of rivers, variously stated to be extended to the depth of from six inches to as many feet. Their flight is graceful and light, resembling that of the Swallows. Their food consists of winged insects, especially bees and wasps, which they not only catch when they are wandering at large through the air, but watch for near their nests. The inhabitants of Crete and Cyprus are said to catch them by the help of a light silk line, to which is attached by a fish-hook a wild bee. The latter in its endeavour to escape soars into the air, and the Bee-eater seizing it becomes the prey of the aerial fisherman.

FAMILY CORACIIDÆ

THE ROLLER CORÁCIAS GÁRRULUS (*Plate XXXVIII*)

Head, neck, and under parts, tinged with various shades of light blue, varied with green ; back and scapulars reddish brown ; tail blue, green, and black. Length twelve inches and a half. Eggs smooth shining white. A very rare visitor to the British Isles in summer.

THE winter home of the Roller is Africa. About the middle of April it crosses the Mediterranean, and seems to prefer the east of Europe to the west as a summer residence, being more abundant in Germany and the south of Russia than in France, though many proceed no further than Sicily and Greece. Its food consists mainly of beetles and other insects. The name Roller, being derived directly from the French *Rollier*, should be pronounced so as to rhyme with ' dollar '.

FAMILY UPUPIDÆ

THE HOOPOE UPUPA EPOPS (*Plate XXXVIII*)

Crest orange-red, tipped with black ; head, neck, and breast, pale cinnamon ; back, wings, and tail, barred with black and white ; under parts white. Length twelve inches ; width nineteen inches. Eggs lavender-grey, changing to greenish olive. A rare passage migrant in the British Isles, chiefly in spring and in the southern and eastern counties of England, which has occasionally nested in the south of England.

LITTLE appears to be known of the habits of this very foreign-looking bird from observation in Great Britain. The season at which it is seen in this country is usually spring, though a few instances have occurred of its having bred with us. In the south of Europe and north of Africa it is of common occurrence as a summer visitor, but migrates southwards in autumn. Its English name is evidently derived from the French *Huppe*, a word which also denotes ' a crest ', the most striking characteristic of the bird. It is called also in France *Puput*, a word coined, perhaps, to denote the noise of disgust which one naturally makes at encountering an unpleasant odour, this, it is said, being the constant accompaniment of its nest, which is always found in a filthy condition, owing to the neglect of the parent birds in failing to remove offensive matter, in conformity with the laudable practice of most other birds. It lives principally on the ground, feeding on beetles and ants. On trees it sometimes perches but does not climb, and builds its nest in holes in trees and walls, rarely in clefts of rocks. It walks with a show of dignity when on the ground, erecting its crest from time to time. In spring the male utters a note not unlike the coo of a Wood Pigeon, which it repeats several times, and from which its English and Latin names and the French names mentioned above are no doubt derived. But it is no musician and is as little anxious to be heard as seen. The nest is a simple structure composed of a few scraps of dried grass and feathers, and contains from four to six eggs.

ORDER PICIFORMES

FAMILY PICIDÆ

THE GREEN WOODPECKER PICUS VIRIDIS (*Plate XXXIX*)

Upper plumage green ; under, greenish ash ; crown, back of the head, and moustaches, crimson ; face black. Female—*less crimson on the head ; moustaches black. Length thirteen inches ; breadth twenty-one inches. Eggs glossy white. A resident in England and Wales, and a very rare straggler to Scotland.*

ONE of the most interesting among the natural sounds of the country, is that of the

Woodpecker tapping the hollow beech tree:

yet one may walk through the woods many times and hear no tapping at all, and even if such a sound be detected and traced to its origin, it will more often be found to proceed from the Nuthatch, who has wedged a hazel-nut into the bark of an oak, than from the hammering of a Woodpecker. Yet often indeed it may be observed ascending, by a series of starts, the trunk of a tree, inclining now a little to the right, and now to the left, disappearing now and then on the side farthest from the spectator, and again coming into view somewhat higher up. Nor is its beak idle ; this is employed sometimes in dislodging the insects which lurk in the rugged bark, and sometimes in tapping the trunk in order to find out whether the wood beneath is sound or otherwise. Just as a carpenter sounds a wall with his hammer in order to discover where the brickwork ends and where lath and plaster begin, so the Woodpecker sounds the wooden pillar to which it is clinging, in order to discover where the wood is impenetrable alike by insects and itself, and where the former have been beforehand with it in seeking food or shelter. Such a canker-spot found, it halts in its course, tears off piecemeal a portion of bark and excavates the rotten wood beneath, either as far as the fault extends or as long as it can find food. It is, then, by no means a mischievous bird, but the reverse ; as it not only destroys a number of noxious insects, but points out to the woodman, if he would only observe aright, which trees are beginning to decay and consequently require his immediate attention. This aspect of the Woodpecker's operations is the right one and not the old idea that ' it is a great enemy of old trees in consequence of the holes which it digs in their trunks ', as some old writer states.

But with all his digging and tapping, the sound by which the vicinity of a Green Woodpecker is most frequently detected, especially in spring and summer, is the unmistakable laughing note which has gained for him the name of ' Yaffle '. No more perhaps than the mournful cooing of the dove does this indicate merriment ; it is harsh, too, in tone ; yet it rings through the woods with such jovial earnestness that it is always welcome. On such occasions the bird is not generally, I think, feeding, for if the neighbourhood from which the sound proceeded be closely watched, the Yaffle may frequently be observed to fly away, with a somewhat heavy dipping flight, to another tree or grove, and thence, after another laugh, to proceed to a second. It is indeed oftener to be seen on the wing than hunting for food on the trunks of trees. Very frequently too it may be observed on the ground, especially in a meadow or common in which ants abound.

The admirable adaptation of the structure of the Woodpecker to its mode of life is well pointed out by Yarrell. Its sharp, hooked toes, pointing two each way, are eminently fitted for climbing and clinging. The keel of the breast-bone is remarkably shallow ; hence, when ascending (its invariable mode of progress) a tree, it is enabled to bring its body close to the trunk without straining the muscles of the legs. Its tail is short, and composed of unusually stiff feathers, which in the process of climbing are pressed inwards against the tree, and contribute greatly to its support. The beak is strong and of considerable length, and thus fitted either for digging into an ant-hill or sounding the cavities of a tree ; and the tongue, which is unusually

long, is furnished with a curious but simple apparatus, by which
it is extended so that it can be thrust into a hole far beyond the point
of the bill, while its tip is barbed with small filaments, which, like
the teeth of a rake, serve to pull up the larva or insect into its mouth.
The Woodpecker builds no nest, but lays five or six glossy white eggs on
the fragments of the decayed wood in which it has excavated its hole.

Other names by which this bird is known are Popinjay, Woodspite,
Rain-bird, Hew-hole, and Woodwele.

THE GREATER SPOTTED WOODPECKER DRYOBATES MAJOR
(Plate XXXIX)

*Crown and upper plumage black ; a crimson patch on the back of the head ;
a white spot on each side of the neck ; scapulars, lesser wing-coverts, and
under plumage, white ; abdomen and under tail-coverts crimson ; iris red.
Female—without the crimson on the head. Length nine inches and a half ;
breadth fourteen inches. Eggs glossy white. A resident in England and
Wales and the mainland of Scotland ; also a scarce winter visitor throughout
the British Isles.*

IN habits this bird closely resembles the Green Woodpecker. It
is of less common occurrence, but by no means rare, especially in the
wooded districts of the southern and midland counties. A writer
in the *Zoologist* [1] is of opinion that it shows a decided partiality
to fallen timber. ' In 1849 ', he says, ' a considerable number of
trees were cut down in an open part of the country near Melbourne,
which were eventually drawn together and piled in lots. These lay
for some time, and were visited almost daily by Great Spotted Woodpeckers. Their habits and manners were very amusing, especially
whilst searching for food. They alighted on the timber, placed the
body in a particular position, generally with the head downward '
[differing in this respect from the Green Woodpecker], ' and commenced pecking away at the bark. Piece by piece it fell under their
bills, as chips from the axe of a woodman. Upon examining the
bark, I found that the pieces were chipped away in order that the
bird might arrive at a small white grub which lay snugly embedded
in the bark ; and the adroitness of the bird in finding out those
portions of it which contained the greatest number of grubs, was
certainly very extraordinary. Where the birds were most at work
on a particular tree, I shelled off the bark and found nearly thirty
grubs in nine square inches ; but on shelling off another portion
from the same tree, which remained untouched, no grub was visible.
Yet how the bird could ascertain precisely where his food lay was
singular, as in both cases the surface of the bark appeared the same
and bore no traces of having been perforated by insects. During
the day one bird chipped off a piece thirty inches long and twenty
wide—a considerable day's work for so small a workman.' Another
observer states that this bird rarely descends to the ground, and affects
the upper branches of trees in preference to the lower. Its note is

[1] Vol. viii, p. 3115.

an abrupt 'tchick-tchick'. Both species are charged with resorting to gardens and orchards during the fruit season, not in quest of insect food; but no instance of this has come under my own notice. It is said, too, that they eat nuts. This statement is most probably correct. I myself doubt whether there are many birds of any sort which can resist a walnut; and I would recommend any one who is hospitably disposed towards the birds which frequent his garden, to strew the ground with fragments of these nuts. To birds who are exclusively vegetarians, if indeed there be any such indigenous to Britain, they are a natural article of diet, and as from their oily nature they approximate to animal matter, they are most acceptable to insectivorous birds. They have an advantage over almost every other kind of food thus exposed, that they are not liable to be appropriated as scraps of meat and bread are, by prowling cats and dogs. A walnut, suspended from the bough of a tree by a string, will soon attract the notice of some inquisitive Tit, and, when once detected, will not fail to receive the visits of all birds of the same family which frequent the neighbourhood. A more amusing pendulum can scarcely be devised. To ensure the success of the experiment, a small portion of the shell should be removed.

THE LESSER SPOTTED WOODPECKER DRYOBATES MINOR
(*Plate XXXIX*)

Forehead and lower parts dirty white; crown bright red; nape, back, and wings, black, with white bars; tail black, the outer feathers tipped with white and barred with black; iris red. Length five inches and a half; breadth twelve inches. Eggs glossy white. A resident in England and Wales north to Cheshire and Yorkshire.

THIS handsome little bird resembles its congeners so closely, both in structure and habits, that it scarcely needs a lengthened description. Owing to its fondness for high trees and its small size it often escapes notice. It lays its eggs on the rotten wood, which it has either pecked, or which has fallen, from the holes in trees; they are not to be distinguished from those of the Wryneck.

THE WRYNECK JYNX TORQUILLA (*Plate XXXIX*)

Upper plumage reddish grey, irregularly spotted and lined with brown and black; a broad black and brown band from the back of the head to the back; throat and breast yellowish red, with dusky transverse rays; rest of the under plumage whitish, with arrow-shaped black spots; outer web of the quills marked with rectangular alternate black and yellowish red spots; tail-feathers barred with black zigzag bands; beak and feet olive-brown. Length six inches and a half; breadth eleven inches. Eggs glossy white. A summer visitor to England and Wales, breeding regularly in south-eastern England, but only occasionally elsewhere.

THE note of the Wryneck is so peculiar that it can be confounded with none of the natural sounds of the country; a loud, rapid, harsh

cry of *pay-pay-pay* from a bird about the size of a lark may be referred
without hesitation to the Wryneck. Yet it is a pleasant sound after
all—' the merry pee-bird ' a poet calls it—and the untuneful minstrel
is the same bird which is known by the name of ' Cuckoo's Mate ',
and so is associated with May-days, pleasant jaunts into the country,
hayfields, the memory of past happy days and the hope of others
to come. This name it derives not from any fondness it exhibits
for the society of the cuckoo, as it is a bird of remarkably solitary
habits, but because it arrives generally a few days before the cuckoo.
Not less singular than its note is its plumage, which, though unmarked
by gaudiness of colouring, is very beautiful, being richly embroidered
as it were with brown and black on a reddish grey ground. In habits,
it bears no marked resemblance to the Woodpeckers ; it is not much
given to climbing and never taps the trunks of trees ; yet it does
seek its food on decayed trees, and employs its long horny tongue
in securing insects. It darts its tongue with inconceivable rapidity
into an ant-hill and brings it out as rapidly, with the insects and their
eggs adhering to its viscid point. These constitute its principal food,
so that it is seen more frequently feeding on the ground than hunting
on trees. But by far the strangest peculiarity of the Wryneck, stranger
than its note and even than its worm-like tongue, is the wondrous
pliancy of its neck, which one might almost imagine to be furnished
with a ball and socket joint. A country boy who had caught one of
these birds on its nest brought it to me on a speculation. As he held
it in his hand, I raised my finger towards it as if about to touch its
beak. The bird watched most eagerly the movement of my finger,
with no semblance of fear, but rather with an apparent intention of
resenting the offer of any injury. I moved my finger to the left ; its
beak followed the direction—the finger was now over its back, still the
beak pointed to it. In short, as a magnetic needle follows a piece
of steel, so the bird's beak followed my finger until it was again in
front, the structure of the neck being such as to allow the head to
make a complete revolution on its axis, and this without any painful
effort. I purchased the bird and gave it its liberty, satisfied to have
discovered the propriety of the name Torquilla.[1] I may here remark
that the name Jynx [2] is derived from its harsh cry. Besides this,
the proper call-note of the bird, it utters, when disturbed in its nest,
another which resembles a hiss ; whence and partly, perhaps, on
account of the peculiar structure of its neck, it is sometimes called
the Snake-bird. Nest, properly speaking, it has none ; it selects a
hole in a decaying tree and lays its eggs on the rotten wood. Its
powers of calculating seem to be of a very low order. Yarrell records
an instance in which four sets of eggs, amounting to twenty-two,
were successively taken before the nest was deserted ; a harsh experiment, and scarcely to be justified except on the plea that they were
taken by some one who gained his livelihood by selling eggs, or was
reduced to a strait from want of food. A similar instance is recorded
in the *Zoologist*, when the number of eggs taken was also twenty-two.

---

[1] From the Latin *torqueo*, ' to twist '.   [2] Greek *ἴυγξ* from *ἰύζω*, to ' shriek '.

ORDER PASSERIFORMES

FAMILY ALAUDIDÆ

THE SKYLARK ALAUDA ARVENSIS (*Plate XL*)

Upper parts reddish brown, the centre of each feather dark brown ; a faint whitish streak above the eyes ; throat white ; neck and breast whitish, tinged with yellow and red, and streaked with dark brown ; tail moderate. Length seven inches and a quarter. Eggs greyish, thickly speckled with dark grey and brown. A resident, breeding throughout the British Isles ; also a passage migrant and winter visitor.

THE Skylark, a bird whose flight and song are better known perhaps than those of any other bird, needs but a simple biography. The favourite bird of the poets, its story might be told in extracts compiled from various authors whose muse has led them to sing of Nature. Much, however, that has been written is but an amplification of the golden line, ' Hark, the Lark at Heaven's gate sings ! ' and not a little is an exaggerated statement of the height to which it ascends, and the time which it remains suspended in mid-air. But the Skylark needs no panegyrists, so, with all due deference to those who have struck the lyre in its honour, I will endeavour to describe its habits and haunts in humble prose.

The Skylark is a generally diffused bird, adapted by the conformation of its claws for perching on the ground, and by its length and power of wing for soaring high in the air. Accordingly, its food consists of small insects and seeds, which it collects among the herbage of stubble-fields, meadows and downs, or in newly ploughed fields. To this fare, it adds in winter and spring the tender stalks of sprouting corn. Hence it is regarded with deadly hostility by farmers, and hence, too, the quiet of the country used to be much disturbed at these seasons, by boys employed to frighten it away by screaming and plying a peculiar kind of rattle. During autumn and winter, Larks congregate in large flocks, and occupy their time principally in searching for food on the ground. If disturbed, they rise in a scattered manner, wheel about in the air until the flock is formed again, chirping from time to time, and then withdraw, not in a compact body, but at unequal distances from the earth and from each other, to a new feeding-ground, over which they hover with circling flight for some time before alighting. On trees they never perch ; though one or two may occasionally be seen settled on a quickset hedge or a railing. In North Britain, at the approach of severe weather, they flock together and migrate southwards. Great

Herring Gull

Kittiwake   Little Gull, *imm.*

Black-headed Gull

XXXIII

Common Gull

Greater Black-backed Gull

Glaucous Gull

Lesser Black-backed Gull

XXXIV

Puffin	Black Guillemot
Razorbill	Guillemot

XXXV

Turtle Dove

Stock Dove   Rock Dove

Wood Pigeon

XXXVI

Brown or Tawny Owl

Short-eared Owl

Long-eared Owl (young)

Barn Owl and Egg

XXXVII

Kingfisher

Roller

Hoopoe

Bee-eater

XXXVIII

Wryneck   Greater Spotted Woodpecker ♀
Green Woodpecker ♂   Lesser Spotted Woodpecker ♂

XXXIX

Shorelark

Woodlark

Skylark

XL

Swift

Swallow ♂

Sand Martin

House Martin

XLI

Jackdaw

Hooded Crow

Rook

Carrion Crow

XLII

Jay

Raven

Chough

Magpie

XLIII

Blue Tit

Crested Tit

Cole Tit

Marsh Tit

XLIV

Great Tit

Firecrest♂

Long-tailed Tit

Goldcrest ♂

XLV

Tree Creeper

Bearded Tit ♂ ♀

Nuthatch

Wren

XLVI

Missel Thrush   Song Thrush

Fieldfare   Redwing

Blackbird's Nest and Eggs
Blackbird, 14th day

Just Hatched
Day after
4th Day

6th Day
9th Day
11th Day

XLVIII

numbers also visit England from the Continent, arriving in November, when they used to be caught in nets and traps for the table. Early in spring the flocks break up, when the birds pair, and for three or four months, every day and all day long, when the weather is fine (for the Lark dislikes rain and high winds), its song may be heard throughout the breadth of the land. Rising as it were by a sudden impulse from its nest or lowly retreat, it bursts forth, while as yet but a few feet from the ground, into exuberant song, and with its head turned towards the breeze, now ascending perpendicularly, and now veering to the right or left, but not describing circles, it pours forth an unbroken chain of melody, until it has reached an elevation computed to be, at the most, about a thousand feet. To an observer on earth, it has dwindled to the size of a mere speck ; but, as far as my experience goes, it never rises so high as to defy the search of a keen eye. Having reached its highest elevation, its ambition is satisfied without making any permanent stay, and it begins to descend, not with a uniform downward motion, but by a series of droppings with intervals of simple hovering, during which it seems to be resting on its wings. Finally, as it draws near the earth, it ceases its song and descends more rapidly, but before it touches the ground it recovers itself, sweeps away with almost horizontal flight for a short distance and disappears in the herbage. The time consumed in this evolution is at the most from fifteen to twenty minutes, more frequently less ; nor have I ever observed it partially descend and soar upwards again. A writer in the *Magazine of Natural History* maintains that ' those acquainted with the song of the Skylark, can tell, without looking at them, whether the birds be ascending or stationary in the air, or on their descent ; so different is the style of the song in each case '. Mr. Yarrell is of the same opinion, and I have little doubt that they are correct, though I am not certain that I have myself attained the skill of discriminating. In July, the Lark ceases its soarings and song together, but in fine weather, in October, it receives a new inspiration and is musical again. From time to time, during winter, if the season be mild, it resumes its aerial habits, but it neither ascends so high nor sings so long, two or three minutes becoming now the limits of its performance. Like most other birds, it sings least about noon and the first two hours of the afternoon ; but it begins before sunrise, having been heard at midsummer as early as two o'clock in the morning, and it sometimes continues its song till late on into the night, having been heard at ten o'clock when it was quite dark. Occasionally, too, it sings on the ground ; and, in a cage, as all the world knows, it pours out its melody with as much spirit, as if its six inches of turf could be measured by acres, and the roof of its little cage were the vault of heaven. The following stanza in French is equally successful in imitating the song of the Skylark and describing its evolutions :

> La gentille Alouette avec son tirelire,
> Tirelire, relire et tirelirant, tire
> Vers la voûte du ciel ; puis son vol en ce lieu
> Vire, et semble nous dire : Adieu, adieu, adieu.

The Lark builds its nest in a hollow in the ground, the rut of a cart-wheel, the depression formed by a horse's hoof, or in a hole which it scrapes out for itself. The nest is composed of dry grass, and lined with finer fibres. It lays four or five eggs, and rears two broods in the year. It displays great attachment to its young, and has been known, when disturbed by mowers, to build a dome over its nest, as a substitute for the natural shelter afforded by the grass while standing, and to remove its young in its claws to another place of concealment. In a cage, even the male is an excellent nurse. Mr. Weir mentions one which brought up several broods entrusted to its care, and a similar instance has fallen under my own notice. Larks frequently become the prey of the Hobby and Merlin, which pounce on them as they are on the point of leaving the ground, and bear them off with as much ease as they would a feather. But if an intended victim discovers its oppressor in time, it instantly begins to ascend with a rapidity which the other cannot follow, carried on as it is by the impetus of its horizontal flight. The Hawk, foiled for this time, renews the chase and endeavours to soar above its quarry ; if it succeeds, it makes a second swoop, sometimes with deadly effect ; but if it fails a second time, the Lark folds its wings, drops like lead to the ground, and, crouching among the herbage, often escapes detection.

THE WOODLARK LULLULA ARBÓREA (*Plate XL*)

Upper parts reddish brown, the centre of each feather dark brown ; a distinct yellowish white streak above the eye passing to the back part of the head ; lower parts yellowish white, streaked with dark brown ; tail short. Length six inches and a half. Eggs greyish white, speckled and sometimes faintly streaked with brown. A local resident in southern England and Wales ; north of Shropshire, Staffordshire, Nottinghamshire and Lincolnshire now only a rare straggler.

THE Woodlark is much less frequent than the Skylark, and is confined to certain districts. It is distinguished by its smaller size, short tail, a light mark over the eye, and by its habit of perching on trees, where the Skylark is never known to alight. It builds its nest very early in the season, sometimes so soon as the end of March, and probably rears several broods in the year, as it has been found sitting as late as September. It is consequently among the earliest songsters of the year, and among the last to bid adieu to summer. It sings on until the occurrence of severe frosts, and its note is among the sweetest and most touching sounds of nature. The song, though of less compass and less varied than that of the Skylark, is superior in liquidness of tone, and is thought to resemble the syllables ' *lulu* ', by which name the bird is known in France. When soaring it may be distinguished from the Skylark not only by its song, but by its ascending in circles, which it describes, poets tell us, and perhaps correctly, with its nest for a centre. Sometimes, especially during sunshine after a summer shower, it alights on the summit of a lofty tree, to ' unthread its chaplet of musical pearls ', and its simpler *lulu* notes may be heard as it flies from place to place while but a few feet above the surface of the ground. In autumn, Woodlarks assemble in small sociable parties (but not in large flocks), and keep together during the winter. Early in spring these societies are broken up into pairs, and the business of the season commences. The nest is composed of bents and a little moss, and is lined with finer grass, and, though built on the ground, is generally concealed with more art than that of the Skylark, the birds availing themselves of the shelter afforded by a bush or tuft of grass.

THE SHORE LARK EREMOPHILA ALPESTRIS (*Plate XL*)

Throat, forehead, and ear-coverts, yellow ; over the forehead a black band ; lore, moustache, and gorget, black ; upper parts reddish brown ; breast and flanks yellowish white ; abdomen white. Length nearly seven inches. Eggs greyish white, spotted with pale blue and brown. A rare winter visitor to the British Isles, principally to the east and south coasts.

FAMILY HIRUNDINIDÆ

THE SWALLOW HIRUNDO RÚSTICA (*Plate XLI*)

Forehead and throat chestnut-brown ; upper parts, sides of the neck, and a bar across the breast, black, with violet reflections ; lower parts dull reddish white ; tail very long and forked. Female—with less red on the forehead and less black on the breast ; under parts whiter ; outer tail-feathers shorter. Length six inches and a half, width thirteen inches and a quarter. Eggs white, spotted with brown and dark red. A summer visitor, breeding throughout the British Isles, except the Outer Hebrides, Orkneys, and Shetlands, where it only occasionally nests.

THERE are many features in the life of the Swallow so prominent, that no undomesticated bird is more thoroughly known. Like the Sparrow, it accompanies man wherever he fixes his dwelling ; but, unlike the Sparrow, it is liable to be mistaken for no other bird ; its flight is peculiar and all but ceaseless ; at least, it is rarely seen except in motion ; and it is absent during the greater portion of the year, so giving to itself a twofold notoriety, being regretted at the season of its departure and welcomed at its return. These three circumstances, its migratory habits, its mode of flight, and attachment to the dwellings of man, have been the cause why, in all ages, it has been invested with especial interest. Its return is universally greeted as prophetic of summer weather ; the very proverb that ' one Swallow does not make a summer ', only indicates a popular belief ; and its departure is among the first intimations of approaching winter. The Swallow consequently is the type of migratory birds ; if the Swallow is come, all take it for granted that the other summer birds have arrived, and when its twitter is no longer heard, we know that all the other birds of passage are gone or going. Of the Swallow, therefore, it is said pre-eminently, ' God sends us the Swallow in the first days of summer, to relieve us of the insects which the summer suns are calling into life. The home of the Swallow is all the habitable earth ; it knows nothing of winter or winter's cold.' In remote ages the Swallow was considered to be endowed with supernatural intelligence ; it refused to build its nest in a certain town because it was polluted with crime ; in another, because it had been frequently burnt down ; it foretold tempests ; and, above all, it was noted for having taught men the healing properties of a certain herb,[1] by employing it to give sight to its young. Not only was it thus skilled in the healing art, but was in itself a medicine of no ordinary virtue. Even in the time of our countryman Ray, not three hundred years ago, its efficacy in various complaints was seriously believed : the whole body burnt was considered a specific for weak eyes, quinsy, and inflamed uvula ; the heart was prescribed in epilepsy and in quartan ague, it was good also for strengthening the memory ; the blood was good for the eyes, especially if drawn from under the right wing : a little stone sometimes found in the stomach of young birds, called *chelidonius*, tied to the arm, or hung around the neck, was a remedy against children's fits. This was to be searched for before or at the August full moon, in the eldest of a brood. Even the nest had its virtues, being, if applied externally, good for quinsy, redness of the eyes, and the bite of a viper.

A century later ' good old White ' published his account of the Swallow, to which the reader is referred as an admirable model of bird-biography, not only for the age, but as an authentic history full of fresh interest to the reader in all ages. The only point on which White had doubts was whether Swallows all migrate, or whether some of the young do not occasionally stay behind, and hibernate in hollow trees, holes of rocks, and the banks of pools and rivers. Individuals are said occasionally to remain, perhaps in consequence of having been disabled by accident at the season when the migratory instinct was in its active force, or from some other cause unknown to us. Several instances of such have been recorded by authors who, whether accurate observers or not, certainly believed that they were reporting truly. That they were seen only on warm days is of course no evidence that they had been roused from a state of torpor by the unusual warmth. Sunny days in winter tempt people to walk abroad and to resort to the same places which winter-gnats would choose for their gambols. Here, too, the stray Swallow would be found ; but in dark stormy weather the gnats and the Swallow would stay at home, and the ornithologist would have little temptation to do otherwise. I happen to be myself among the number of those who on personal evidence believe that individual Swallows

---

[1] Chelidonium : Celandine or Swallow-wort, from χελιδών, ' a Swallow '.

do remain in England long after the period of general migration. I was walking through a limestone quarry at Saltram on the bank of the Plym, in Devonshire, many years ago, on the twenty-fourth of December, when I saw a Swallow, whether a Chimney-Swallow or Martin I cannot positively affirm, wheeling about, and evidently hawking for gnats near the face of the cliff. The season was a mild one, the air still, and the sun shining brightly against the limestone rocks, from which much heat was reflected. That the bird had been kept in captivity until the migratory season had passed and then released is not probable. On any other supposition it must have remained either of its own free will, which is not likely, or from incapacity to accompany its congeners. Left alone it probably found a sheltered retreat in the face of the cliff, and sallied forth whenever the weather was inviting, making the most of the short days, and, on the finest, contenting itself with a scanty meal. The temperature of the west of England in winter it is quite able to bear ; in fact, it is not uncommon there for a whole winter to pass without any weather so severe as that which has characterized the whole of the present April (1860), though Swallows have returned, and contrive to find food enough to keep themselves alive. If, therefore, the bird which I saw managed to live on till Christmas Eve, there is no reason why it should not survive the whole of the winter. But as ' one Swallow does not make a spring ', so neither is one sufficient to upset a theory. There remains, therefore, the rule with the one exception to prove it, that Swallows do migrate. The Swallow is a migratory bird wherever it is found, that is in most of the countries of Europe, Asia, and Africa. The first Swallows arrive in this country about the eleventh of April, and are followed by others at various intervals, until the middle or end of May. On their arrival, they resort to those places which, being most sheltered, abound most in winged insects, these being frequently the courses of rivers and canals. As the season advances, they spread themselves more generally over the country, still, however, being most numerous in the vicinity of water. In May they build their shallow open nests of mud and straw lined with feathers, a few feet down a chimney, in an outhouse, a bell-tower, the shaft of a deserted mine, or any other place which is at once dry and dark, rarely in more exposed places. They lay four or five eggs, and rear two or three broods in a season. The young being, from the usual situation of the nest, unable to leave their nursery until they are fully fledged, require to be fed a long time, but they continue to be, partially at least, dependent on the parent birds for many days after they have learnt to hawk for themselves. The process of feeding is carried on while both old and young are on the wing ; or the young, perched on the top of a house or the branch of a tree, receive in turn the morsels which their more skilful parents have caught for them. In autumn, many days before migration is actually about to take place, Swallows, old and young, assemble in large flocks, especially towards evening, and roost on trees in the vicinity of water. At this season they seem to be more socially disposed, even during the day, than at any other period of their sojourn with us. In October they take their departure collectively, and so strongly is the migratory instinct then in force that it overcomes parental affection, powerful though this feeling is in the Swallow ; some of the late broods being left behind.

THE HOUSE MARTIN DELICHON ÚRBICA (*Plate XLI*)

Head, nape, and upper part of the back, black with violet reflections ; lower part of the back, and all the under parts, pure white ; feet and toes covered with downy feathers ; tail forked, moderate. Length five inches and a half. Eggs pure white. A summer visitor, breeding throughout the British Isles, except the Outer Hebrides and Shetlands.

THE Swallow and the Martins are so much alike in their leading habits, namely, migration, mode of flight, and food, that a description of either will in many respects be applicable to the other. The House Martin generally arrives a few days after the Swallow, and resorts to similar localities. In the early part of the season the most sheltered places are sought out, and the two species may frequently be seen hawking for flies in company. Later in the season its numbers are observed to be greatly increased, and it is joined by the Swift and Sand Martin. Not that any society is entered into by the different species, or that they even sport together ; but one may often stand on the bank of a canal, or by the margin of a pond, and see all four kinds glance by in varied succession, and in proportions which differ according as one or the other is most abundant in the neighbourhood. Acute listeners can, it is said, hear a snapping noise made by the bird as it closes its beak on a captured insect, but I must confess that though I have often tried to detect this sound, I have never succeeded. Swift as their passage is, and similar though the flight of all the species, no difficulty is found in distinguishing them. The Chimney-Swallow is sufficiently marked by its long forked tail and red chin ; the House Martin by the snow-white hue of its abdomen and lower part of the back, and by its shorter tail, which is also forked ; the Sand Martin by its smaller size, its greyish brown back and dirty-white under plumage, as well as by its shorter, slightly forked tail ; and the Swift can be distinguished at any distance by its shape, which resembles a bent bow, with the body representing an arrow ready to be shot. On a nearer view, the Swift is marked by its general black hue relieved only by a spot of white on the chin, which it requires a sharp eye to detect. All the species have the power of suddenly, and with the greatest rapidity, altering their course by a slight movement of the wings and tail.

Immediately on its arrival in this country, the Martin pays a visit to its old dwelling, clings to its walls, peeps in or even enters many times a day. It has been proved by several experiments, that the same birds return year after year to their old nests, and it is hard to believe, so thoroughly delighted do they seem, that they are guided simply by an impassive instinct. If so, why should they hang about the ' old house at home ' so many days before they begin to set in order again the future nursery ? No elaborate plans of alterations and improvements are to be devised ; last year's family are launched on the world, and are quite equal to building for their own accommodation. No collecting of materials is requisite. The muddy edge of the nearest pond will provide plaster enough and to spare to carry out all necessary repairs ; shreds of straw are to be had for the picking up, and farmyard feathers are as plentiful as of yore. It would seem then a reasonable conclusion, that a bird endowed with an instinct powerful enough to guide it across the ocean, and a memory sufficiently powerful to lead it to the snug window corner of the same cottage where it reared its first brood, may live in the past as well as the present, and that its seeming joyousness is a reality, even mixed perhaps with hopeful anticipations of the future.

As the reader may, if he will, have ample opportunity of watching the habits of a bird that probably builds its nest under the eaves of his own house, whether he dwell in a town, a village, or a lonely cottage, it is unnecessary to enter into further details of its biography.

THE SAND MARTIN RIPÁRIA RIPÁRIA (*Plate XLI*)

All the upper parts, cheeks, and a broad bar on the breast, mouse-colour ; throat, fore part of the neck, abdomen, and under tail-coverts, white ; legs and feet naked, with the exception of a few small feathers near the insertion of the hind toe ; tail forked, rather short. Length five inches. Eggs pure white. A summer visitor, breeding throughout the British Isles except the Shetlands.

WHILE the other British species of Swallow resort from choice to the haunts of man, the Sand or Bank Martin is indifferent about the matter. Provided that it can find a convenient place for excavating its nest, other considerations are omitted. It is said to be partial to the vicinity of water, but even this selection is rather to be attributed to the accidental circumstance that perpendicular cliffs often have rivers running at their base, than to any decided preference shown by the bird for such situations. Railway cuttings carried through a sandy district offer, perhaps, equal attraction ; and it is probable that a majority of the colonies planted within the last twenty years overlook, not the silent highway of the river, but the unromantic parallel bars of iron which have enabled man to vie almost with the Swallow in rapidity of flight.

The word colonies is applicable to few British birds besides the Sand Martin. Others of the tribe not infrequently construct their nests in close proximity with each other, and, when thus associated, are most neighbourly—hunting in society, sporting together, and making common cause against an intrusive Hawk ; but still this is no more than a fortuitous coming together. It so happens that a certain district offers good hunting-ground, and the eaves or windows of a certain house are peculiarly well adapted for sheltering nests ; so a number of Window Martins, not having taken counsel together, but guided each by independent choice, find themselves established sometimes so close together that their nests have party walls, like the houses in a street. They accordingly make acquaintances, and are sociable to a limited extent. But Sand Martins go beyond this, they are comrades banded together by municipal laws, which no doubt they understand and obey, inhabiting dwellings which constitute a joint settlement, returning without fail to the familiar haunt after every annual migration, or if they desert a station, leaving no stragglers behind, and pitching their camp anew in some locality which common consent has pronounced to be an eligible one. They are not, however, exclusive in their fraternization ; as they hunt in society with their relatives the Swallows, and even accompany them in distant flights. I have repeatedly observed Sand Martins flying about with others of the same tribe many miles away from their homes. They may readily be distinguished, as I have stated before, by their dingy mouse-coloured hue, smaller size, and less forked tails. I have never had an opportunity of watching a colony engaged in their mining operations at the busy period of their year, that of nidification ; but from the description by Professor Rennie (*Bird Architecture*) and that by Mr. R. D. Duncan, quoted by Macgillivray, the sight must be most interesting. The task of the older birds must be a light one ; not so, however, that of the younger members of the flock. The former have neither walls nor roofs to repair ; the holes which served them as nests the previous year afford the same accommodation as before. All that is needed is, that the remains of the old nest should either be removed or receive the addition of a few straws and feathers to protect the eggs and young from direct contact with the cold sand ; their labours then are over. But the new colonists have a toilsome work to perform before they can enjoy the gratification of bringing up a family. The settlement is fixed probably in the perpendicular face of a bank of sand, gravel, or clay, at an elevation from the ground which varies from a few to a great many feet. Their claws are sharp and well adapted for clinging, the beak short, rigid, and pointed, no less well suited for excavating. Grasping the perpendicular surface of the bank with their claws, and steadying themselves by means of their tails they commence operations by pricking a small hole with their bills. This hole they gradually enlarge by moving round and round, and edging off the sand with the side of their bills, which they keep shut. Their progress is slow at first, but after they have made room to stand on the excavation, they proceed rapidly, still working with their bills, and carefully pushing out the loosened sand with their feet. At one time the male, at another the female, is the excavator. When their burrowing is impeded by the resistance of a stone, they either dig round it and loosen it, or, if it prove so large as to defy removal, they desist and begin another cell. The form of the hole varies both in size and shape, but it rarely exceeds three or four inches in diameter, and more or less approaches the circular form. The depth varies from a few inches to three feet, and the direction seems to depend on the nature of the soil encountered. In all, however, the extremity of the hole is enlarged to a diameter of five or six inches, and is situated above the level of the entrance, so that no rain-water can lodge. The work is performed only in the mornings, and is consequently carried over several days. The nest itself consists of straws of grass and feathers, and is placed in the terminal chamber. The eggs are five or six in number, pure white, and of a rather long shape.

FAMILY ORIOLIDÆ

THE GOLDEN ORIOLE ORIOLUS ORIOLUS (*Plate LIX*)

Plumage golden yellow ; lore, wings, and tail, black, the tail yellow at the tip,
Female—olive-green above, greyish white tinged with yellow beneath, and streaked with greyish brown ; wings dark brown, the quills edged with olive grey ; tail olive, tinged with dark brown. Length ten inches. Eggs white with a few isolated dark brown or black spots. A rare spring and summer visitor to the British Isles, breeding occasionally in southern England.

THIS brilliant bird, resembling the Thrushes in form, and habits, but apparelled in the plumage of the Tropics, would seem to have no right to a place among British birds, so little is its gorgeous livery in keeping with the sober hues of our other feathered denizens. There can, however, be no doubt of the propriety of placing it among our visitors, though it comes but seldom and makes no long stay. It is a visitor to the southern seaboard counties and often seen in Cornwall and the Scilly Isles. Were it left unmolested, and allowed to breed in our woods, it is probable that it would return with its progeny, and become of comparatively common occurrence ; but though there are on record one or two creditable exceptions, when real naturalists have postponed the glory of shooting and adding to their collection a British specimen, to the pleasure of watching its ways on British soil, yet its biography is not to be written from materials collected in this country. On the European continent it is a regular visitor, though even there it makes no long stay, arriving in the beginning of May and taking its departure early in autumn. It is most common in Spain, southern France, and Italy, but is not infrequent in many other parts of France, in Belgium, and the south of Germany, and Hungary.

'His note', says Cuthbert Collingwood, 'is a very loud whistle, which may be heard at a great distance, but in richness equalling the flute stop of a fine-toned organ. This has caused it to be called *Loriot* in France. But variety there is none in his song, as he never utters more than three notes consecutively, and those at intervals of half a minute or a minute. Were it not for its fine tone, therefore, his song would be as monotonous as that of the Missel Thrush, which in modulation it greatly resembles.'

The nest of the Oriole is described as a marvel of architectural skill, excelling in elegance of form, richness of materials, and delicacy of workmanship combined with strength. It is overlaid externally, like that of the Chaffinch, with the silvery white lichen of fruit trees, which gives it the appearance of being a part of the branch which supports it. But the mansion of the Oriole is more skilfully concealed than that even of the Chaffinch. The latter is placed *on* a branch of which it increases the apparent size, and so attracts attention. The nest of the Oriole, on the contrary, is suspended between the two forks of a horizontal branch, which intercept the side view of it. The materials employed are the lichen above mentioned, wool, cobwebs, and feathers, but all of a white hue. When not placed in a fruit tree, it is attached by a kind of cordage to the twigs of a poplar or birch tree, or even to a bunch of mistletoe, hanging in mid-air like the car of a balloon. A cradle thus sedulously constructed we should expect to find watched with unusual solicitude. And such is the case ; it is defended most valiantly against the attacks of marauding birds, and so devoted is the mother bird that she has been known to suffer herself to be carried away sitting on her eggs, and to die of starvation. Surely a bird so beautiful and so melodious, so skilful an architect and so tender a nurse, deserves rather to be encouraged than exterminated. Nests have been found in several of our counties, more especially in Kent. The plumage of the female bird differs considerably from that of the male in richness of tint, and the young of both sexes resemble the female.

FAMILY CORVIDÆ

THE CHOUGH PYRRHÓCORAX PYRRHÓCORAX (*Plate XLIII*)

Plumage black, with purple and green reflections ; beak and feet coral-red ; claws black. Length sixteen inches ; width thirty-two inches. Eggs yellowish white, spotted with ash-grey and light brown. Resident in south-western England, Wales, the Isle of Man, the Inner Hebrides, and Ireland ; chiefly on the coasts.

CONTINENTAL authors state that the bird which we call the Chough or Red-legged Crow frequents the highest mountain regions and the confines of perpetual snow, and that hence it is sometimes known by the name of 'Jackdaw of the Alps'. Like the rest of its tribe, it is omnivorous, and lives in societies, like the common Jackdaw and Rook, but rarely deserting, and then only when pressed by hunger, the place of its birth. It builds its nest in inaccessible cliffs, and leads the same kind of life with its sable relatives the Crows and Jackdaws. The name Chough was probably in ancient times used as a common appellation of all the members of the family Corvidæ which have black plumage, this one being distinguished as the ' Cornish Chough ', from the rocky district which it frequented. The famous lines in *King Lear*—

> The Crows and Choughs that wing the midway air
> Show scarce so gross as beetles :

point probably to the Jackdaw, which is abundant on the rocky coast of Kent, where the Chough has not been observed, though there is a traditional account of a pair which many years ago escaped from confinement and bred there. By its flight it is scarcely to be distinguished from the Jackdaw ; but if it comes near enough to the observer to betray the vermilion colour of its legs, it may be known at once, and, seen on the ground, its long curved bill, and more slender form, sufficiently distinguish it from all others to which it assimilates in colour and size.

Not many years since, the Chough was far from uncommon in several parts of the coast of Devon and Cornwall. It is now much less frequent, though it still lingers in the latter county. It also haunts the precipitous coast of several other parts of Great Britain, and is found also in many parts of Ireland ; in the Channel Islands, especially in Guernsey, it is fairly common, but always preferring the least frequented localities. The peculiar habits of a bird so uncommon and secluded are little known, so far at least as they are characteristic of the bird in its wild state. In captivity its ways differ little from those of the rest of its tribe. It is inquisitive, intrusive, captious in temper, disposed to become attached to those who treat it well, fond of attracting notice ; in a word, it surpasses in intelligence most other tribes of birds, ranking among those members of the brute creation whose instinct amounts to something more than a formal compliance with certain laws which the rational creation has arbitrarily set down for their government. Insects and the *rejectamenta* of the seashore and occasionally grain form its diet. It builds its nest of sticks, and lines it with wool and hair, preferring a cleft in a rock, but not refusing any old ruin conveniently situated for its purpose. It lays four or five eggs.

THE RAVEN corvus córax (*Plate XLIII*)

Plumage black with purple reflections ; tail rounded, black, extending two inches beyond the closed wings ; beak strong, black as well as the feet ; iris with two circles, the inner grey, the outer ash-brown. Length twenty-five inches ; width four feet. Eggs dirty green, spotted and speckled with brown. Resident in the British Isles, but exterminated in most of the eastern counties of Scotland and in the eastern and midland counties of England.

THE Raven, the largest of the Corvidæ, and possessing in an eminent degree all the characteristics of its tribe except sociability, is the bird which beyond all others has been regarded with feelings of awe by the superstitious in all ages. In both instances in which specific mention of it occurs in Holy Writ, it is singled out from among other birds as gifted with a mysterious intelligence. Sent forth by Noah when the ark rested on the mountains of Ararat, it perhaps found a congenial home among the lonely crags strewed with the carcases of drowned animals, and by failing to return, announced to the patriarch that a portion of the earth, though not one fit for his immediate habitation, was uncovered by the waters. At a subsequent period, honoured with

the mission of supplying the persecuted prophet with food, it was
taught to suppress its voracious instinct by the God who gave it.   The
Raven figures prominently in most heathen mythologies, and is almost
everywhere regarded with awe by the ignorant even at the present time.
In Scandinavian mythology it was an important actor ; and all readers
of Shakespeare must be familiar with passages which prove it to have
been regarded as a bird of dire omen.

> The sad presaging Raven tolls
> The sick man's passport in her hollow beak,
> And in the shadow of the silent night
> Doth shake contagion from her sable wing.
>
> *Marlowe.*

In the judgment of others, its friendly mission to the Tishbite invested
it with a sanctity which preserved it from molestation.

Apart from all traditional belief, the Raven derives its ill-omened
character as a herald of death from the rapidity with which it discerns,
in the vicinity of its haunts, the carcase of any dead animal.   In the
coldest winter days, at Hudson's Bay, when every kind of effluvium
is greatly checked if not arrested by frost, buffaloes and other beasts
have been killed when not one of these birds was to be seen ; but in
a few hours scores of them have been found collected about the spot
to pick up the blood and offal.   ' In Ravens ', says a writer in the
Zoologist, ' the senses of smell and sight are remarkably acute and
powerful.   Perched usually on some tall cliff that commands a wide
survey, these faculties are in constant and rapid exercise, and all the
movements of the bird are regulated in accordance with the information thus procured.   The smell of death is so grateful to them that
they utter a loud croak of satisfaction instantly on perceiving it.   In
passing any sheep, if a tainted smell is perceptible, they cry vehemently.
From this propensity in the Raven to announce his satisfaction in the
smell of death has probably arisen the common notion that he is aware
of its approach among the human race, and foretells it by his croakings.'
The same observant author, as quoted by Macgillivray, says again :
' Their sight and smell are very acute, for when they are searching the
wastes for provision, they hover over them at a great height ; and yet
a sheep will not be dead many minutes before they will find it.   Nay,
if a morbid smell transpire from any in the flock, they will watch it
for days till it die.'

To such repasts they are perhaps guided more by scent than by
sight, for though they not infrequently ascend to a great height in the
air, they do not then appear to be on the look-out for food.   This
duty is performed more conveniently and with greater success by
beating over the ground at a low elevation.   In these expeditions
they do not confine themselves to carrion, but prey indiscriminately
on all animals which they are quick enough to capture and strong
enough to master.   Hares, rabbits, rats, mice, lizards, game of various
kinds, eggs, and the larger insects, all of these enter into their diet, and,
wanting these, they resort to the seashore for refuse fish, or ransack
dunghills in villages, before the inhabitants are astir, for garbage of
all sorts.   Pliny even relates that in a certain district of Asia Minor

they were trained to hawk for game like the noble Falcons. Few of these qualifications tend to endear them to mankind ; and as they are dreaded by shepherds on account of their being perhaps more than suspected of making away with sickly lambs when occasion offers, and of plundering poultry yards, Ravens are become, in populous districts, almost unknown birds. I have only seen them myself on the rocky seashore of Devon and Cornwall, in the wilds of Dartmoor, and the Highlands of Scotland. There was for many successive years a nest built on a ledge of granite near the Bishop Rock, in Cornwall, a huge mass of sticks, and what appeared to be grass, inaccessible from below, but commanded by a venturous climber from above. Where it still continues to breed inland, it places its nest, constructed of sticks and lined with the wool and fur of its victims, either on an inaccessible rock, or near the summit of a lofty tree, the ill-omened ' Raven-tree ' of romances. In the north of Scotland, in the Orkneys and Hebrides, where it is still abundant, it builds its nest in cliffs which it judges to be inaccessible, both inland and on the seashore, showing no marked preference for either. Even the Eagle treats the Raven with respect, and leaves it to its solitude, not so much from fear of its prowess, as worn out by its pertinacious resistance to all dangerous intruders. Hence, in some districts, shepherds encourage Ravens, because they serve as a repellent to Eagles ; while in others, where Eagles are of unusual occurrence, they allow them to build their nests undisturbed, but when the young are almost fledged, destroy them by throwing stones at them from above. Nevertheless the original pair continues to haunt the same locality for an indefinite term of years, and it is not a little singular that if one of them be killed, the survivor will find a mate in an incredibly short space of time.

The geographical range of the Raven is very extensive. Through-out all the zones of the Northern Hemisphere it is to be found ; and having this wide range, its physical constitution is strong, and it lives to a great age, amounting, so the ancients tell us, to twenty-seven times the period of a man's life. The note of the Raven is well described by the word ' *croak* ', but it is said by those who have had the opportunity of observing it under various circumstances, to utter another sound, resembling the word ' *whii-ur* '. With this cry it very commonly intermixes another, sounding like ' *clung* ', uttered very much as by a human voice, only a little wilder in the sound. From the cry *croak* the Raven no doubt derives its Latin name *Corvus*, the French *Corbeau*, and its common Scottish appellation *Corbie*.

THE CARRION CROW CORVUS CORÓNE (*Plate XLII*)

Black, with green and violet reflections ; tail slightly rounded, extending an inch and a quarter beyond the closed wings ; iris dark hazel ; lower part of the beak covered with bristly feathers ; beak and feet black. Length nineteen inches ; breadth three feet. Eggs bluish green, spotted and speckled with ash-grey and olive. A resident in England and Wales and the mainland of Scotland.

BREEDING early in the year, like the Raven, the Carrion Crow builds its nest in some tree which, from its loftiness or other reason, is difficult of ascent, where its young ones are hatched about the time that most other birds are laying their eggs, and when the lambing season is at its height. Then, too, its habits are most fully developed. Its young are clamorous for food, and will not be satisfied with a little. So the old bird sallies forth to scour the districts least frequented by man, and makes every living thing its prey, provided that by force or cunning it can overpower it. If Grouse are plentiful, it is said that one pair, what with stealing the eggs and carrying off the young, will in a season destroy more of them than the keenest sportsman. It will pounce on the leveret and bear it screaming from the side of its mother. It watches sheep which have strayed from the fold, and mangles the newly born or weakly lambs, carrying them piecemeal to the young ones at home. If mowers are at work, the wary birds alight on some lofty tree, taking care to keep at a safe distance, and when a nest has been laid bare by the scythe, their incredibly sharp eye discerns the prize which, whether it consist of eggs or callow young, is borne off in triumph. Lest their depredations should be discovered by the accumulation of eggshells, feathers, and bones, which are the natural consequence of these raids, they carefully carry to some distance everything that would tend to betray them, so that one might pass directly beneath the scene of these enormities unsuspicious of the evil existing overhead. Keen as this bird is in pursuit of such delicate fare, he can be, when occasion serves, as unclean a feeder as the Vulture, and he can, on the other hand, make a meal off corn. Mr. Knox states that in the Weald of Sussex, it resorts to the brooks and ponds, which abound in fresh-water mussels (*Anodon*), and feeds on them most voraciously, especially after floods, when they lie scattered on the mud. The same author states that in winter it resorts to the seashore, and feeds on the oysters, mussels, small crabs, marine insects, worms, and dead fish which are cast up by the waves during the prevalent south-westerly storms. It has been frequently observed, he adds, to ascend to a great height in the air with an oyster in its claws, and after letting it fall on the beach, to descend rapidly with closed pinions and devour the contents. A similar instance of apparent reasoning is recorded of the same bird by Pliny, but with the substitution of walnuts for oysters.

With such wandering habits, it seems at first sight strange that the phrase ' as the Crow flies ' should be adopted to mark distances in a straight line across the open country ; yet when it is borne in mind how many persons confound the Crow with the Rook, and even talk of the ' Crows in a rookery ', the suggestion will at once occur to the mind that the term owed its origin to its far gentler and more respectable relation, the Rook, whose evening flights from the feeding-ground are among the most familiar sights of the country, and are invariably performed in a line so straight, that if a whole flock could be tracked through the air on any one evening it would be found scarcely to deviate from that of the preceding or the following. It is to be feared that this inaccurate application of names has done the Rook ill service ; yet the two birds are totally distinct. Crows are solitary birds, rarely being seen in more than pairs together ; Rooks are eminently sociable. Crows shun the haunts of men ; Rooks court the vicinity of his dwellings. Crows are carnivorous ; Rooks feed principally on the grubs of beetles, worms, and noxious insects, rewarding themselves occasionally for their services by regaling on corn and fruits, but rarely touching carrion or molesting living animals.   In appearance the two birds are much alike ; the Crow, however, is somewhat smaller, the beak is stouter at the point and encircled at the base with numerous short feathers, while the bill of the Rook is encroached on by a white membrane which is almost bare of feathers. Both are noted for their intelligence ; the Crow has been known to remove its eggs from its nest when apprehensive of danger ; it was held in high consideration in the days of augury, and certain of its movements were considered to be indicative of changes in the weather.   It builds its nest of sticks, and lines it with moss, straw, hair, and wool, and lays from four to six eggs.   Like the Raven, it is a widely diffused bird, and attains a great age, outliving (the ancients said) nine generations of men, showing great attachment to any spot in which it has once fixed its home, and suffering neither its own progeny nor any other large birds to nestle in its vicinity.

This Crow is becoming more numerous of late in the close vicinity of London.   It comes constantly to some of our suburban gardens.

THE HOODED, GREY, OR ROYSTON CROW
CORVUS CORNIX (*Plate XLII*)

Head, throat, wings, and tail, black, the rest of the plumage ash-grey ; tail rounded ; beak and feet black ; iris brown. Length nineteen and a half inches ; breadth three feet two inches. Eggs bluish green, mottled with ash-grey and olive. A resident in Ireland, the Isle of Man, and western and northern Scotland, including the Hebrides, Orkneys, and Shetlands ; also a winter visitor to south-eastern Scotland and the eastern counties of England ; elsewhere in England and Wales only a rare visitor.

THE Hooded Crow closely resembles the Carrion Crow, scarcely differing from it in fact except in colour.   They are, however, perfectly distinct species, and for the most part exercise their calling in separate haunts.   In Norway Hooded Crows are very abundant, and, though not congregating so as to form a society like the Rook, they may be seen simultaneously employed in searching for food in groups which collectively amount to a hundred or more.   One can scarcely traverse the shores of the salt-water lochs of Scotland without seeing a pair, or, in the latter part of the year, a small party of four or five of these birds, gravely pacing the shingle and sand in quest of food.   As far as my own experience goes, I should consider the Hooded Crow as ' half sea-bird ', but it is said to be met with, in summer, in the very centre of the Grampians and other inland districts.   Its proper diet consists of the smaller marine animals, such as crabs, echini, and molluscs, alive or dead, fish and carrion.   At high-water it retires inland, and skulks about the low grounds in quest of the eggs and young of Moor-fowl, thereby gaining the execrations of gamekeepers ; takes a survey of any adjacent sheep-walks, on the chance of falling in with a new-born lamb, or sickly ewe, whence it has but an ill name among shepherds ; and returns when the tide has well ebbed, to finish the day's repast on food of a nature light and easy of digestion. It is less wary of man than the Carrion Crow, and often comes within shot, but, being far too numerous to admit of being exterminated, is but little assailed. In the comparatively mild climate of the Scottish sea-coast, these birds find an abundant supply of food all the year round and as there is no sensible diminution of their numbers in winter, it is supposed that those which frequent the English coast from October to March have been driven southwards by the inclement winters of high latitudes. They are then frequently observed on the coast of Norfolk and Sussex in parties of thirty or more, and it has been remarked that the hunting-grounds of the two species are defined by singularly precise limits, the neighbourhood of Chichester being frequented by the Carrion Crow, that of Brighton by its congener. It is abundant on the sea-coast of Norfolk in the winter, where I have seen it feeding with Gulls, Plovers, etc. In musical capabilities it is inferior even to its relative, its solitary croak being neither so loud nor so clear. The nest of the Hooded Crow is large, composed of twigs, seaweeds, heath, feathers, and straws, and is placed on rocks, tall trees, low bushes, and elsewhere, according to circumstances.

THE ROOK CORVUS FRÚGILEGUS (*Plate XLII*)

Plumage black, with purple and violet reflections ; base of the beak, nostrils, and region round the beak, bare of feathers and covered with a white scurf ; iris greyish white ; beak and feet black. Length eighteen inches ; breadth three feet. Eggs pale green, thickly blotched with olive and dark brown. A resident throughout the British Isles, except the Shetlands and treeless districts ; also a winter visitor.

As the Hooded Crow is essentially the type of the Corvidæ in Scandinavia and the Isles of Scotland, so in England the representative of the tribe is the Rook, a bird so like the Crow that it is called by its name almost as frequently as by its own, yet so different in habits that, instead of being under a perpetual and universal ban, it is everywhere encouraged and indeed all but domesticated. There are few English parks that do not boast of their rookery, and few proprietors of modern demesnes pretending to be parks, who would not purchase at a high price the air of antiquity and respectability connected with an established colony of these birds. Owing to their large size and the familiarity with which they approach the haunts of men, they afford a facility in observing their habits which belongs to no other birds ; hence all treatises on Natural History, and other publications which enter into the details of country life in England, abound in anecdotes of the Rook. Its intelligence, instinctive appreciation of danger, voracity, its utility or the reverse, its nesting, its morning repasts and its evening flights, have all been observed and more or less faithfully recorded again and again ; so that its biography is better known than that of any other British bird. It would be no difficult task to compile from these materials a good-sized volume, yet I doubt not that enough remains untold, or at least not sufficiently authenticated, to furnish a fair field of inquiry to any competent person who would undertake to devote his whole attention to this one bird for a considerable period of time. Such a biographer should make himself master of all that has been recorded by various authorities, and should then visit a large number of rookeries in all parts of the kingdom, collecting and sifting evidence, making a series of personal observations, and spreading his researches over all seasons of the year. Such an inquiry, trivial though it may seem, would be most useful, for the Rook, though it has many friends, has also many enemies, and, being everywhere abundant, its agency for good or evil must have serious results. The following account being imperfect from want of space, the reader who wishes to know more about this interesting bird must refer to our standard works on Ornithology, and, above all, record and compare his own personal observations.

In the early spring months Rooks subsist principally on the larvæ and worms turned up by the plough, and without gainsay, they are then exceedingly serviceable to the agriculturist, by destroying a vast quantity of noxious insects which, at this period of their growth, feed on the leaves or roots of cultivated vegetables. Experience has taught them that the ploughman either has not the power or the desire to molest them ; they therefore approach the plough with perfect fearlessness, and show much rivalry in their efforts to be first to secure the treasures just turned up. During the various processes to which the ground is subjected in preparation for the crop, they repeat their visits, spreading more widely over the field, and not only pick up the grubs which lie on the surface, but bore for such as, by certain signs best known to themselves, lie concealed. I need not say that in all these stages the wisdom of the farmer is to offer them every inducement to remain ; all that they ask is to be let alone. Not so, however, when the seed-crop is sown. Grain, pulse, and potatoes are favourite articles of diet with them, and they will not fail to attack these as vigorously as they did the grubs a few days before. They are therefore undeniably destructive at this season, and all available means should be adopted to deter them from alighting on cultivated ground. About the second week in March they desert the winter roosting-places, to which they had nightly congregated in enormous flocks, leave off their wandering habits, and repair as if by common consent to their old breeding-places. Here, with much cawing and bustling, they survey the ruins of their old nests, or select sites for new ones, being guided by their instinct to avoid all those trees the upper branches of which are too brittle for their purpose either because the trees are sickly or in an incipient state of decay. Hence, when it has occasionally happened that a nestless tree in a rookery has been blown down, the birds have been saluted as prophets, while in reality the tree yielded to the blast before its fellows because it was unsound, the Rooks knowing nothing about the matter except that signs of decay had set in among the upper twigs while as yet all seemed solid beneath. How the birds squabble about their nests, how they punish those thievishly disposed, how they drive away intruders from strange rookeries, how scrupulously they avoid, during building, to pick up a stick that has chanced to drop, how the male bird during incubation feeds his mate with the most luscious grubs brought home in the baggy pouch at the base of his bill, how every time that a bird caws while perched he strains his whole body forward and expands his wings with the effort, all these things, and many more, I must pass over without further notice, leaving them to be verified by the reader with the help of a good field-glass. I must, however, mention, in passing, the custom so generally adopted by sportsmen, of shooting the young birds as soon as they are sufficiently fledged to climb from their nests to the adjoining twigs, or to perform their first tentative flight over the summits of the trees. It is supposed to be necessary to keep down their numbers, but this is a disputed point. I have, however, little doubt that Rooks during the whole of their lives associate the memory of these *battues* with the appearance of a man armed with a gun. Many people believe that Rooks know the smell of powder : they have good reason to know it ; but that they are as much alarmed at the sight of a stick as a gun in the hand of a man, may be proved by any one who, chancing to pass near a flock feeding on the ground, suddenly raises a stick. They will instantly fly off, evidently in great alarm.

While the young are being reared, the parent birds frequent corn-fields and meadows, where they search about for those plants which indicate the presence of a grub at the root. Such they unscrupulously uproot, and make a prize of the destroyer concealed beneath. They are much maligned for this practice, but without reason ; for, admitting that they kill the plant as well as the grub, it must be borne in mind that several of the grubs on which they feed (cockchafer and daddy-long-legs) live for several years underground, and that, during that period, they would, if left undisturbed, have committed great ravages. I have known a large portion of a bed of lettuces destroyed by a single grub of *Melolontha,* having actually traced its passage underground from root to root, and found it devouring the roots of one which appeared as yet unhurt. Clearly, a Rook would have done me a service by uprooting the first lettuce, and capturing its destroyer.

I must here advert to a peculiar characteristic of the Rook which distinguishes it specifically from the Crow. The skin surrounding the base of the bill, and covering the upper part of the throat, is, in the adult birds, denuded of feathers. Connected with this subject many lengthy arguments have been proposed in support of two distinct opinions : one, that the bareness above mentioned is occasioned by the repeated borings of the bird for its food ; the other, that the feathers fall off naturally at the first moult, and are never replaced. It is now known that the latter view is correct.

In very dry summer weather, Rooks are put to great shifts in obtaining food. Grubs and worms descend to a great depth to get beyond the influence of the drought, and the soil is too parched and hard for digging ; they then retire to the seashore, to marshes, fresh-water and salt, to cabbage and potato gardens, and in the last-named localities they are again disposed to become marauders. To fruit gardens they are rarely permitted to resort, or they would commit great ravages. As the season advances, ripe walnuts are a very powerful attraction, and when they have discovered a tree well supplied with fruit, a race ensues between them and the proprietor as to which shall appropriate the greater share, so slily do they watch for opportunities, and so quick are they in gathering them and carrying them off in their beaks. In long winter frosts, or when the ground is covered with snow, they are again reduced to straits. Some resort to the seashore and feed on garbage of all kinds, some to turnip-fields where they dig holes in the bulbs. They have also been observed to chase and kill small birds, which, as near starvation as themselves, have been unable to fly beyond their reach, and I have even seen a Rook catch a small fish.

I must not conclude this imperfect sketch without noticing a peculiar habit of Rooks, which is said to portend rain. A flock will suddenly rise into the air almost perpendicularly, with great cawing and curious antics, until they have reached a great elevation, and then, having attained their object, whatever that may be, drop with their wings almost folded till within a short distance of the ground, when they recover their propriety, and alight either on trees or on the ground with their customary grave demeanour. Occasionally in autumn, as White of Selborne remarks,

> Sooth'd by the genial warmth, the cawing Rook
> Anticipates the spring, selects her mate,
> Haunts her tall nests, and with sedulous care
> Repairs her wicker eyrie, tempest torn.

Similar instances of this unseasonable pairing are recorded by modern ornithologists.

Efforts are sometimes made, and not always unsuccessfully, to induce Rooks to establish a colony in a new locality. One plan is to place some eggs taken from a Rook's nest in that of some large bird which has happened to build in the desired spot, that of a Crow for instance, a Magpie, Jackdaw, Jay, or perhaps a Mistle Thrush. If the young are reared, it is probable that they will return to breed in the same place in the following year. Another plan which has been tried with success is to place several bundles of sticks, arranged in the form of nests, among the highest branches of the trees which it is desired to colonize. Stray Rooks in quest of a settlement, mistaking these for ruins of old nests, accept the invitation and establish themselves if the locality suits them in other respects.

THE JACKDAW CORVUS MONÉDULA (*Plate XLII*)

Crown of the head and upper parts black, with violet reflections ; back of the head and nape grey ; lower parts duller black ; iris white ; beak and feet black. Length thirteen inches ; breadth twenty-seven inches. Eggs very light blue, with scattered spots of ash-colour and dark brown.   Resident almost throughout the British Isles, except the Shetlands ;   also a winter visitor.

THIS lively and active bird, inferior in size as well as dignity to the Rook, yet in many respects resembles it so closely that it might be fabled to have made the Rook its model, and to have exercised its imitative powers in the effort to become the object of its admiration. A vain effort, however ; for nature has given to it a slender form, a shriller voice, a partially grey mantle, and an instinct which compels it to be secretive even in the placing of its nest.   Its note, which may be represented either by the syllable ' jack ' or ' daw ', according to the fancy of the human imitator, sounds like an impertinent attempt to burlesque the full ' caw ' of the Rook ; it affects to be admitted into the society of that bird on equal terms ; but whether encouraged as a friend, or tolerated as a parasite whom it is less troublesome to treat with indifference than to chase away, is difficult to decide.   Most probably the latter ; for although it is common enough to see a party of Jackdaws dancing attendance on a flock of Rooks, accompanying them to their feeding-grounds, and nestling in hollow trunks of trees in close proximity to rookeries, they are neither courted nor persecuted ; they come when they like and go away when they please.   On the other hand, no one, I believe, ever saw a flock of Rooks making the first advances towards an intimacy with a flock of Jackdaws, or heard of their condescending to colonize a grove, because their grey-headed relatives were located in the neighbourhood.   On the sea-coast, where Rooks are only casual visitors, the Jackdaw has no opportunity of hanging himself on as an appendage to a rookery, but even here he must be a client.   With the choice of a long range of cliff before him, he avoids that which he might have all to himself, and selects a portion which, either because it is sheltered from storms, or inaccessible by climbers, has been already appropriated by Sea-mews.

The object of the Jackdaw in making church-towers its resort is pretty evident.   Where there is a church there is at least also a village, and where men and domestic animals congregate, there the Jackdaw fails not to find food ; grubs in the fields, fruit in the orchards, and garbage of all kinds in the waste ground.   Here, too, it has a field for exercising its singular acquisitiveness.   Wonderful is the variety of objects which it accumulates in its museum of a nest, which, professedly a complication of sticks, may comprise also a few dozen labels stolen from a Botanic Garden, an old tooth-brush, a child's cap, part of a worsted stocking, a frill, etc.   Waterton,[1] who strongly defends it from the charge of molesting either the eggs or young of Pigeons, professes himself unable to account for its pertinacious habit of collecting sticks for a nest placed where no such support is seemingly necessary, and, cunning though it is, comments on its want of adroitness in introducing sticks into its hole : ' You may see the Jackdaw ', he says, ' trying for a quarter of an hour to get a stick into the hole, while every attempt will be futile, because, the bird having laid hold of it by the middle, it is necessarily thrown at right angles with the body, and the Daw

[1] *Essays on Natural History*, First Series, p. 109.

cannot perceive that the stick ought to be nearly parallel with its body before it can be conveyed into the hole. Fatigued at length with repeated efforts, and completely foiled in its numberless attempts to introduce the stick, it lets it fall to the ground, and immediately goes in quest of another, probably to experience another disappointment on its return. When time and chance have enabled it to place a quantity of sticks at the bottom of the hole, it then goes to seek for materials of a more pliant and a softer nature.' These are usually straw, wool, and feathers ; but, as we have seen, nothing comes amiss that catches its fancy. In addition to rocks, towers, and hollow trees, it sometimes places its nest in chimneys or in rabbit-burrows, but never, or in the rarest instances, among the open boughs of a tree. It lays from four to six eggs, and feeds its young on worms and insects, which it brings home in the pouch formed by the loose skin at the base of its beak. When domesticated, its droll trickeries and capability of imitating the human voice and other sounds are well known. By turns affectionate, quarrelsome, impudent, confiding, it is always inquisitive, destructive, and given to purloining ; so that however popular at first as a pet, it usually terminates its career by some unregretted accident, or is consigned to captivity in a wicker cage.

THE MAGPIE PICA PICA (*Plate XLIII*)

Head, throat, neck, and back, velvet-black ; scapulars and under plumage white ; tail much graduated and, as well as the wings, black, with lustrous blue and bronze reflections ; beak, iris, and feet, black. Length eighteen inches ; breadth twenty-three inches. Eggs pale dirty green, spotted all over with ash-grey and olive-brown. Resident in England, Wales, and Ireland, and in some districts of Scotland.

THE Magpie, like the Crow, labours under the disadvantage of an ill name, and in consequence incurs no small amount of persecution. Owing to the disproportionate length of its tail and shortness of its wings its flight is somewhat heavy, so that if it were not cunning and wary to a remarkable degree, it would probably well-nigh disappear from the catalogue of British Birds. Yet though it is spared by none except avowed preservers of all birds (like Waterton, who protected it ' on account of its having nobody to stand up for it '), it continues to be a bird of general occurrence, and there seems indeed to be but little diminution of its numbers. Its nest is usually constructed among the upper branches of a lofty tree, either in a hedge-row or deep in a wood ; or if it has fixed its abode in an unwooded district, it selects the thickest thorn-bush in the neighbourhood and there erects its castle. This is composed of an outwork of thorns and briers supporting a mass of twigs and mud, which is succeeded by a layer of fibrous roots. The whole is not only fenced round but arched over with thorny sticks, an aperture being left, on one side only, large enough to admit the bird. In this stronghold are deposited generally six eggs, which in due time are succeeded by as many young ogres, who are to be reared to birds by an unstinted supply of the most generous diet. Even before their appearance the old birds have committed no small havoc in the neighbourhood ; now, however, that four times as many mouths have to be filled, the hunting-ground must either be more closely searched or greatly extended. Any one who has had an opportunity of watching the habits of a tame Magpie, must have observed its extreme inquisitiveness and skill in discovering what was intended to be concealed, joined, moreover, to an unscrupulous habit of purloining everything that takes its roving fancy. Even when surrounded by plenty and pampered with delicacies it prefers a stolen morsel to what is legally its own. Little wonder then that when it has to hunt on its own account for the necessaries of life, and is stimulated besides by the cravings of its hungry brood, it has gained an unenviable notoriety as a prowling bandit. In the harrying of birds' nests no schoolboy can compete with it ; Partridges and Pheasants are watched to their retreat and plundered mercilessly of their eggs and young ; the smaller birds are treated in like manner ; hares and rabbits, if they suffer themselves to be surprised, have their eyes picked out and are torn to pieces ; rats, mice, and frogs are a lawful prey ; carrion, offal of all kinds, snails, worms, grubs, and caterpillars, each in turn pleasantly vary the diet ; and, when in season, grain and fruit are attacked with as much audacity as is consistent with safety ; and might, whenever available, gives a right to stray chickens and ducklings. The young birds, nurtured in an impregnable stronghold, and familiarized from their earliest days with plunder, having no song to learn save the note of caution and alarm when danger is near, soon become adepts in the arts of their parents, and, before their first moult, are a set of inquisitive, chattering marauders, wise enough to keep near the haunts of men because food is there most abundant, cautious never to come within reach of the fowling-piece, and cunning enough to carry off the call-bird from the net without falling themselves into the snare. Even in captivity, with all their drollery, they are unamiable.

Magpies, though generally distributed, are far more numerous in some districts than others. In Cornwall they are very abundant ; hence I have heard them called Cornish Pheasants. In Ireland they are now very common. It is stated that they are in France more abundant than in any other country of Europe, where they principally build their nests in poplar-trees, having discovered, it is said, ' that the brittle nature of the boughs of this tree is an additional protection against climbers ! ' ' In Norway ', says a writer in the *Zoologist*,[1] ' this bird, usually so shy in this country, and so difficult to approach within gunshot, seems to have entirely changed its nature : it is there the most domestic and fearless bird ; its nest is invariably placed in a small tree or bush adjoining some farm or cottage, and not unfrequently in the very midst of some straggling village. If there happens to be a suitable tree by the roadside and near a house, it is a very favourable locality for a Norwegian Magpie's nest. I have often wondered to see the confidence and fearlessness displayed by this bird in Norway ; he will only just move out of your horse's way as you drive by him on the road, and should he be perched on a rail

[1] Vol. viii. p. 3085.

by the roadside he will only stare at you as you rattle by, but never think of moving off. It is very pleasant to see this absence of fear of man in Norwegian birds ; a Norwegian would never think of terrifying a bird for the sake of sport ; whilst, I fear, to see such a bird as the Magpie sitting quietly on a rail within a few feet, would be to an English boy a temptation for assault which he could not resist. I must add, however, with regard to Magpies, that there is a superstitious prejudice for them current throughout Norway ; they are considered harbingers of good luck, and are consequently always invited to preside over the house ; and, when they have taken up their abode in the nearest tree, are defended from all ill ; and he who should maltreat the Magpie has perhaps driven off the *genius loci*, and so may expect the most furious anger of the neighbouring dwelling, whose good fortune he has thus violently dispersed'. Faith in the prophetic powers of the Magpie even yet lingers in many of the rural districts of England also.

THE JAY GÁRRULUS GLANDÁRIUS (*Plate XLIII*)

Feathers of the crest greyish white, streaked with black ; a black moustache from the corners of the beak ; general plumage reddish grey, darker above ; primaries dingy black ; secondaries velvet-black and pure white ; inner tertials rich chestnut ; winglet and greater coverts barred with black, white, and bright blue ; upper and under tail-coverts pure white ; iris bright blue ; beak black ; feet livid brown. Length thirteen and a half inches ; breadth twenty-two inches. Eggs dull green, minutely and thickly speckled with olive-brown. Resident in England and Wales, and in some districts of Scotland and Ireland ; also an irregular winter visitor.

THERE exists among gamekeepers a custom of selecting a certain spot in preserved woods, and there suspending, as trophies of their skill and watchfulness, the bodies of such destructive animals as they have killed in the pursuit of their calling. They are generally those of a few stoats or weasels, a Hawk, a Magpie, an owl, and two or three Jays. All these animals are judged to be destructive to game, and are accordingly hunted to the death, the Jay, perhaps, with less reason than the rest, for though it can hardly resist the temptation of plundering, either of eggs or young, any nest, whether of Partridge or Pheasant, that falls in its way, yet it does not subsist entirely upon animal food, but also upon acorns and various other wild fruits. Its blue feathers are much used in the manufacture of artificial flies. Nevertheless, owing to their cautious and wary habits, there are few wooded districts in which they are not more or less numerous. Their jarring unconnected note, which characterizes them at all seasons, is in spring and summer varied by their song proper, in which I have never been able to detect anything more melodious than an accurate imitation of the noise made by sawyers at work, though Montagu states that ' it will, sometimes, in the spring utter a sort of song in a soft and pleasing manner, but so low as not to be heard at any distance ; and at intervals introduces the bleating of a lamb, mewing of a cat, the note of a Kite or Buzzard, hooting of an Owl, or even neighing of a horse. These imitations are so exact, even in a natural wild state, that we have frequently been deceived.' The Jay generally builds its nest in a wood, either in the top of a low tree, or against the trunk of a lofty one, employing as material small sticks, roots, and dry grass, and lays five eggs. There seems to be a difference of opinion as to the sociability of the family party after the young are fledged, some writers stating that they separate by mutual consent, and that each shifts for itself; others, that the young brood remains with the old birds all the winter. For my own part, I scarcely recollect ever having seen a solitary Jay, or to have heard a note which was not immediately responded to by another bird of the same species, the inference from which is that, though not gregarious, they are at least social.

When domesticated, the Jay displays considerable intelligence; it is capable of attachment, and learns to distinguish the hand and voice of its benefactor.

THE NUTCRACKER NUCÍFRAGA CARYOCATACTES (*Plate LVIII*)

Plumage sooty brown, spotted on the back and under parts with white; tail black, barred with white at the extremity; beak and feet horn-colour; iris brown. Length thirteen inches. Eggs light buff, with a few greyish brown spots. A very rare winter visitor to the British Isles, chiefly to southern and eastern England.

THE Nutcracker Crow must not be confounded with the Nuthatch; the former is a large bird, as big as a Jay, and is only an occasional visitor in this country, whose habits partake of those of the Crows and Woodpeckers.

FAMILY PARIDÆ

THE GREAT TIT, OX-EYE, OR TOMTIT PARUS MAJOR
(*Plate XLV*)

Head, throat, and a line passing down the centre of the breast, black; back olive-green; cheeks and a spot on the nape white; breast and abdomen yellow. Length six inches; breadth nine. Eggs white, speckled with light rusty. Resident in the British Isles except the Outer Hebrides, Orkneys and Shetlands.

As this bird is no larger than a Sparrow, its surname 'Great' must be understood to denote only its superiority in size to other birds of the same family. It is, however, great-hearted, as far as boldness and bravery entitle it to this epithet, being ready to give battle to birds far its superiors in size, foremost to join in mobbing an intrusive Owl, and prepared to defend its nest against robbers of all kinds. Its powers of locomotion are considerable, as it is strong in flight, active on the ground, and as a climber is surpassed by few rivals. Its stout and much-curved hind claw gives it great facility in clinging to the twigs and branches of trees, sides of ricks, and even the walls of houses.   Such situations it resorts to in quest of its favourite food, caterpillars and pupæ of all kinds, and it is most amusing to watch it while thus engaged. Attitude seems to be a matter of no consequence ; it can cling with perfect security to anything but a smooth surface.   On trees it hangs from the branches, with its back either downwards, or turned sideways, and explores crevices in walls with as little regard to the vertical position of the surface to which it clings, as if it were examining a hole in the level ground.   Its efforts to disengage a chrysalis from its cocoon are very entertaining.   One scarcely knows which most to admire, the tenacity of its grasp, the activity with which it turns its head and body, or the earnestness and determination with which it clears away every obstacle until it has secured the prize.   It does not, however, limit its food to insects ; it is accused of feeding occasionally on the buds of fruit-trees, but it is doubtful whether the bird has any other object in attacking these, than that of hunting out the insects that infest them. It is said also to be very fond of nuts, which it sticks into crevices in the bark of trees, and cracks by repeated blows of its beak.   Whether it has this power, I do not know ; but that it will *eat* nuts of every kind, it is easy to prove by fastening the kernels of filberts or walnuts to the trunks of trees by means of stout pins.   Tits, great and little, and Nuthatches, if there be any in the neighbourhood, will soon discover them, and if once attracted may thus be induced to pay daily visits to so productive a garden.   A Great Tit of unusual intelligence, which frequents my garden at the present time, has been frequently observed to draw up by its claws a walnut suspended by a string from the bough of an apple-tree, and to rifle its contents, being itself all the while leisurely perched on the twig, and keeping the nut firm by a dexterous use of its claws.   A charge, amounting to a grave accusation against the Great Tit, and one which cannot be palliated by the plea that he has accomplices, is, that when driven by hunger and he has the opportunity, he attacks other small and weakly birds, splits their skulls by means of his strong, sharp beak, and picks out their brains. One story in particular I find, of a Great Tit having been placed in a well-filled aviary.   In the course of a single night, he had killed every one of his companions, with the exception of a Quail, and when he was discovered, he was in the very act of dealing to this the *coup de grâce*.   His skill and discrimination in pecking holes in the sunniest side of ripe apples and pears are well known ; but to this reward for his services in destroying caterpillars he is justly entitled.

The Great Tit builds its nest generally in the hole of a tree, employ-ing as materials moss and leaves, and, for the lining, hair and feathers ; but as its habits lead it to our gardens, it comes into close contact with human beings and becomes familiar with them.   Hence it occasionally builds its nest in quaint places, which bear ever so distant a resemblance to its natural haunts.   An unused pump affords it an excellent har-bour ; and the drawer of an old table, left in an outhouse, has been found thus occupied.

The notes of the Great Tit are various, but not musical.   Its spring song must be familiar to every one ; though not every one who hears it knows who is the musician. It consists of but two notes, repeated frequently, and sounding as if made by a bird alternately drawing in and sending out its breath ; both together give a fair imitation of the sharpening of a saw. Besides this, it indulges in a variety of chirps, twitters, and cheeps, some angry, some deprecatory, and some pert, which a practised ear only can refer to their proper author.

THE BLUE TIT, ALSO CALLED TOMTIT PARUS CŒRÚLEUS
(Plate XLIV)

Crown of the head blue, encircled with white ; cheeks white, bordered with dark blue ; back olive-green ; wings and tail bluish ; greater coverts and secondaries tipped with white ; breast and abdomen yellow, traversed by a dark blue line. Length four inches and a half ; breadth seven inches and a half. Eggs as in the preceding, but smaller. Resident in the British Isles, except the Outer Hebrides, Orkneys, and Shetlands.

THE Blue Tit or Tomtit so closely resembles the Great Tit in its habits, that, with trifling exceptions, a description of one would be equally applicable to the other. Though much smaller than his relative, the Tomtit is equally brave and pugnacious, and is even more quarrelsome, for he will fight with birds of his own kind ; and the Great Tit, if obliged to contest with him the possession of a prize, retires from the field. His food, too, consists principally of insects, but he is also very partial to meat. This taste leads him much to the neighbourhood of houses and other places where he can indulge in carnivorous propensities. A dog-kennel, with its usual accompaniment of carrion, is a favourite resort, and there are probably few butchers' shops in country villages which he does not frequently visit. A bit of bacon suspended from the branch of a tree is a great attraction. He evinces little fear of man, and will hunt about the trees in our gardens without seeming to notice the presence of a stranger. He frequently pays visits, too, to roses trained against cottages, and will occasionally flutter against the glass to secure a spider or gnat that he has detected while passing. His power of grasping is very great. I have seen him cling to the moulding of a window for several minutes, without relinquishing his hold, though the projecting surface was merely a smooth beading. All this while he was engaged in tearing to pieces the cocoon which some caterpillar had constructed in a crevice ; and so intent was he on his occupation, that he took no notice of the tenants of the room, though they were only a few feet distant from him. He is more frequently seen on the ground than either of the other species, and where it is the custom to throw out crumbs and the scrapings of plates, for the benefit of little birds, the Blue Tit rarely fails to present itself among Sparrows and Redbreasts.

The Tomtit builds its nest of moss, and lines it with hair, wool, and feathers. This it places in a hole, either in a wall or tree, and is at so great pains to combine comfort and security for its brood, that it has been known to excavate, in a decayed stump, a chamber large enough for its nest, and to carry away the chips in its beak to

some distant place, lest, we may suppose, they should betray its retreat.
More frequently, however, it selects a natural hollow, as, for instance,
the stump of a small tree in a hedge, of which all the inner part is
decayed ; nor does it despise human appliances if they will answer
its purpose ; a disused pump, a bottle, or a flower-pot, have all been
known to serve its turn.   It lays seven or eight eggs, but a nest containing eighteen is on record ; and in defence of its family, shows great
courage.   If a nest be molested, the bird, instead of endeavouring to
escape, retains its place and makes an unpleasant hissing noise, and
if this be not enough to deter the intruder, pecks his fingers with great
vigour.   Hence it has received the popular name of ' Billy Biter '.
As a songster, it does not rank high : yet it has some variety of notes,
which it utters in short snatches, expressive rather than musical, as
if the bird were trying to talk rather than to sing.

THE CRESTED TIT PARUS CRISTÁTUS (*Plate XLIV*)

*Feathers of the crown elongated and capable of being erected, black, edged with
white ; cheeks and sides of the neck white ; throat, collar, and a streak across
the temples, black ; all the other upper parts reddish brown ; lower parts
white, faintly tinged with red.   Length four inches and three-quarters.   Eggs
white, spotted with blood-red.   Resident in northern Scotland in pine forests
in the valleys of rivers flowing into the Moray Firth.*

Its food consists of insects, berries of the juniper, and seeds of the
Scots pine.   It builds its nest in hollow trees, or in the deserted nests
of squirrels and crows, and lays as many as eight eggs.

THE COLE TIT PARUS ATER (*Plate XLIV*)

*Crown of the head, throat, and front of the neck, black ; cheeks and nape
white ; upper parts grey ; wings bluish grey, with two white bands ; under
parts white, tinged with grey.   Length four inches and a half ; breadth nearly
eight.   Eggs like the last.   Resident throughout the British Isles, except the
Outer Hebrides, Orkneys, and Shetlands.*

THIS and the following species resemble each other so closely in
size, habits, general hue, and note, that at a distance it is difficult
to distinguish them.   There are, however, strong points of difference ;
the head and neck of the present species being glossy black, with
a patch of pure white on the nape of the neck and on the cheeks, while
the head of the Marsh Tit is of a dull sooty black, without any
admixture of white, nor is there a white spot on the cheeks.   The
Cole Tit is in many districts a common bird, inhabiting woods and
hedgerows, and feeding on insects, for which it hunts with unceasing
activity among the branches and twigs of trees.   Its note is less
varied than that of the Blue Tit, but sweeter in tone.   It builds
its nest in the holes of trees and walls, of moss, hair, and feathers
and lays six or seven eggs.

THE MARSH TIT PARUS PALUSTRIS (*Plate XLIV*)

Forehead, crown, head, and nape, black ; upper parts grey ; wings dark grey, lighter at the edges ; cheeks, throat, and breast, dull white. Dimensions and eggs as in the last. Resident in England and Wales.

As has been said, the Marsh Tit and Cole Tit are so much alike that it requires a sharp eye to distinguish them at a distance. On a closer inspection, however, the characters mentioned in the preceding paragraph become apparent. The Marsh Tit is a bird of common occurrence, being in some places less abundant, in others more so than the Cole Tit, while in others, again, the two are equally frequent. In those districts with which I am myself most familiar, it is hard to say which kind preponderates. Though it freely resorts to woods and plantations remote from water, it prefers, according to Montagu, low, wet ground, where old willow-trees abound, in the holes of which it often makes its nest. Its note, I have already observed, is very like that of the Cole Tit, being less harsh than that either of the Blue or Great Tit. The peculiar double note, which I know no other way of describing than by comparing it to the syllables ' *if-he* ', rapidly uttered, and repeated in imitation of a sob, characterizes, in a more or less marked degree, the spring song of all four. Another characteristic of the same species is, that all the members of a brood appear to keep much together for several months after they are fledged. At the approach of winter, they break up their societies, and are for the most part solitary till the return of spring. The Marsh Tit, like the Tomtit, has been observed to enlarge the hole which it has selected for its nest, and to carry the chips in its bill to a distance, and it is equally courageous in defence of its eggs and young.

THE WILLOW TIT PARUS ATRICAPILLUS

Extremely like the Marsh Tit but the black of the crown is dull, not glossy ; the secondaries and greater wing-coverts are tipped with buffish, making a broad light patch on the closed wing ; the sides of the neck, flacks, and under tail-coverts, are usually deeper buff ; and the outer tail-feathers are usually shorter in proportion. Eggs similar to those of the Marsh Tit. Resident in England, Wales, and southern Scotland.

THIS species is so much like the Marsh Tit that it can rarely be identified with certainty except by those familiar with its characteristic notes. In most districts it is rarer than the Marsh Tit but in some localities it is commoner and it extends into Scotland where the Marsh Tit is unknown. The Willow Tit almost always excavates a hole for nesting in a rotten stump and its nest is generally far less bulky than that of the Marsh Tit, being a thin pad of rabbit-down mixed with fibre, often with a few feathers.

THE LONG-TAILED TIT ÆGITHALOS CAUDATUS (*Plate XLV*)

Head, neck, throat, breast, and a portion of the outer tail-feathers, white ; back, wings, and six middle feathers of the tail, black ; a black streak above the eye ; sides of the back and scapulars tinged with rose-red ; under parts reddish white ; tail very long ; beak very short. Length five inches and three-quarters ; breadth six inches and three-quarters. Eggs white, minutely and sparingly speckled with light red or plain white. Resident in the British Isles, except the Outer Hebrides, Orkneys, and Shetlands.

ALL the Tits, of whatever species, are more or less sociable in their habits, hunting about during autumn in parties of half a dozen or more ; but some of them are given to be quarrelsome, not only towards other birds—like the Great Tit, who actually murders them for the sake of picking out their brains—but among themselves, as the Blue Tit, who has been noticed so intently engaged in combat with another bird of his own kind, that the observer caught them both in his hat. The Long-tailed Tits, however, are sociable after another sort. From the time that a young brood leaves the nest until the next pairing season, father, mother, and children keep together in irreproachable harmony. Exploring the same clump of trees in society, perfectly agreed as to whither their next flitting shall be, no one showing any disposition to remain when the rest are departing, molesting no one, and suffering as far as it can be ascertained no persecution, they furnish a charming example of a happy family. Nomad in their habits, save that they indulge in no questionable cravings for their neighbours' property, they satisfy their wants with the natural produce of any convenient halting-place, when they have exhausted which they take their flight, in skirmishing order, but generally in a straight line, and strictly following the lead of their chief, to some other station ; and when overtaken by night, they halt and encamp where chance has left them. Their only requisite is, in summer, the branch of a tree ; in winter, some sheltered place where they can huddle together, and sleep until the next day's sun calls them to resume their erratic course.[1] Their food, during those journeys, consists of caterpillars, small beetles, and the pupæ of insects generally, and this diet they seem never or very rarely to vary.[2] The ripest fruits do not tempt them to prolong their stay in a garden, and insects that crawl on earth are in two senses beneath their notice. Their rapid progress from tree to tree has been compared to a flight of arrows. Singular as is their flight, they are no less amusing while employed in hunting for food, as they perform all the fantastic vagaries of the Tits, and their long straight tails add much to the grotesqueness of their attitudes. Seen near at hand, their appearance may be called comical. Their abundant loose feathers, the prevailing hue

[1] The name proposed for the Long-tailed Tit, by Dr. Leach, *Mecistura vagans*, is most appropriate. ' Long-tailed Wanderer ', for such is its import, describes the most striking outward characteristic of the bird, and its unvarying habit.

[2] A young friend informed me that he had once shot one, with a beechnut in its mouth. This it must have picked up from the ground, as the season was winter.

of which is grey, suggest the idea of old age, and, together with the short hooked beak, might give a caricaturist a hint of an anti-quated human face, enveloped in grey hair. Many of the provincial names of the bird are associated with the ridiculous ; thus, Long-tailed Mufflin, Long-tail Mag, Long-tail Pie, Poke-pudding, Hack-muck, Bottle Tom, Mum-ruffin, and Long-pod, pet names though they are, are also whimsical, and prepare one beforehand for the information that their owner is ' just a little eccentric '. But whatever be their name, I never hear the well-known ' *zit, zit* ', the pass-word which keeps them together, and which always accompanies their journeyings, without stopping to watch the little family on their flight.

The nest of this species is of most exquisite workmanship and beautiful texture. Its form is that of a large cocoon broadest at the base, or that of a fir cone. It is sometimes fastened to the stem of a tree, sometimes placed in a fork, but more frequently built into the middle of a thick bush, so that it can only be removed by cutting away the branches to which it is attached. The outer surface is composed principally of the white lichen which is most abundant in the neighbourhood, and so is least likely to attract attention. All the scraps are woven together with threads of fine wool ; the dome is felted together, and made rain-proof by a thick coating of moss and lichen, wool, and the web of spiders' eggs. The walls are of moss. The interior is a spherical cell, lined with a profusion of feathers. A softer or warmer bed it would be hard to imagine. At the distance of about an inch from the top is a circular opening scarcely large enough to admit one's thumb. In this luxurious couch, which it has cost the female bird some three weeks of patient industry to complete, she lays ten or twelve eggs, which all in good time are developed into as many Bottle Tits ; but by what skilful management the ten or twelve long tails are kept unruffled, and are finally brought to light as straight as arrows, I can offer no opinion. Nests are occasionally found containing as many as eighteen eggs. In these cases it has been affirmed that two or more females share a common nursery, and incubate together. Certainly it is difficult to imagine how a single pair can manage to supply with food so many hungry young birds, but there is no direct evidence of their being two distinct broods.

THE BEARDED TIT OR REEDLING PANURUS BIÁRMICUS
(*Plate XLVI*)

Head bluish grey ; between the bill and eye a tuft of pendant black feathers prolonged into a pointed moustache ; throat and neck greyish white ; breast and abdomen white, tinged with yellow and pink ; upper parts light orange-brown ; wings variegated with white, black, and red ; tail long, orange-brown, the outer feathers variegated with white and black. In the female *the moustache is of the same colour as the cheek, and the grey on the head is absent. Length six inches. Eggs white, with a few wavy lines of dark red. Resident in*

*the Broads district of Norfolk and Suffolk ; elsewhere in the British Isles
now only an occasional straggler.*

THIS pretty bird is of very local occurrence, being found in considerable numbers in several marshy districts where reeds abound,
but in others being totally unknown. Their habits resemble those
of the true Tits, but instead of spending their lives in trees, they
confine themselves to the marshes, and are constantly employed in
running up and down the stems of the reeds, hunting for their food,
which consists of small molluscs (or water-snails) and the seeds of
the reeds. Like the Tits, too, they are sociable, always being observed
in pairs or families ; not congregating like Sparrows for the sake
of mutual protection but seemingly from the pure love of each other's
company. When in flight over the reeds they utter in chorus their
musical note, which resembles the monosyllable *ping !* pronounced
first slow and single, then two or three times in a more hurried
manner, uttered in a clear and ringing though soft tone. Towards
the end of April the Bearded Tit begins building its nest. This is
composed externally of the dead leaves of reeds and sedges, and
lined with the feathery tops of reed. It is generally placed in a tuft
of coarse grass or rushes near the ground on the margin of the dikes,
in the fen ; sometimes among the reeds that are broken down, but
never suspended between the stems. The eggs are from seven to
eight in number, rather smaller than those of the Great Tit, and
less pointed, white, and sparingly marked with pale red lines or
scratches.

FAMILY SITTIDÆ

THE NUTHATCH SITTA EUROPÆA (*Plate XLVI*)

*Upper plumage bluish grey ; a black streak across the eye ; cheeks and throat
white ; under plumage dull orange red ; outer tail-feathers black, with a
white spot near the end, tipped with grey, the two central ones grey ; beak
bluish black, the lower mandible white at the base ; feet light brown. Length
six inches. Eggs white, spotted with two shades of purplish red. Resident
in England and Wales, except the Isle of Wight, the Lake district, and
Northumberland.*

STANDING, one winter's day, by the side of a pond, near a row of
tall elms, and watching some boys sliding, I heard the few short
twittering notes of a Nuthatch overhead, and it at once occurred
to me how I should describe the note in such a way that it should
be infallibly recognized. It is precisely like the sound made by a
pebble thrown so as to bound along ice. This is the winter note.
On fine sunny days in February it begins to add to its simple call
a more musical sound, approaching a whistle. Further on in the
season, the twitter is heard no more, and is exchanged altogether for
a not unmelodious whistle, several times repeated, rarely protracted

into a bubbling sound, such as it might be supposed to make if it were rattling a pea in its throat. On these occasions it is usually perched in the branches of a tree, and may be distinguished by its bluish grey back, dull red breast, and short tail. The Nuthatch is not an accomplished musician, and claims, therefore, to be pointed out by other characteristics. This is no difficult task to undertake ; for no British bird is more decidedly marked in its habits. In the first place, it has strong clasping claws, which admirably adapt it for climbing ; and though it does not possess the rigid tail of the Wood-peckers to aid it in this operation, it has a short tail which never comes in the way. In most counties of England where old timber is (except the extreme western and northern, where it is rare) any one walking through a woodland district and keeping a sharp look-out may observe a bluish bird, somewhat larger than a Sparrow, creeping by starts up the trunk of any rough barked tree. It is so intent on its occupation—that of searching for insects in the crevices of the bark—that it takes no notice of the observer, but pursues its course after a method of its own, but according to no rule that we can detect. Now it disappears on one side of the trunk and then shows itself a few inches higher on the other ; now it is lost to sight for a longer interval—one would think it was hiding, or had taken its departure—but no, there it is again, creeping, back downwards, along a horizontal branch ; arrived at the extremity it utters a double twitter, perhaps, and flies either to a new tree or to another branch of the same. This time it creeps from the extremity of a branch towards the bole of the tree, equally at ease whatever may chance to be its position, and no more affected by gravity than a fly. Arrived at the main stem it keeps on its course, still advancing by starts, and accompanying every movement, as, indeed, it has been doing all along, by an almost imperceptible twinkling of its wings, something like that which has gained for the Hedge Sparrow the sobriquet of ' Shuffle-wing '. That no other bird but the Nut-hatch has the power of creeping down a tree I cannot say, for I once observed a Tree-creeper descend for a few inches ; but no other British bird does habitually hunt after this method ; by this habit consequently it may be discriminated. Equally comfortable in all positions, if it has any choice, or desires to rest, it clings to the upright trunk of a tree, head downwards.

The Nuthatch is singular, too, in its mode of nidification. The only nest which I have thoroughly examined was built in the hollow of an apple-tree, and was composed entirely of scraps of birch-bark. The *Naturalist* contains a description of one made of beech-bark, though probably here, too, *birch* is meant; others are described as being made of dry leaves and moss ; but, whatever the materials may be, the nest itself is invariably placed in the hole of a tree. There are good reasons for believing that in case of necessity the bird enlarges the cavity to make its dwelling sufficiently commodious, chips of wood having been sometimes found in the vicinity ; but what makes the Nuthatch singular among British birds is, that it not only enacts the carpenter when occasion arises, but adds the vocation of plasterer.

In the case above alluded to I do not know that its powers were called out in either of these capacities. As a plasterer it had no occasion to work, for the opening to the hole was so small that it required to be cut away in order to admit a boy's hand, but many instances are recorded when it selected a hole with a large orifice which it contracted by lining it with a thick coat of mud and gravel. This parapet, constructed either to keep out bulky intruders or to keep in the young birds, if injured or destroyed, will be found restored after a short lapse of time ; and so devoted a mother is the hen bird that she will suffer herself to be taken rather than desert her brood. I have rarely noticed a Nuthatch on the ground during winter, but in spring and summer it adds to its diet terrestrial insects and worms and is said also to be partial to red currants—not a singular taste. But the fruit which has an especial charm for the Nuthatch is that from which it derives its name.[1] Its keen eye detects the ripening filbert in the garden or orchard before the hazels in the wood are beginning to turn brown, and it then despises less dainty food. One by one the clusters are pecked open and their contents purloined, carried, perhaps, to some convenient storehouse for future banquetings. At any rate the owner of filbert trees where these birds abound has need to keep a daily watch, or his share in the produce will prove exceedingly small. I have seen trees bearing a fine crop of husks but nearly all empty. The proprietor had suffered them to remain till they were ripe, the Nuthatches had taken a different view of the case and preferred them unripe rather than not at all. But what, it may be asked, can a bird little larger than a Sparrow find to do with a filbert, or even a hazel-nut ? Here we have a fresh distinctive feature in the biography of the Nuthatch. The bird carries off its prey in its beak, and when in want of a meal wedges the nut in the crevice of some rough barked tree, such as an oak, an elm, or a walnut. This done, he takes his stand, head downwards, above the nut, throws back his head to gather force for a blow, and then brings it violently forwards many times in rapid succession, aided, too, by the weight of his body and a clapping of the wings in exact time with each stroke. By dint of repeated blows thus dealt by his strong beak, even the hard shell of a filbert at last gives way ; a small hole is the result, which is soon enlarged, and the kernel becomes the hardly earned prize. Any one who will take the trouble to examine the trunks of old oaks and elms will be sure to find shells still remaining wedged into the bark, and if during a ramble in the woods in autumn or winter, or even in early spring, he should happen to hear a smart tapping, let him follow the direction of the sound, and he will stand a fair chance of discovering the clever little nut-cracker at work. If in the course of his operation the bird happens to dislodge a nut, so nimble is he that before it reaches the ground he will have caught it in his beak. Acorns and the nuts of yew-berries, and probably other hard seeds, are similarly treated by the Nuthatch ; cherrystones, I suspect, are beyond his powers, yielding only to the massive beak of the Hawfinch. The Nuthatch

[1] From the French *hacher*, ' to chop ' ; hence also ' hatchet '.

B.B.   ·   H

may easily be induced to visit gardens by wedging hazel or Spanish nuts into the bark of trees ; a walnut fastened on by a pin is equally effectual. But no more enticing bait can be set than a lump of fat meat, which should be tied tightly by a string to the horizontal branch of an apple-tree or any other tree, a good view of which can be commanded from the house. If the weather be severe and the ground covered with snow, it is surprising what a variety of birds will come to partake of the unknown food. Robins, Sparrows, Tits of several kinds, Chaffinches, and others flock for a share, not without sundry bickerings, alarms, and semblances of fighting. But should a Nuthatch happen to appear, all retire until his highness is satisfied. He enters upon the scene in a way of his own. Other birds alight on a bough or twig at some little distance from the banquet and make gradual advances. Not so the Nuthatch ; he darts forward in a horizontal line, as if propelled by a missile, sticks by his claws to whatever part of the branch he happens to touch, not caring in what attitude he alights, stops for a second as if to assure himself in what direction his head is pointing, creeps nimbly round to the morsel, takes his stand on it and hammers away until he has separated a large lump. This he then seizes in his beak and retires to a place of seclusion, leaving the inferior animals to squabble to their hearts' content over the crumbs which he has dislodged, and presently he discomfits them again by a reappearance. What his powers as a combatant may be I cannot say ; great, it may be supposed, for no one is inclined to do him battle, and he is not sociably disposed even towards those of his own kind.

FAMILY CERTHIIDÆ

THE TREE CREEPER CÉRTHIA FAMILIÁRIS (*Plate XLVI*)

Upper plumage mottled with yellowish brown, dark brown, and white ; a pale streak over the eyes ; throat and breast buff-white, becoming dusky towards the tail ; wings brown, tipped with white and barred with white brown, and dull yellow ; tail-feathers reddish brown, stiff and pointed. Length five inches ; breadth seven inches. Eggs white, with small yellowish red spots. Resident throughout the British Isles, except the Outer Hebrides, Orkneys, and Shetlands.

THE Tree Creeper, though a common bird, is less familiarly known than many others of much rarer occurrence, yet, if once observed, can be confounded with no other. In size it ranks with the Tits, Willow Wren, etc., but is less likely to attract notice than any of these, as it never alights on the ground, nor perches on the small twig of a tree. Its note, too, is weak, simple, and unpretending, amounting to no more than an occasional ' *cheep* ', which it utters from time to time while hunting for food, and while performing its short flights. Any one, however, who wishes to see the bird, and knows what to search for, can scarcely fail of success if he looks well about him during a stroll through almost any wood of full-grown trees. Half-way up the trunk of a rugged elm or oak he will observe a small portion of bark, as it were, in motion ; the motion, and not the colour, betrays the presence of a small brown bird, which is working its way by a succession of irregular starts up the trunk. Frequently it stops for a few seconds, and is evidently pecking at some small insect, quite noiselessly, however. Its beak is not adapted for hammering ; it confines its attention therefore to such insects as live on the surface of the bark. It utters a low ' cheep ', and proceeds, not in a straight line up the tree, but turning to the right or left according as it descries a probable lurking-place of its prey : presently it disappears on the other side of the trunk, and again comes in view a few feet higher up. Now it reaches a horizontal branch ; along this it proceeds in like manner, being indifferent whether it clings sideways, or hangs with its back downwards. Arrived at the smaller subdivisions of the bough it ceases to hunt ; but, without remaining an instant to rest, flies to the base of another bough, or more probably, to another tree, alighting a few feet only from the ground, and at once beginning a new ascent. This mode of life it never varies : from morning to night, in winter and in summer, it is always climbing up the boles of trees, and when it has reached the top, flying to the base of others. On one solitary occasion I observed one retrace its steps for a few inches, and stand for a second or two with its head downwards ; but this is a most unusual position, as indeed may be inferred from the structure of its tail, the feathers of which are rigid, and more or less soiled by constant pressure against the bark. It frequently visits orchards and gardens in the country, displaying little fear of man, preferring perhaps to hunt on the far side of a tree when any one is looking on ; but not very particular even about this, and certainly never thinking it necessary to decamp because it is being watched. To this indifference to the presence of human beings, it owes its name ' *familiaris* ', and not, as it might be imagined, to any fondness for their society, which, in fact, it neither courts nor shuns. It is a quiet inoffensive creature, congregating with no other birds, and being rarely, except in spring, seen in company with even its own species. It builds its nest of small roots and twigs, scraps of bark and grass, and lines it with wool and feathers. A hole in a pollard willow is a favourite place for a nest ; in default of this a hollow in any other tree is selected, or the space between the stump of a tree and a detached portion of bark. It lays from six to nine eggs, which are exceedingly like those of the smaller Tits.

FAMILY CINCLIDÆ

THE DIPPER CINCLUS CINCLUS (*Plate LIX*)

Upper plumage dark brown, tinged with ash ; throat and breast pure white ; abdomen brownish red ; bill blackish ; feet horn-colour. Female—*colours nearly the same, but of a dingy hue. Length seven inches. Eggs pure white. Resident in hilly districts throughout the British Isles, except the Shetlands and eastern England.*

ANY one who has wandered by the mountain rivers of Scotland, North Wales, or Derbyshire, can have scarcely failed to notice a bird, somewhat less than a Blackbird, black above, with white throat and breast, dart with rapid and direct flight from a low rock on the river's bank, and alight on a wet mossy stone rising but a few inches above the water, where the stream runs swiftest and the spray sparkles brightest. But for the roar of the torrent you might hear his song, a low melodious strain, which he often carries far on into the winter. His movements while he is thus perched are peculiar ; a jerking upwards of the tail and dipping forward of the head remind us of the Wren, a bird with which he has, however, nothing really in common. Water Thrush is one of his names ; but he is better known by the names, Dipper and Water Ouzel. Though neither furnished with web-feet like the Ducks, nor with long legs like the waders, the Dipper is decidedly an aquatic bird, for he is never seen at any distance from a stream or mountain tarn ; in his habits he resembles no other of his tribe—a water bird with a song— a song bird that wades, and swims. That he should be so far only singular in his habits is not enough. Although he is a wader he wades differently from other birds ; and he uses his wings like oars. The Dipper uses both legs and wings in search of prey, examining the pebbles, feeding on molluscs and the larvæ of insects.

I might greatly extend my sketch of this interesting bird, but I have space only to add, that it builds a compact nest of moss, felted so as to be impervious to water, and lined with dead leaves, under a bank overhanging a stream, in the hole of a wall near a mill-dam, or between two rocks under a cascade, but always in such a situation that both old and young birds can throw themselves into the water immediately on being alarmed. I have read of one instance in which a nest was built under a waterfall in such a position, that the bird could not go to and fro without penetrating every time a vertical sheet of water. The nest is domed, and can be entered only by a small hole in front. It contains usually five or six whitish eggs, somewhat smaller than those of the Thrush.

FAMILY TROGLODYTIDÆ

THE WREN TRÓGLODYTES TRÓGLODYTES (*Plate XLVI*)

Upper plumage reddish brown with transverse dusky bars ; quills barred alternately with black and reddish brown ; tail dusky, barred with black ; over the eyes a narrow light streak ; under parts light reddish brown ; the sides and thighs marked with dark streaks. Length three inches and three-quarters ; breadth six inches and a half. Eggs white with a few yellowish red spots towards the larger end, sometimes without spots. Resident throughout the British Isles.

THROUGHOUT the whole of England the Wren is invested with a sanctity peculiar to itself and the Redbreast. In the west of England I was familiar, as a child, with the doggerel rhymes :

> Whoso kills a Robin or a Wran
> Shall never prosper boy nor man.

In the north it is protected by a similar shield :

> Malisons, malisons, mair than ten,
> Who harries the queen of heaven's Wren.

In the Isle of Man a legend exists that there ' once on a time ' lived a wicked enchantress who practised her spells on the warriors of Mona, and thereby stripped the country of its chivalry. A doughty knight at length came to the rescue, and was on the point of surprising her and putting her to death, when she suddenly transformed herself into a Wren and flew through his fingers. Every year, on Christmas Day, she is compelled to reappear in the island under the form of a Wren, with the sentence hanging over her, that she is to perish by human hands. On that day, consequently, every year, a grand onslaught is made by troops of idle boys and men on every Wren which can be discovered. Such as are killed are suspended from a bough of holly and carried about in triumph on the following day (St. Stephen's Day), the bearers singing a rude song descriptive of the previous day's hunt. The song is preserved in Quiggin's *Guide to the Isle of Man*, as it was sung in 1853 ; and, strange to say, it agrees almost word for word with a song which was current twenty years ago, and is so perhaps now, among the rustic population of Devonshire, though the actual hunt has in the latter case fallen into disuse.

In several parts of Ireland, especially the south, there still exists a legend to the effect that a party of Irish soldiers were on the point of surprising their enemies (either Danes or Royalists, for the story varies) who lay fatigued and asleep, when a Wren perched on the drum and awoke the sentinels. An unhappy legend for the poor bird. For some weeks previous to Christmas, peasants assemble to revenge the treachery of the offender in the persons of his descendants. Every Wren that is seen is hunted to death, and the bodies are carefully saved till St. Stephen's Day, when they are suspended from a decorated holly-bough and carried from house to house by the captors, accompanied by a song of which, in Connemara, this is the burden :

> The Wran, the Wran, the king of all birds,
> St. Stephen's Day was caught in the furze ;
> Although he is little, his family's great ;
> So come out, kind ladies, and give us a trate.

The version of the song in Hall's *Ireland*, as it is sung in the neighbourhood of Cork, scarcely differs from the above, and a similar one may be heard on the same day within twenty miles of Dublin.

That a custom so absurdly singular should exist in places so remote, is in itself evidence that it is of ancient origin, though whence derived it would be idle to inquire.

The true story of the Wren is simple enough. It is a minute bird of unpretending plumage, distinguished easily by its erect tail and its habit of hiding in bushes and hedges, not clinging like the Creeper to the perpendicular or horizontal bough of a tree, but hopping from twig to twig, and occasionally taking a short direct flight to another place of concealment, but rarely exposing itself by doing more than this. When hunting for its food, which consists almost exclusively of insects, it searches diligently holes and crannies of all kinds, and in all substances. I have known one make its way habitually through a zinc pipe into a greenhouse, and do much service there by picking aphides from the slender stalks of herbaceous plants, which bent into the form of an arch under even its trifling weight. While thus occupied it has suffered me to come within arm's length, but has taken no notice of me. Generally, it displays little fear of man ; but, though in winter it resorts to the neighbourhood of houses in quest of food, it shows no disposition, like the Redbreast, to enter on terms of intimacy, nor is it sociable either with its own kind or other birds. Its call-note is a simple ' *chip, chip* ', which often betrays its vicinity when it is itself concealed from sight. Its proper song is full, loud, clear, and powerful, rapidly executed and terminating in a trill or shake, followed by two or three unimportant notes. This it utters occasionally in autumn and winter. About the middle of March the song of the Wren is among the most frequent sounds of the country. At this season one may often hear in a garden the roundelay of a Wren poured forth from the concealment of a low shrub ; and, immediately that it is completed, a precisely similar lay bursts forth from another bush some twenty yards off. No sooner is this ended than it is answered, and so the vocal duel proceeds, the birds never interfering with each other's song, but uttering in turns the same combinations and arrangement of notes, just as if they were reading off copies of a score printed from the same type.[1]

But the season is coming on when the Wren has to be occupied with other things than singing down a rival. Nest-making is with this bird something more than the laying of a few sticks across one another. It is not every one who has at once the time, the inclination and the steadiness of purpose to watch, from beginning to end, the completion of a Wren's nest. To most people, one or other of these qualifications is wanting, and to not a few all three. A friend of Mr. Macgillivray, however, performed the task, and furnished him with a most satisfactory detailed account of what passed under his observation. The nest was commenced at seven o'clock in the morning of the thirtieth of May, by the female bird's placing the decayed leaf of a lime-tree in the cleft of a Spanish juniper. The male took no part in the work, but regaled his busy partner by singing to her all day long. At one period of the day she brought in bundles of leaves four, five, and even six times in the space of ten minutes.

[1] I have heard the same musical contest in August.

At other times, when greater care was needed in the selection of materials, she was sometimes absent for eight or ten minutes, but such was her industry that at seven o'clock the whole of the external workmanship was finished, the materials being dry leaves, felted together with moss. On the following day both birds joined in the work, beginning as early as half-past three o'clock in the morning, the materials being now moss and a few feathers. So the work proceeded, day after day, until the eighth of June, when the structure was completed, being a compact ball of dried leaves felted with moss and thickly lined with finer moss and feathers, domed over and having a small circular opening on one side. Dried leaves form the exterior of most Wrens' nests, unless they are placed in situations where such an appearance would attract the attention of a passer-by. On a mossy bank, the outside would probably consist of moss ; under the root of a tree, of twigs ; in a hay-stack, of hay, and so on, the bird being guided by its instinct to select the least conspicuous material. The number of eggs laid is usually six, but as many as fifteen or sixteen have been observed. Any one residing in the country, who has given his attention to birds' nests, must have remarked what a large proportion of the Wrens' nests which he has discovered are in an unfinished state and contain no eggs. These are called ' cock ' nests. In winter wrens resort in numbers to old nests and to holes in walls for mutual warmth and shelter.

FAMILY TURDIDÆ

THE MISTLE (OR MISSEL) THRUSH TURDUS VISCIVORUS
(Plate XLVII)

Upper plumage ash brown ; space between the bill and eye greyish white ; wing-coverts edged and tipped with greyish white ; under parts white, faintly tinged here and there with reddish yellow, marked all over with deep brown spots, which on the throat and breast are triangular, in other parts oval, broader on the flanks ; under wing-coverts white ; three lateral tail-feathers tipped with greyish white. Young spotted on the head and back with buff and black. Length eleven inches ; breadth eighteen inches. Eggs greenish or reddish white, spotted with brownish red. Resident throughout the British Isles, except the Shetlands ; also a passage migrant and winter visitor.

THE largest British song bird, distinguished from the Song Thrush not only by its superior size, but by having white under wing-coverts, and the whole of the under part of the body buffish white, spotted with black. It is a generally diffused bird, and is known by various local names ; in the west of England its popular name is Holm Thrush, or Holm Screech, derived most probably, not, as Yarrell surmises, from its resorting to the oak in preference to other trees, but from its feeding on the berries of the holly, or holm ; the title ' Screech ' being given to it from its jarring note when angry or alarmed, which closely resembles the noise made by passing the finger-nail rapidly along the teeth of a comb. Its French name, 'Draine', and German, 'Schnarre', seem to be descriptive of the same harsh '*churr*'. In Wales, it has from its quarrelsome habits acquired the name of Penn y llwyn, or, master of the coppice. Another of its names, Throstle Cock, expresses its alliance with the Thrushes, and its daring nature; and another, Storm Cock, indicates 'not that it delights in storms more than in fine weather, but that nature has taught it to pour forth its melody at a time of the year when the bleak winds of winter roar through the leafless trees'. The song of the Mistle Thrush is loud, wild, and musical. Waterton calls it 'plaintive', Knapp 'harsh and untuneful'. I must confess that I agree with neither. This note, generally the earliest of the spring sounds (for the Redbreast's song belongs essentially to winter), is to my ear full of cheerful promise amounting to confidence—a song of exultation in the return of genial weather. The bird sings generally perched on the topmost branch of some lofty tree, and there he remains for hours together out-whistling the wind and heeding not the pelting rain. This song, however, is not continuous, but broken into passages of a few notes each, by which characteristic it may be distinguished alike from that of the Thrush or the Blackbird, even when mellowed by distance to resemble either. The Mistletoe Thrush is essentially a tree-loving bird. During winter its food mainly consists of berries, among which those of the mountain ash and yew have the preference, though it also feeds on those of the hawthorn, ivy, juniper, and the strange plant from which it derives its name. Towards other birds it is a very tyrant, selfish and domineering in the extreme; to such a degree, indeed, that even when it has appeased its appetite it will allow no other bird to approach the tree which it has appropriated for its feeding-ground. I have seen it take possession of a yew-tree laden with berries, and most mercilessly drive away, with angry vociferations and yet more formidable buffets, every other bird that dared to come near. Day after day it returned, until the tree was stripped of every berry, when it withdrew and appeared no more.

As soon as the unfrozen earth is penetrable by its beak, it adds to its diet such worms and grubs as it can discover; and, if it be not belied, it is given to plunder the nests of other birds of their eggs and young. It may be on this account that Magpies, Jays, and other large woodland birds, robbers themselves, entertain an instinctive dislike towards it. Certainly these birds are its bitter enemies; but in the breeding season it eludes their animosity by quitting the woods, and resorting to the haunts of man. Its harsh screech is now rarely heard, for its present object is not defiance, but immunity from danger. Yet it takes no extraordinary pains to conceal its nest. On the contrary, it usually places this where there is little or no foliage to shadow it, in a fork between two large boughs of an apple, pear, or cherry tree, sometimes only a few feet from the ground, and sometimes twenty feet or more. The nest is a massive structure, consisting of an external basket-work of twigs, roots, and lichens, within which is a kind of bowl of mud containing a final lining of grass and roots. The bird is an early builder. It generally lays five eggs and feeds its young on snails, worms, and insects.

THE FIELDFARE turdus piláris (*Plate XLVII*)

Head, nape, and lower part of the back, dark ash-colour ; upper part of the back and wing-coverts chestnut brown ; lore black ; a white rim above the eyes ; throat and breast yellowish red, with oblong dark spots ; feathers on the flanks spotted with black and edged with white ; abdomen pure white, without spots ; under wing-coverts white ; beak brown, tipped with black. Length ten inches ; breadth seventeen inches. Eggs light blue, mottled all over with dark red-brown spots. A winter visitor to the British Isles ; also a passage migrant.

THE Fieldfare is little inferior in size to the Mistle Thrush, with which, however, it is not likely to be confounded even at a distance, owing to the predominant bluish tinge of its upper plumage. In the west of England, where the Thrush is called the Greybird, to distinguish it from its ally the Blackbird, the Fieldfare is known by the name of Bluebird, to distinguish it from both. It is a migratory bird, spending its summer, and breeding, in the north of Europe, and paying us an annual visit in October or November. But it is impatient of cold, even with us, for in winters of unusual severity it migrates yet farther south, and drops in upon our meadows a second time in the spring, when on its way to its summer quarters. Fieldfares are eminently gregarious ; not only do they arrive at our shores and depart from them in flocks, but they keep together as long as they remain, nor do they dissolve their society on their return to the north, but build their nests many together in the same wood. In this country, they are wild and cautious birds, resorting during open weather to watercourses and damp pastures, where they feed on worms and insects, and when frost sets in betaking themselves to bushes in quest of haws and other berries ; or in very severe weather resorting to the muddy or sandy seashore. They frequent also commons on which the juniper abounds, the berries of this shrub affording them an abundant banquet. Unlike the Blackbird and Thrush, they rarely seek for food under hedges, but keep near the middle of fields, as if afraid of being molested by some concealed enemy. When alarmed, they either take refuge in the branches of a high tree in the neighbourhood, or remove altogether to a distant field. The song of the Fieldfare I have never heard : Toussenel doubts whether it has any ; Yarrell describes it as ' soft and melodious ' ; Bechstein as ' a mere harsh disagreeable warble ' ; while a writer in the *Zoologist* who heard one sing during the mild January of 1846, in Devon, describes it as ' combining the melodious whistle of the Blackbird with the powerful voice of the Mistle Thrush '. Its call-note is short and harsh, and has in France given it the provincial names of Tia-tia and Tchatcha. This latter name accords with Macgillivray's mode of spelling its note, *yack*, *chuck*, harsh enough, no one will deny. For a description of it in its summer haunts we must refer to Hewitson, who visited Norway mainly with the object of observing the habits of the Fieldfare and Redwing. ' Our attention was attracted by the harsh cries of several birds which we at first supposed must be Shrikes, but which afterwards proved to be Fieldfares. We were now delighted by the discovery of several of their nests, and were surprised to find them (so contrary to the habits of other species of the genus with which we are acquainted) breeding in society. Their nests were at various heights from the ground, from four to thirty or forty feet or upwards ; they were, for the most part, placed against the trunk of the spruce fir ; some were, however, at a considerable distance from it, upon the upper surface and towards the smaller end of the thicker branches : they resembled most nearly those of the Ring Ouzel ; the outside is composed of sticks and coarse grass and weeds gathered wet, matted with a small quantity of clay, and lined with a thick bed of fine dry grass : none of them yet contained more than three eggs, although we afterwards found that five was more commonly the number than four, and that even six was very frequent ; they are very similar to those of the Blackbird, and even more so to the Ring Ouzel. The Fieldfare is the most abundant bird in Norway, and is generally diffused over that part which we visited, building, as already noticed, in society ; two hundred nests or more being frequently seen within a very small space.'

THE SONG THRUSH TURDUS ERICETORUM (*Plate XLVII*)

Upper parts brown, tinged with olive ; wing-coverts edged and tipped with reddish yellow ; cere yellowish ; throat white in the middle, without spots ; sides of neck and breast reddish yellow, with triangular dark brown spots ; abdomen and flanks pure white, with oval dark brown spots ; under wing-coverts pale orange-yellow ; bill and feet greyish brown. Length eight inches and a half ; breadth thirteen inches. Eggs blue, with a few black spots, mostly at the larger end. Resident throughout the British Isles ; also a summer visitor, passage migrant, and winter visitor.

THE Thrush holds a distinguished place among British birds, as contributing, perhaps, more than any other to the aggregate charms of a country life. However near it may be, its song is never harsh, and heard at a distance its only defect is, that it is not nearer. It possesses, too, the charm of harmonizing with all other pleasant natural sounds. If to these recommendations we add that the Thrush frequents all parts of England, and resorts to the surburban garden as well as the forest and rocky glen, we think we may justly claim for it the distinction among birds, of being the last that we would willingly part with, not even excepting its allowed master in song himself, the Nightingale.

The food of the Thrush during winter consists of worms, insects, and snails. The first of these it picks up or draws out from their holes, in meadows and lawns ; the others it hunts for among moss and stones, in woods and hedges, swallowing the smaller ones whole, and extracting the edible parts of large snails by dashing them with much adroitness against a stone. When it has once discovered a stone adapted to its purpose, it returns to it again and again, so that it is not uncommon in one's winter walks to come upon a place thickly strewn with broken shells, all, most probably, the ' chips ' of one workman. As spring advances, it adds caterpillars to its bill of fare, and as the summer fruits ripen, it attacks them all in succession ; strawberries, gooseberries, currants, raspberries, cherries, and, on the Continent, grapes suit its palate right well ; and, when these are gone, pears and apples, whether attached to the tree or lying on the ground, bear, too often for the gardener, the marks of its beak on their ripest side. During all this period it relieves the monotony of its diet by an occasional repast on animal food ; as, indeed, in winter it alternates its food whenever opportunity occurs, by regaling itself on wild berries. Yet, despite the mischief which it perpetrates in our gardens by devouring and spoiling much of the choicest fruit—for your thrush is an epicure, and tastes none but the ripest and best—the service which it renders as a devourer of insects more than compensates for all. So the gardener, if a wise man, will prefer the scarecrow to the gun, the protecting net to that which captures.

I know two adjoining estates in Yorkshire. On one the gardener shoots blackbirds and thrushes in fruit time. On the other they are protected. The latter yields always more fruit than the former.

The Thrush holds a high rank, too, among birds as an architect. Its nest is usually placed in a thorn-bush, a larch or young fir tree, a furze-bush, an apple or pear tree, or an ordinary hedge, at no great elevation from the ground, and not concealed with much attempt at art. Indeed, as it begins to build very early, it is only when it selects an evergreen that it has much chance of effectually hiding its retreat. The nest externally is composed of feather-moss, intermatted with bents, twigs, and small roots, and terminates above in a thicker rim of the same materials. Thus far the bird has displayed her skill as basket-maker. The outer case is succeeded by a layer of cow-dung, applied in small pellets, and cemented with saliva. The builder, with a beak for her only trowel, has now completed the mason's work. But she has yet to show her skill as a plasterer ; this she does by lining her cup-like chamber with stucco made from decayed wood, pulverized and reduced to a proper consistency, kneading it with her beak. With this for her sole instrument, except her round breast, to give to the whole the requisite form, she has constructed a circular bowl sufficiently compact to exclude air and water, as true and as finely finished as if it had been moulded on a potter's wheel, or turned on a lathe.

The Thrush lays four or five eggs, and rears several broods in the season, building a new nest for each brood. During incubation the female is very tame, and will suffer herself to be approached quite closely without deserting her post. In the vicinity of houses, where she is familiar with the human form, she will even take worms and other food from the hand.

THE REDWING TURDUS MUSICUS (*Plate XLVII*)

Upper plumage olive-brown ; lore black and yellow ; a broad white streak above the eye ; lower plumage white, with numerous oblong dusky spots, middle of the abdomen without spots ; under wing-coverts and flanks bright orange-red ; bill dusky ; feet grey. Length eight inches ; breadth thirteen inches. Eggs greenish blue, mottled with dark brownish red spots. A winter visitor to the British Isles which has occasionally nested in northern Scotland.

THE Redwing (called in France *Mauvis*, whence an old name for the Song Thrush, ' Mavis ') is the smallest of the Thrushes with which we are familiar. It is, like the Fieldfare, a bird of passage, reaching us from the north about the same time with the Woodcock, in October. It resembles the Song Thrush more than any other bird of the family, but may readily be distinguished even at some distance by the light stripe over the eye, and its bright red under wing-coverts. In some parts of France it is much sought after by the fowler, its flesh being considered by many superior to that of the Quail and Woodcock. It owes perhaps some of this unfortunate distinction to the fact of its arriving in France in time to fatten on grapes, for in this country it is often too lean to be worth cooking. Being impatient of cold, it is less abundant in the north of England than the south ; but even in the mild climates of Devon and Cornwall, where it congregates in large numbers, it is so much enfeebled by unusually severe weather, as to be liable to be hunted down by boys with sticks, and a Redwing starved to death used to be no infrequent sight in the course of a winter's ramble. As long as the ground remains neither frozen nor snowed up the open meadows may be seen everywhere spotted with these birds, but when the earth becomes so hard as to resist their efforts in digging up worms and grubs, they repair to the cliffs which border the sea-coast, where some sunny nook is generally to be found, to woods in quest of berries, or to the water-courses of sheltered valleys. At these times they are mostly silent, their only note, when they utter any, being simple and harsh ; but in France they are said to sing towards the end of February, and even in this country they have been known to perch on trees in mild weather, and execute a regular song. Towards the end of April or beginning of May, they take their departure northwards, where they pass the summer, preferring woods and thickets in the vicinity of marshes. Mr. Hewitson states that while he was travelling through Norway ' the Redwing was but seldom seen, and then perched upon the summit of one of the highest trees, pouring forth its delightfully wild note. It was always very shy, and upon seeing our approach would drop suddenly from its height, and disappear among the underwood. Its nest, which we twice found with young ones (although our unceasing endeavours to find its eggs were fruitless), was similar to that of the Fieldfare. The Redwing is called the Nightingale of Norway, and well it deserves the name.'

THE BLACKBIRD TURDUS MERULA (*Plates XLVIII and XLIX*)

Male—plumage wholly black ; bill and orbits of the eyes orange-yellow ; feet black. Female—upper plumage sooty brown ; throat pale brown, with darker spots ; breast reddish brown, passing into dark ash-brown ; bill and legs dusky. Length ten inches ; breadth sixteen inches. Eggs greenish grey, spotted and speckled with light red-brown. Resident throughout the British Isles ; also a winter visitor and passage migrant.

WITH his glossy coat and yellow beak the Blackbird is a handsomer bird than the Thrush ; his food is much the same : he builds his nest in similar places ; he is a great glutton when gooseberries are ripe, and his rich mellow song is highly inspiriting. But he is suspicious and wary ; however hard pressed he may be by hunger, you will rarely see him hunting for food in the open field. He prefers the solitude and privacy of ' the bush '. In a furze-brake, a coppice, a wooded water-course, or a thick hedgerow, he chooses his feeding ground, and allows no sort of partnership. Approach his haunt, and if he simply mistrusts you, he darts out flying close to the ground, pursues his course some twenty yards and dips again into the thicket, issuing most probably on the other side, and ceasing not until he has placed what he considers a safe distance between himself and his enemy. But with all his cunning he fails in prudence ; it is not in his nature to steal away silently. If he only suspects that all is not right, he utters repeatedly a low cluck, which seems to say, ' This is no place for me, I must be off.' But if he is positively alarmed, his loud vociferous cry rings out like a bell, informing all whom it may concern that ' danger is at hand, and it behoves all who value their safety to fly '. Most animals understand the cry in this sense, and catch the alarm. Many a time has the deer-stalker been disappointed of a shot, who, after traversing half a mile on his hands and knees between rocks and shrubs, has just before the critical moment of action started some ill-omened Blackbird. Out bursts the frantic alarum, heard at a great distance ; the intended victim catches the alarm, once snuffs the air to discover in what direction the foe lies concealed, and bounds to a place of security. A somewhat similar note, not, however, indicative of terror, real or imagined, is uttered when the bird is about to retire for the night, and this at all seasons of the year. He would merit, therefore, the title of ' Bellman of the woods '. Neither of these sounds is to be confounded with the true *song* of the Blackbird. This is a full, melodious, joyful carol, many of the notes being remarkable for their flutelike tone—' the whistling of the Blackbird '—and varying greatly in their order of repetition ; though I am inclined to believe that most birds of this kind have a favourite passage, which they repeat at intervals many times during the same performance.

The song of the Blackbird does not meet the approbation of bird-fanciers : ' It is not destitute of melody,' says Bechstein, ' but it is broken by noisy tones, and is agreeable only in the open country.' The art of teaching the Blackbird is of old date, for we find in *Pepys' Diary*, May 22, 1663, the following passage : ' Rendall, the house carpenter at Deptford, hath sent me a fine Blackbird, which I went to see. He tells me he was offered twenty shillings for him as he came along, he do so whistle. 23d. Waked this morning between four and five by my Blackbird, which whistled as well as ever I heard any ; only it is the beginning of many tunes very well, but then leaves them and goes no further.'

The song of the Blackbird is occasionally heard during the mild days of winter, but it is not until spring sets in that it can be said to be in full, uninterrupted song. It then repairs to some thick bush or hedge, especially at the corner of a pond, and builds its nest, a bulky structure, the framework of which is composed of twigs and roots ; within is a thin layer of mud lined with small fibrous roots, bents, and moss. The nest contains four or five eggs, and the young birds are fed with worms. In the breeding season Blackbirds are far more venturesome than at any other time, as they frequently select a garden in which to build their nest, with the double object, perhaps, of procuring plenty of worms for their nestlings, and of launching them when fledged where they will have great facilities for regaling themselves on summer fruits. In such localities the appearance of a cat near their nest greatly excites their wrath. From being timid they become very courageous, scolding with all their might, darting down so near as almost to dash in her face, and generally ending by compelling her to beat a retreat.

The female Blackbird differs materially from the male, its plumage being of a dingy brown hue, the breast light and spotted, the beak dark brown with yellowish edges. White and pied specimens of both sexes are occasionally met with.

We would draw attention to the extraordinary size of the bird just out as compared with the egg. On the sixth day the feather shafts with the tips of the encased feathers sticking out of them are quite formed, although two days earlier they were hardly more than indicated. On the ninth day feathers nearly cover the whole of the skin —on the eleventh day they do this completely. In Plates XLVIII and XLIX the bird was drawn after it had flown from the nest.

THE RING OUZEL TURDUS TORQUATUS (*Plate XLIX*)

Plumage black, edged with greyish white ; a large crescent-shaped pure white spot on the throat ; bill and legs dusky. Female with the gorget smaller and tinged with red and grey, and the rest of the plumage greyer. Length ten inches. Eggs greenish white, spotted with reddish brown and grey. A summer resident in the mountainous and hilly districts of the British Isles, except the Outer Hebrides and Shetlands ; also a passage migrant. Individuals occasionally remain for the winter.

RING OUZEL is hardly an appropriate name for this bird ; for in reality it does not wear a ring round its neck, but a white gorget on its breast, the contrast between which and its black plumage is very striking. It frequents the mountainous parts of Scotland and hilly parts of northern and western England, Wales, and Ireland. Though never so abundant as the Blackbird and Thrush are in the plains, it is far from uncommon. It is a migratory bird, arriving in this country in March, and returning to its southern winter quarters—Spain, Greece, Mediterranean islands, and north-west Africa—early in autumn; not so early, however, as to miss the vintage season of the south of Europe. In summer it travels as far north as Sweden and Norway, where, on the authority of Mr. Hewitson, it is often seen 'enlivening the most bleak and desolate islands with its sweet song. It shares with the Redwing the name of Nightingale, and often delighted us in our midnight visits amongst the islands.' Its habits and food while it remains with us are very similar to those of the Blackbird, and its nest, generally built among stones and bushes, near the ground, is constructed of the same materials with the nest of that bird. Towards the end of their sojourn in Britain, Ring Ouzels descend to the level countries, and are not infrequently met with in gardens, whither they repair for the sake of feeding on fruit and berries.

THE REDBREAST OR ROBIN ERÍTHACUS RUBÉCULA
(Plate LI)

Upper parts brownish grey, tinged with olive ; forehead, lore, and breast, red, the red edged with ash-grey ; abdomen white. Length five inches and three quarters. Eggs yellowish white, spotted with light reddish brown. Resident throughout the British Isles, except the Shetlands ; also a passage migrant and winter visitor.

THE Redbreast is everywhere invested with a kind of sanctity beyond all other birds. Its wonted habit of making its appearance, no one knows whence, to greet the resting traveller in places the most lonely— its evident predilection for the society of the out-of-door labourer, whatever his occupation—the constancy with which it affects human habitations—and the readiness with which, without coaxing, or taming, or training, it throws itself on human hospitality—engender an idea that there must be some mysterious connection between the two—that if there were no men, there would be no Redbreasts. Trust on one side engenders confidence on the other, and mutual attachment is the natural result. There is something, too, beyond the power of explanation in the fact that the Robin is the only bird which frequents from choice the homes of men.

The habits of the Redbreast are so well known, that to describe them would be simply to write down what every one has seen or may see.

It generally builds its nest in a hole, near the bottom of a hedge or under the stump of a tree, in an ivy-clad wall, or amidst the creepers trained round the veranda of a cottage. I have seen it also placed in a niche in a wall intended for the reception of a vase, in a beehive stored away on the rafters of an outhouse, and under a wisp of straw accidentally left on the ground in a garden. It is usually composed of dry leaves, roots, bents, and moss, lined with hair and wool, and contains five or six eggs. The young birds are of a brown tint, and have the feathers tipped with yellow, which gives them a spotted appearance.   Until they acquire the red breast, they are very unlike the parents, and might be mistaken for young Thrushes, except that they are much smaller.   They may be often observed in gardens for many days after they have left the nest, keeping together, perching in the bushes, and clamorous for food, which the old birds bring to them from time to time.   Towards the end of August, the young birds acquire the distinctive plumage of their species, and are solitary in their habits until the succeeding spring.   The call-notes of the Redbreast are numerous, and vary beyond the power of description in written words ;   the song is loud, and it is needless to say, pleasing, and possesses the charm of being continued when all our other feathered songsters are mute.

THE BLUETHROAT LUSCINIA SUECICA (*Plate LXIX*)

Upper parts ash-brown ;   throat and neck azure-blue, with a central red or white spot ;   beneath the blue a black border, then a narrow white band, succeeded by a broader band of red ;   under parts white ;   basal half of the tail rust-colour, the other half black.   Female has gorget whitish, with dark breast band and stripes at sides, often with some blue and rufous markings.   Length six inches.   Eggs greenish blue, with reddish brown spots.   A regular passage migrant through the British Isles, chiefly in autumn and on the east coasts of England and Scotland :   unknown in Ireland.

THE NIGHTINGALE LUSCINIA MEGARHYNCHA (*Plate LI*)

Upper plumage russet-brown ;   tail bright rust-red ;   under plumage buffish white ;   flanks pale ash-colour.   Length six and a quarter inches ;   breadth nine and a half inches.   Eggs uniform olive-brown.   A summer visitor to England, breeding regularly south and east of a line from the Humber to the Severn, and very locally or rarely a short distance farther north and west.

THE southern, eastern, and some of the midland counties of England, enjoy a privilege which is denied to the northern and western—an annual visit, namely, from the Nightingale.   It is easy enough to understand why a southern bird should bound its travels northwards by a certain parallel, but why it should keep aloof from Devon and Cornwall, the climate of which approaches more closely to that of its favourite continental haunts than many of the districts to which it unfailingly resorts, is not so clear.   Several reasons have been assigned —one, that cowslips do not grow in these counties ;   this may be dismissed at once as purely fanciful ;   another is, that the soil is too rocky :   this is not founded on fact, for both Devon and Cornwall abound in localities which would be to Nightingales a perfect Paradise, if they would only come ;   a third is, that the proper food is not to be found there :   but this reason cannot be admitted until it is proved that the portions of the island to which the Nightingale does resort abound in some kind of insect food which is not to be found in the extreme southern counties, and that the Nightingale, instead of being, as it is supposed, a general insect-eater, confines itself to that one ; and this is a view of the question which no one has ventured to take. My own theory—and I only throw it out for consideration—is that the Nightingale is not found in these two counties on account of their peculiar geographical position. The continental Nightingales are observed to take their departure in autumn, either eastward through Hungary, Dalmatia, Greece, and the islands of the Archipelago ; or southwards across the Straits of Gibraltar, but none by the broad part of the Mediterranean. Hence we may infer that the bird dislikes a long sea voyage, and that when in spring it migrates northward and westward, it crosses the English Channel at the narrowest parts only,[1] spreads itself over the nearest counties in the direction of its migration, but is instinctively prevented from turning so far back again to the south as the south-west peninsula of England. From Scotland it would be naturally excluded by its northern position, and from Ireland by the Welsh mountains and the broad sea.

For the dwellers in these unfavoured districts alone is my description of the Nightingale intended ; for, where it abounds, its habits are too well known to need any description. Twenty-four hours of genial May weather spent in the country with a good use of the eyes and ears, will reveal more of the life and habits of the bird than is contained in all the ornithological treatises that have been written on the subject, and they are not a few.

No great amount of caution is necessary in approaching the Nightingale while singing at night. One may walk unrestrainedly across the fields, talking in an ordinary tone of voice, and not even find it necessary to suppress conversation when close to a singing bird. Either he is too intent on his occupation to detect the presence of strangers, or he is aware of the security in which he is wrapped by the shades of night, or he is actually proud of having listeners. In the neighbourhood of my present residence in Hertfordshire, Nightingales are numerous. They arrive about the seventeenth of April, and for the first few days assemble year after year in the bushes and hedges of a certain hillside, the position of which it would be unsafe to indicate particularly, and taking their station two or three hundred yards apart from each other, set up a rivalry of song which is surpassingly beautiful. At this season, one may hear five or six chanting at once ; every break in the song of the nearest being filled up by the pipings or wailings of the more distant ones. The male birds arrive several days before the female, and employ the interval, it is fancifully said, in contending for the prize in a musical contest. This period is anxiously watched for by bird-catchers, who have learnt by experience that birds entrapped before they have paired will bear confinement in a cage, but that those captured after the arrival of their mates pine to death. The Nightingale being a fearless bird and of an inquisitive nature is easily snared ; hence, in the neighbourhood of cities, the earliest and therefore strongest birds fall ready victims to the fowler's art.

[1] This is the opinion of Gilbert White.

It must not be supposed that this bird sings by night only. Every day and all day long, from his first arrival until the young are hatched (when it becomes his duty to provide for his family), perched in a hedge or on the branch of a tree, rarely at any considerable height from the ground, he pours forth his roundelay, now, however, obscured by the song of other birds. But not even by day is he shy, for he will allow any quietly disposed person to approach near enough to him to watch the movement of his bill and heaving chest. At the approach of night he becomes silent, generally discontinuing his song about an hour before the Thrush, and resuming it between ten and eleven. It is a disputed point whether the Nightingale's song should be considered joyous or melancholy. This must always remain a question of taste. My own opinion is, that the piteous wailing note which is its most characteristic nature, casts a shade of sadness as it were over the whole song, even those portions which gush with the most exuberant gladness. I think, too, though my assertion may seem a barbarous one, that if the Nightingale's song comprised the wailing notes alone, it would be universally shunned as the most painfully melancholy sound in nature. From this, however, it is redeemed by the rapid transition, just when the anguish of the bird has arrived at such a pitch as to be no longer supportable, to a passage overflowing with joy and gladness. In the first or second week of June he ceases his song altogether. His cataract of sweet sounds is exhausted, and his only remaining note is a harsh croak exactly resembling that of a frog, or the subdued note of a raven, *wate-wate* or *cur-cur*. On one occasion only I have heard him in full song so late as the fourth week in June : but this probably was a bird whose first nest had been destroyed, and whose song consequently had been retarded until the hatching of a second brood. From this time until the end of August, when he migrates eastward, he may often be observed picking up grubs, worms, and ants' eggs on the garden lawn, or under a hedge in fields, hopping from place to place with an occasional shake of the wings and raising of the tail, and conspicuous whenever he takes one of his short flights by his chestnut-brown tail-coverts.

The Nightingale's nest is constructed of dead leaves, principally of the oak, loosely put together and placed on the ground under a bush. Internally it is lined with grass, roots, and a few hairs. It contains four or five eggs of a uniform olive-brown.

THE REDSTART PHŒNICURUS PHŒNICURUS (*Plate L*)

Forehead white ; throat black ; head and upper part of the back bluish grey ; breast, tail-coverts, and tail (except the two central feathers, which are brown), bright rust-red ; second primary equal to the sixth. Female—upper parts grey, tinged with red ; larger wing-coverts edged with yellowish red ; throat and abdomen whitish ; breast, flanks, and under tail-coverts, pale red. Length five inches and a quarter. Eggs uniform blue. A summer visitor breeding in

England, except Cornwall ; Wales ; and Scotland, except the Outer Hebrides, Orkneys, and Shetlands : also a passage migrant.

ALTHOUGH of no great size this summer visitor is pretty sure to attract attention by its peculiar colouring ; its red tail and white forehead being sufficient to distinguish it from every other British bird. It is familiar, too, in its habits, commonly resorting to gardens, and searching for its favourite food, worms and insects, on the lawn, and in orchards. It is local rather than rare, for while there are some places to which it regularly resorts every year, there are others in which it is never seen. Redstarts arrive in this country about the end of April, and soon set about the work of building their nest. This they generally place in a hole in a wall or hollow of a tree, but sometimes by the mossy stump or amongst the exposed roots of a tree. Occasionally they select a quaint domicile, a garden pot, for example, left bottom upwards, or a sea-kale bed. A still stranger instance is that of a pair of Redstarts, who, themselves or their descendants, were for twenty years located in the box of a wooden pump. On one occasion, the pump being out of order, the owner employed workmen to repair it. This proceeding offended the birds, who deserted it for three years, and then, forgetting or forgiving the intrusion, returned to their unquiet home. Another pair constructed their nest for ten successive years in the interior of an earthenware fountain placed in the middle of a garden. But though not averse to the haunts of men, the Redstart shows much anxiety when its nest is approached, flitting about restlessly and uttering a plaintive cry. I happened once to be walking in a friend's garden, and heard what I supposed to be the chirping of two birds proceed from a large apple tree close by. As the notes were not familiar to me, I went round the tree several times in order to discover whence they proceeded. One of the notes was like the noise which may be made by striking two pebbles together, the other a querulous chirp, and they seemed to come from different parts of the tree. The author of the music, however, allowed me several times to come very near him, and I satisfied myself that both sounds proceeded from the same bird, a male Redstart, whose nest, I afterwards heard, was built in an adjoining shed. This singular power of ventriloquizing, or making its note apparently proceed from a distant place, is possessed also by the Nightingale, as any one may assure himself who will quietly creep up to within a few yards of one of these birds when singing. The song of the Redstart is short but pleasing, and it is emitted both while the bird is at rest and on the wing, principally in the morning, and only during two months of the year. Its food consists of small worms and insects, which last it is very expert at catching on the wing ; and in summer, it regales itself on the soft fruits. Its nest is composed of fibrous roots and moss, and is lined with hair, wool, and feathers. It lays about six eggs, which closely resemble those of the Hedge Sparrow, only that they are smaller. In autumn, the Redstarts retire southwards. On the African shores of the Mediterranean they are very abundant, and are caught by the Arabs in traps of the simplest construction. On the continent of Europe, notably in Italy, in spite of their diminutive size, they are highly prized for food. The number of Redstarts (both kinds), Redbreasts, Flycatchers, and Nightingales taken in traps is inconceivable. These birds being of about the same size, and equally excellent in delicacy of flesh, are sold together in all the market towns and are sent to the great cities. Thousands of dozens are thus annually despatched; but this number is as nothing compared with that consumed on the spot.

THE BLACK REDSTART PHŒNICURUS OCHRURUS (*Plate L*)

Upper plumage bluish grey; bill, cheeks, throat, and breast, black, passing into bluish beneath; tail as in the last; greater wing-coverts edged with pure white; second primary equal to the seventh. Female—upper plumage duller; lower bright ash, passing into white; wings dusky, edged with grey; red of the tail less bright. Length five inches and three quarters. Eggs pure shining white. A scarce passage migrant throughout the British Isles; also a winter visitor, chiefly to the coasts of the south-western counties of England; and a rare summer visitor, which has bred occasionally in a number of localities in southern England.

A MUCH less frequent visitor to this country than the preceding, but by no means ranking among our rarest birds, specimens occurring in the winter of every year in some part of England or another, especially in Devon and Cornwall. Its habits are much the same as those of its congener; but it generally chooses a loftier situation for its nest, which is placed in the walls of buildings, at an elevation varying from a few feet to eighty or ninety. Its plumage differs in being much darker in the fore part of the body, while the tail is of a brighter red. The eggs are white. It generally arrives in England about the first week in November, and remains with us all the winter.

THE STONECHAT SAXICOLA TORQUATA (*Plate L*)

Head, throat, bill, and legs, black; sides of the neck near the wing, tertial wing-coverts, and rump, white; breast bright chestnut-red, shaded into yellowish white towards the tail; feathers of the back, wings, and tail, black, with reddish brown edges. Female—feathers of the head and upper parts dusky brown, edged with yellowish red; throat black, with small whitish and reddish spots; less white in the wings and tail; the red of the breast dull. Length five and a quarter inches; breadth eight and a half inches. Eggs pale blue, the larger end often faintly speckled with reddish brown. A resident throughout the British Isles, except the Shetlands; also a summer visitor.

WE can scarcely pass through a furze-brake during the spring and summer months without having the presence of the Stonechat almost forced on our notice. I am acquainted with no small bird whose habits are more marked, or more easily observed. Not even does the Skylark build its nest more invariably on the ground, and 'soaring sings, and singing soars', than does the Stonechat build its nest in a furze-bush, and perch on the topmost twigs of shrubs. In the breeding season, too, it seems not to wander far from its home : we know therefore where a pair are to be found at any time ; and they allow us to approach so close to them, that we can readily distinguish them by the tints of their plumage.

The nest of the pair may be within a few yards of the spot on which we are standing ; but the exact locality no one knows, nor is likely to know but itself. The male is a beautiful creature, with a black head, red breast, and several patches of pure white on its wings, the female much more sober in her attire. Their purpose is evidently to distract our attention from their nest. One is clinging to the top of a juniper, where he fidgets about uttering his *twit-click-click*, which you can easily imitate by whistling once sharply and knocking two stones together twice in rapid succession. The other is perched on the top spine of a furze-bush—they are aspiring birds and must settle on the *top* of whatever they alight on, be it only a dock. Now one dips down and is lost for a few seconds, to appear again, however, directly on the summit of another bush ; now they are on our right hand, now on our left ; now before us, and then behind. Are they describing a circle round their nest for a centre, or are they trying to trick us into the belief that they are better worth caring for than their young ones, and may be caught if we will only be silly enough to chase them ? I do not know ; but whatever their thoughts may be, *we* certainly are in them, and as certainly they are not delighted at our presence. We walk on, and suddenly they are gone ; but presently we encounter another pair of the same birds, who if we loiter about will treat us in exactly the same way, but, if we pass on steadily, will take little notice of us.

We have little more to say of the Stonechat. It is not often heard to sing ; the reason probably being that, when listeners are in the way, it is too anxious about its nest to be musical. Its food is principally insects, which it often catches on the wing. In winter (for they do not all leave us at this season) it feeds on worms, etc. Its nest is remarkable more from its size and position (usually in the centre of a furze-bush), than for neatness of structure. It lays five eggs. Its names Stonechat, Stoneclink, or Stonechatter, are evidently to be traced to the similarity between its note of alarm and the striking together of two pebbles.

THE WHINCHAT SAXICOLA RUBÉTRA (*Plate L*)

Upper plumage dusky brown, edged with reddish yellow ; over the eye a broad white streak ; throat and sides of the neck white ; neck and breast bright yellowish red ; a large white spot on the wings and base of the tail ; extremity of the latter and the whole of the two central feathers dusky brown ; abdomen and flanks yellowish white. Female—yellowish white wherever the male is pure white ; the white spot on the wings smaller ; the red parts dingy. Length five inches ; breadth nine inches. Eggs bluish green, often minutely speckled with light brownish red. A summer visitor, widespread but local in England,

Wales, and Scotland, except the Shetlands ; in Ireland scarce and local, chiefly in the north : also a passage migrant.

A GREAT deal that we have said of the Stonechat will apply equally to the Whinchat, as the two birds much resemble each other in character, size, and habits.   There is this difference, however, between them, that a considerable number of Stonechats remain in Britain during the winter, whereas the Whinchats, almost to a bird, leave our shores in the autumn.   The latter is by no means so common, and is rarely seen except in wild places where the shrub is abundant from which it derives its name of Whinchat, or Furzechat.   For a small bird to have black legs is, it seems, considered in France an indication of peculiar delicacy of flesh.   Both of these birds, therefore, notwithstanding their diminutive size, are much sought after for the table. Both are of restless habits, delighting to perch on the summit of a furze-bush, where they keep the tail in constant motion, occasionally spring into the air after an insect, and then dart off with a dipping flight to another post of advantage.   They repeat the call of ü-*tick !* and their short and simple song, both while at rest and on the wing ; but they are not musical, and ' their flesh is generally more esteemed than their song '.   The Whinchat may be distinguished at a considerable distance by the white streak over the eye.   Both nest and eggs of the two species are very similar.

THE WHEATEAR (STONE-SMATCH) [1] ŒNANTHÉ ŒNANTHÉ
(Plate LI)

Upper parts, in autumn reddish brown, in spring bluish grey ; wings and wing-coverts, centre and extremity of the tail, legs and feet, bill and area which comprises the nostrils, eyes and ears, black ; base and lower portion of the side of the tail pure white ; the chin, forehead, stripe over the eyes, and under parts, are also white, and in autumn the tail-feathers are also tipped with white. Female—upper parts ash-brown, tinged with yellow ; stripe over the eyes dingy ; all the colours less bright.   Length six and a half inches ; breadth twelve inches. Eggs pale bluish green.   A summer resident throughout the British Isles, though local ; also a passage migrant.

DURING a considerable portion of its stay with us, open downs near the sea are the favourite resort of this lively bird, to which it repairs from its transmarine winter quarters towards the second week of March.   Here it may be seen for several weeks flitting from rock to rock, and occasionally soaring to the height of about twenty yards into the air, warbling from time to time its pleasant song, now aloft, and now restlessly perched on a rock, or bank, or low stone wall, calling *chack-chack*—and making itself all the more welcome that few others among our summer visitants have as yet recovered their voices.   We need not suppose that Wheatears prolong their stay on the coast in order to rest after their voyage.   More probably they make marine insects (for these are abundant even in early spring) the principal

[1] Stone-smatch in Yorkshire—from the Saxon, Steinschmätzer in German.

portion of their food, and are taught, by the same instinct which guided them across the sea, to remain where their wants will be fully supplied until land insects have emerged from their winter quarters. As the season advances many of them proceed inland, and repair to barren districts, whether mountainous or lowland, where they may enjoy a considerable expanse without any great admixture of trees. A wide common studded with blocks of stone, a rabbit-warren or sloping upland, is likely to be more or less thickly peopled by these shy birds. Shy we term them, because, disposed as they are to be social among themselves (especially in spring and autumn), they are with respect to other birds most exclusive. Travelling through the waste lands of England, one may sometimes go on for miles and see no winged creatures but an occasional Wheatear, which, with dipping flight, made conspicuous by the snow-white spot at the base of its tail, shoots ahead of us some thirty or forty yards, alights on a stone, and, after a few uneasy upward and downward movements of its tail, starts off again to repeat the same manœuvre, until we begin to wonder what tempts it to stray away so far from home. It does not ordinarily sing during these excursions, but utters its occasional note, very different from its spring song. It builds its nest of grass, moss, and leaves, and lines it with hair or wool, selecting some very secret spot on the ground, a deserted rabbit-burrow or cavity under a rock, where, beyond the reach of any but the most cunning marauder, it lays five or six eggs. Early in August, when the young are fully fledged, the scattered colonies of Wheatears assemble for emigration on open downs near the sea. We have seen a good many of them on the sandy coast of Norfolk and of North Wales ; but it is on the extensive downs of Sussex that they collect in the largest numbers, not in flocks, but in parties of six or eight ; each party perhaps constituting a family. They here retain their shy habits of flying off at the approach of a human being, and are often seen to drop suddenly, where they may remain concealed from sight behind a stone, furze-bush, or bank. The shepherds and others, whose vocation lies on the downs, used to take advantage of the habit of these birds to conceal themselves, and construct a multitude of simple but efficacious traps in which they captured large numbers. The method which they adopted was to cut out from the sward an oblong piece of turf about the size of a brick, which they inverted over the hole from which it was taken so as to form a cross. Beneath this are placed two running nooses of horsehair, in which the poor bird, when it takes refuge in one of the open ends of the hole for conceal-ment, is easily snared. The birds being in fine condition at this season —having, in fact, fattened themselves previously to undertaking their long sea voyage—were highly prized as a dainty article of food. It was formerly the custom for persons who wanted a dish of Wheatears to supply themselves from the traps, placing a penny in every hole from which they took a bird ; but afterwards the influx of visitors to the neighbouring watering-places so much enhanced their value, that the shepherds allowed no such interference. We once tried the experiment of releasing a bird and depositing the penny-piece in the trap, when, from a neighbouring eminence, we were assailed with such a torrent of abuse, that we declined repeating the experiment. In September, all who have escaped the sportsman and fowler wing their way to southern lands. It is thought that the autumnal flocks are partially composed of birds on their way from high latitudes, which stop to recruit their strength on the South Downs previous to final emigration.

FAMILY SYLVIIDÆ

THE GRASSHOPPER WARBLER LOCUSTELLA NÆVIA (*Plate LIV*)

Upper parts light brown, with a tinge of green, and presenting a spotted appearance, owing to the centres of the feathers being darkest ; tail long, rounded at the extremity and tapering towards the base ; under parts whitish brown, the breast marked with darker spots ; feet and toes light brown. Length five and a half inches ; breadth seven and a half. Eggs reddish white, closely speckled with darker red. A summer visitor, breeding regularly in England, Wales, Ireland, and southern Scotland, and occasionally as far north as Skye and the Moray Firth.

As long ago as the time when a stroll of five-and-twenty miles fatigued me less than a journey of ten does now—when I returned from my botanical rambles with tin boxes, hands, and pockets laden with stores of flowers, ferns, and mosses, my homeward path often led me through a certain valley and wood on the skirts of Dartmoor, known by the names of Bickleigh Vale and Fancy Wood. It often happened that twilight was fading into gloom when I reached this stage in my wanderings—the last of the evening songsters had hushed its note ; for this county, beautiful as it is, offers not sufficient attraction to the Nightingale ; yet I never passed this way under such circumstances without feeling myself compelled to stop once and again to listen to the monotonous whirr of what I had been told, and what I believed, to be the note of the large green grasshopper, or locust. Monotonous is, perhaps, not the right word to use, for an acute ear can detect in the long unmusical jar a cadence descending sometimes a semitone, and occasionally almost a whole note ; and it seemed besides to increase in loudness for a few seconds and then to subside a little below the ordinary pitch ; this fall is chiefly at the breeding season. Whether the difference was produced by a rising and lulling of the breeze, or whether the musician actually altered its note and intensity of noise (or must I call it music ?), I could never decide. As long as I fancied the performer to be an insect, I was inclined to believe that one of the first suppositions was correct ; for it seemed hardly possible that the purely mechanical action of an insect's thighs against its body could produce variety of sound—as well expect varied intonations from a mill-wheel or saw-pit. Attentive observation, and the knowledge that the noise in question proceeded not from the exterior of an insect, but from the throat of a bird, has led me to form another conclusion.

I am not surprised at my having fallen into the error ; for the song of this bird is but an exaggeration of the grasshopper's note, and resembles the noise produced by pulling out the line from the winch of a fishing-rod, no less continuous is it, nor more melodious. Many years after-wards, when the memory of these pleasant wanderings had faded away, I happened one evening in May to be passing across a common in Hertfordshire, skirted by a hedge of brushwood, when the old familiar sound fell on my ear like a forgotten nursery melody. The trees not being in their full foliage, I was not without hope that I might be able to get a sight of the performer, whom I now knew to be a bird, and I crept quietly towards the spot whence the noise pro-ceeded. Had it been singing in a copse-wood instead of a hedge, I should certainly have failed, for there is the same peculiarity about its note that there is about that of the insect—you cannot make up your mind exactly whereabouts the instrument which makes the noise is at work. The note, when near, is continuous, monotonous, and of equal loudness throughout ; it might be a minute spinning-wheel revolving rapidly, or a straw pipe with a pea in it blown with a single breath, and then suddenly stopping. But whether the performance is going on exactly before you, a little to the right, or a little to the left, it is hard to decide. I approached to within a few yards of the hedge, and peered through the hazel rods, now decorated with drooping tufts of plaited leaves, but all in vain. I went a step or two nearer ; the sound ceased, and the movement of a twig directed my attention towards a particular bush, on which I saw a little bird, about as big as a Hedge Sparrow, quietly and cautiously dropping branch by branch to the ground. In a few minutes I observed it again a few yards off, creeping with a movement resembling that of the Nuthatch up another bush. Having reached to nearly the summit it became motionless, stretched out its neck, and keeping its mandibles continuously open and slightly elevated, commenced its trill again ; then it shuffled about for some seconds and repeated the strain. It now seemed to descry me, and dropping to the ground as before, reappeared a few yards off. I fancied that while actually singing its feathers were ruffled ; but in the imperfect twilight I could not decide positively. That it kept its mandibles motionless while singing, I had no doubt. Half an hour afterwards, at a quarter to eight, I returned from my walk, and observed it several times go through precisely the same manœuvres. On no occasion did it make a long flight, but even when I scared it by throwing a stone into the hedge near it, it merely dropped to the ground, and in a minute or two was piping from another bush. I have not found, as some authors say, that it resorts only to the vicinity of watery places. The one which I saw on this occasion had located itself for the summer several miles from a stream ; and others which I have heard night after night had settled down on the skirts of a dry common, watered only by the clouds. Its nest is usually carefully concealed in a tassock and is approached by a runway, the bird when alarmed creep-ing rapidly through the tangle like a mouse and rarely flying.

THE SEDGE WARBLER ACROCÉPHALUS SCHŒNOBÆNUS (*Plate LII*)

Upper plumage olive-grey, the centre of each feather tinged with brown ; above the eyes a broad yellowish white stripe ; under, yellowish white, more or less tinged with red ; throat white ; tail rounded, of moderate length of a uniform ash-brown. Length four and a half inches ; breadth seven and a half. Eggs dirty white, mottled all over with dull yellowish brown. A summer visitor breeding throughout the British Isles, except the Orkneys and Shetlands, but rare in the north of Scotland and the Outer Hebrides.

On the banks of reedy and bushy rivers, in marshes, withy holts, wherever, in fact, there is fresh water associated with enough vegetation to shelter and conceal, this bustling little bird is a constant summer visitor ; restless in its habits, and courting notice by its twittering song, from the time of its arrival to that of its departure. It is usually first detected by its rapidly repeated note, which it utters while performing its short flights from bush to bush, and while creeping in and out among reeds and rushes. The fisherman knows it well, and is often tempted to withdraw his eye from his fly or float, to watch its movements on the opposite bank. From its unceasing babble, plough-boys call it a ' chat ', a name which exactly answers to the French name of the group to which it belongs—' *Jaseuses* '. Its note is remarkable neither for volume nor sweetness, and, like that of unfeathered chatterers, seems to carry more noise than meaning. To a certain extent the bird is a mimic, as it imitates such notes of other birds as are within the compass of its little throat. I was walking one morning in May by the banks of a canal not far from a village, when I remarked the exact resemblance between a portion of its song and the chirrup of a House Sparrow. Intermixed with this, I detected the note of some other bird ; but, familiar though it sounded, I ransacked my memory in vain to discover from whom it was purloined. Pursuing my walk towards the houses, I heard the note of some Guinea-fowls ; not the ' come-back ' cry, but the ' click-click ' which every one knows so well. Of this the Sedge Warbler had caught exactly both the key and the time ; the two notes were in fact identical, except that they were performed on instruments of different calibre. Like other chatterers, who, when they have finished their song, are easily provoked to begin again, the Sedge Warbler, if he does occasionally retire to a bed of reeds and there holds his peace, may be excited to repeat his whole story over again, with variations and additions, by flinging a stone into his breathing-place. And not content with babbling all day, he extends his loquacity far into the night ; hence he has been called the Sedge Nightingale, but with doubtful propriety, for, with all the will perhaps to vie with that prince of songsters, the *zinzinare* of the Nightingale is far beyond his powers. Yet in spite of his obtrusiveness, he is an amusing and a pleasant companion to the wanderer by the river's side : his rivalry is devoid of malice, and his mimicry gives no one pain. While at rest—if he is ever to be detected in this state—he may be distinguished from all other birds frequenting similar haunts by his rounded tail, and a light narrow mark over each eye. His food consists of worms, insects, and freshwater molluscs, for which he hunts among the stems of aquatic plants. As an architect, he displays great skill, constructing his nest among low bushes, never at any great distance from the water, about a foot from the ground. It is composed of stems and leaves of dead grass, moss, and fine roots, and lined with hair, wool, feathers, and the down of various marsh plants. The structure is large, compact, and deep, suspended from, rather than built on, its supports. The eggs are usually five or six in number, though as many as seven have been sometimes found.

THE REED WARBLER ACROCÉPHALUS SCIRPACEUS (*Plate LII*)

Upper parts of a uniform reddish brown, without spots ; wing-feathers brown, edged with olive ; a white streak between (not over) the eye and bill ; throat white ; under plumage yellowish white, the sides tinged with reddish ; tail long, rounded. Length five and a half inches ; breadth seven and a half. Eggs dull greenish white, speckled with olive and light brown, especially towards the larger end. A summer visitor, breeding regularly in England north to Cheshire and southern Yorkshire and west to Shropshire and Somerset, and in a few localities in South Wales, Devon, and Cornwall.

BOTH the Sedge and the Reed Warblers are *jaseuses*, or chatterers, with rounded tails ; but the Sedge Warbler has its upper plumage spotted with dark brown, and a white line above its eye, while the upper plumage of the Reed Warbler is of a uniform pale brown, and the light mark is absent from above the eye. The haunts and habits of the two birds are similar, but the Reed Warbler is by far the less common of the two ; for while the Sedge Warbler is sure to be found wherever the Reed Warbler has been observed, the converse by no means follows.

' The nest of the Reed Warbler is often elegantly built, and generally fixed to three or four reed-stems. It is composed of slender blades of grass, interwoven with reed-tops, dry duckweed, and the spongy substance which covers many of the marsh ditches ; and, here and there, a long piece of sedge is wound securely around it ; the lining is of the finer flowering stems of grass, intermixed with a little horsehair. It is a deep and solid structure, so that the eggs cannot easily roll out ; it is firmly fastened to the reeds in tidal ditches and rivers, at the height of three or four feet from the water, but in still ditches often not more than a foot. In windy weather, when wading through the reed-beds, I have seen nests, with both old and young in them, blown nearly to the surface of the water ; but the birds fix their claws firmly to the sides of the nest, with their heads to windward, and thus ride as securely in their cradle as a sailor does in his cot or hammock.' [1] The Cuckoo occasionally chooses the Reed Warbler's nest to lay its eggs in, for the same writer remarks : ' At the latter end of July, 1829, while reading in my garden, which adjoins a market garden, I was agreeably surprised to see a young Cuckoo, nearly full-grown,

[1] Mr. W. H. Thomas, in the *Zoologist*, p. 97.

alight on the railings between the two, not more than a dozen yards from where I was sitting. Anxious to see what bird had reared this Cuckoo, I silently watched his movements, and had not waited more than a minute, when a Reed Warbler flew to the Cuckoo, who, crouching down with his breast close to the rail, and fluttering his wings, opened wide his orange-coloured mouth to receive the insect his foster-mother had brought him. This done, the Reed Warbler flew away for a fresh supply of food. The difference in the size of the two birds was great ; it was like a pigmy feeding a giant. While the Reed Warbler was absent, the Cuckoo shuffled along the rail, and hopped upon a slender post to which it was nailed, and which projected about eight inches above the rail. The Reed Warbler soon returned with more food, and alighted close to the Cuckoo, but on the rail beneath him ; she then began to stretch herself to the utmost to give him the food, but was unable to reach the Cuckoo's mouth, who, like a simpleton, threw his head back, with his mouth wide open, as before. The Reed Warbler, by no means at a loss, perched upon the Cuckoo's broad back, who, still holding back his head, received in this singular way the morsel brought for him.' The song of the Reed Warbler is loudest and at its best during the evening twilight.

THE MARSH WARBLER ACROCÉPHALUS PALUSTRIS
(Plate LII)

Closely similar to the Reed Warbler but upper parts olivaceous-brown without rufous tint, and under parts, especially throat, whiter ; bill dark brown, inside mouth yellow ; legs pale flesh-coloured. Eggs bluish or greenish white, boldly spotted and blotched with olive-brown. A summer visitor, breeding locally in southern England, particularly in the Severn valley.

THE Marsh Warbler nests in drier places than the Reed Warbler and its song is different, being much more melodious, and uttered more boldly. It haunts osier-beds, tangled thickets, and hedges, sometimes at a distance from water, and suspends its nest among thick growths of meadow-sweet, willow-herb, or nettles, or sometimes in bushes. The nest is not so deep or so substantial as that of the Reed Warbler and is composed of grasses or dead plants lined with roots and horse-hair. The eggs are usually four or five in number.

THE BLACKCAP SYLVIA ATRICAPILLA (Plate LIII)

Top and back of the head black, in the female chocolate colour ; upper parts, wings, and tail, ash-grey, slightly tinged with olive ; neck light grey passing into greyish white ; bill and feet black. Length five inches and a half ; breadth eight and a half. Eggs pale greenish white, variously mottled with several shades of brown; sometimes pinkish, mottled with light purple, and speckled with dark purple. A summer visitor, breeding in most districts of England and

Wales, and locally in Scotland north to Inverness-shire and in many parts of Ireland. Individuals frequently remain for the winter.

WHATEVER difference of opinion there may be as to the character of the Nightingale's song—whether it partakes more of joyousness or of melancholy—the gladsomeness of the Blackcap's warble is beyond all dispute. Conceding to the Nightingale the first place among the warblers which visit England, we do not hesitate to claim the second for the Blackcap. Its song is inferior in power and compass to that of the bird of night, but there is about it a delicious eloquence which makes it irresistibly charming. White of Selborne describes it as ' full, sweet, deep, loud, and wild ' ; high but not unmerited praise. If there are no vocal efforts to astonish, there are no piteous wailings to distress, and though the bird retires to rest at a reasonable hour, it continues its song until a late period of the season, long after that of the Nightingale has degenerated to a croak. It has been compared to that of the Redbreast, but it is more mellow and flute-like ; to that of the Thrush, but it is softer and of more compass ; to that of the Lark, but it is more varied. A practised ear will confound it with neither of these, though, strange to say, many persons who have lived all their lives in the country and who take much interest in its pleasant sights and sounds, habitually confound it with the song of one or other of these birds, not knowing to whom they are indebted for one of the principal charms of their gardens. The Blackcap, like several other of the migratory warblers, returns again and again to its old haunts. For six successive years it has been known to build its nest in a bramble which hung down from a rock in a public garden ; and for even a longer period my own garden has been annually visited by a pair who, from unfailingly resorting to the same bushes, must, I have little doubt, be the same pair, though I cannot say that I have found or even searched for their nest. On its first arrival in April, the Blackcap is in the habit of what bird-fanciers call ' recording '—that is, practising over its song in a low tone. During this season of rehearsal it does not care to be seen, but hides away in a thick bush. It is nevertheless by no means shy of being heard, as it will allow the listener to approach within a few yards of its hiding-place without stopping its song, and if disturbed will remove to a very little distance and recommence. After a few days it acquires its full powers of voice.

Its song is now remarkable among the full choir for sweetness, loudness, and long continuance. Its food at this time consists of aphides, caterpillars, and other small insects which infest roses and fruit-trees ; it rarely captures flies on the wing or descends to feed on the ground. In June it begins to sing shorter strains, but with no diminished power. It may then be observed flying from branch to branch of an apple-tree, resting for a few seconds only in the same spot, and busily occupied in collecting grubs or aphides, then indulging in a short strain. In July, when the raspberries ripen, the Blackcap becomes chary of its song, and introduces its young brood to the choicest and juiciest fruit ; in their attentions to which both old and young birds are exceedingly pertinacious, holding scarecrows in extreme contempt, and heeding clapping of hands or the discharge of a gun as little. The young of the first year resemble the adult female in having a chocolate-coloured crown. The song of the Black-cap may be heard occasionally late in the summer ; in September or October both old and young take their departure, and the Redbreast is left without a rival to assert his superiority as a warbler, until the return of spring. The nest is usually placed in a hedge or low bush, a few feet from the ground, and is constructed of bents, and lined with fibrous roots and hair. The male bird assists the female in performing the office of incubation, and is said to relieve the monotony of his occupation by singing, thus often betraying a well-concealed nest.

THE GARDEN WARBLER SYLVIA BORIN (*Plate LIII*)

Upper parts greyish brown, slightly tinged with olive ; orbits white ; below the ear a patch of ash-grey ; throat dull white ; breast and flanks grey, tinged with rust-colour ; rest of the under parts dull white. Length five inches and three-quarters ; breadth eight and a half. Eggs greenish white, speckled with two shades of greenish brown. A summer visitor, breeding in most districts of England and Wales, and locally in Scotland north to Perthshire and in a few districts of Ireland.

THOUGH tolerably well dispersed throughout England, this bird is by no means so abundant as the Blackcap, which it resembles in size and habits, but it arrives later, coming early in May. Its song is little if at all inferior to that of the bird just named, and it is far from im-probable that some of the sweet strains for which the Blackcap gets credit, particularly late in the summer, may be produced by the Garden Warbler ; I have heard its song so late as the fifth of October. By some authors it is called the Greater Pettychaps, by others the *Fauvette*, which latter name is by some French ornithologists applied to the group containing this bird and several allied species. Its nest and eggs are so like those of the Blackcap as to be discriminated with difficulty.

THE WHITETHROAT SYLVIA COMMUNIS (*Plate LIII*)

Head ash-grey ; rest of the upper parts grey, tinged with rust-colour ; wings dusky, the coverts edged with red ; lower parts white, faintly tinged on the breast with rose-colour ; tail dark brown, the outer feather white at the tip and on the outer web, the next only tipped with white. Female without the rose tint on the breast, but with the upper plumage more decidedly tinged with red ; feet brown. Length five inches and a half ; breadth eight and a half. Eggs greenish white, thickly spotted with reddish and greenish brown. Young, leaving nest, differ very little from adult birds. A summer visitor, breeding throughout the British Isles, except the Orkneys and Shetlands.

THE Whitethroat is in England the most common of all the migratory warblers, and is generally diffused. It is essentially a hedge-bird, neither taking long flights nor resorting to lofty trees. Early in May it may be detected in a hawthorn or other thick bush, hopping from twig to twig with untiring restlessness, frequently descending to the ground, but never making any stay, and all the while incessantly babbling with a somewhat harsh but not unpleasant song, composed of numerous rapid and short notes, which have but little either of variety or compass. Occasionally it takes a short flight along the hedge, generally on the side farthest from the spectator, and proceeds to another bush a few yards on, where it either repeats the same movements, or perches on a high twig for a few seconds. From time to time it rises into the air, performing curious antics and singing all the while. Its short flight completed, it descends to the same or an adjoining twig, and so it seems to spend its days. From its habit of creeping through the lower parts of hedges, it has received the popular name of ' Nettle-creeper '. From the grey tone of its plumage, it is in some districts of France called ' *Grisette* ', and in others, from its continuous song, ' *Babillarde* ', names, however, which are popularly applied without distinction to this species and the next. While singing it keeps the feathers of its head erected, resembling in this respect the Blackcap and several of the other warblers. Though not naturally a nocturnal musician, it does not, like most other birds, when disturbed at night, quietly steal away to another place of shelter, but bursts into repeated snatches of song, into which there seems to be infused a spice of anger against the intruder.[1] Its food consists of insects of various kinds ; but when the smaller fruits begin to ripen, it repairs with its young brood to our gardens, and makes no small havoc among raspberries, currants, and cherries. It constructs its nest among brambles and nettles, raised from two to three feet from the ground, of bents and the dry stems of herbs, mixed with cobweb, cotton from the willow, bits of wool, and horsehair. It usually lays five eggs.

THE LESSER WHITETHROAT ṡYLVIA CURRÚCA
(*Plate LIII*)

Head and lore dark ash-grey ; rest of the upper parts greyish ash, tinged with brown ; wings brown, edged with ash-grey ; tail dusky, outer feather as in the last, the two next tipped with white ; lower parts pure silvery white ; feet deep lead-colour. Length five inches and a quarter. Eggs greenish white, spotted and speckled, especially at the larger end, with ash and brown. A summer visitor, breeding in England and Wales ; but in Scotland a rare passage migrant and to Ireland only an occasional straggler.

GILBERT WHITE in his charming history says: ' A rare, and I think a new little bird frequents my garden, which I have very great reason to think is the Pettichaps ; it is common in some parts of the kingdom ; and I have received formerly dead specimens from Gibraltar. This bird much resembles the Whitethroat, but has a more white, or rather silvery breast and belly ; is restless and active, like the Willow-wrens, and hops from bough to bough, examining every part for food ; it

---

[1] This night song is rarely heard except in the months of May and June.

also runs up the stems of the crown-imperials, and, putting its head into the bells of those flowers, sips the liquor which stands in the nectarium of each petal.   Sometimes it feeds on the ground like the Hedge Sparrow, by hopping about on the grass plots and mown walks.' The little bird of which the amiable naturalist gives so interesting a description, was, there is little doubt, that which is now called the Lesser Whitethroat, then a ' new bird ', inasmuch as it had not been made a distinct species, and necessarily a ' rare bird ', not because a few only visited Britain, but because, until his time set the example, competent observers of birds were rare.   It differs externally from the preceding in its smaller size, and the darker colour of its beak, upper plumage, and feet, and resembles it closely in its habits, though I have never observed that it indulges in the eccentric perpendicular flights, which have gained for its congener, the Greater Whitethroat, the quaint sobriquet of ' singing skyrocket '.   It feeds, too, on insects, and is not found wanting when raspberries and cherries are ripe.   But no matter what number of these it consumes, it ought with its companions to be welcomed by the gardener as one of his most valuable friends.   For it should be borne in mind that these birds, by consuming a portion of a crop of ripe fruit, do not at all injure the trees, but that the countless aphides and caterpillars which they devoured at an earlier period of the year, would, if they had been allowed to remain, have feasted on the leaves and young shoots, and so not only have imperilled the coming crop, but damaged the tree so materially as to impair its fertility for some time to come.   Those birds, therefore, which in spring feed on insects and nourish their young on the same diet, may be considered as necessary to protect from injury the trees which are destined to supply them with support when insect food becomes scarce. Consider what would be the result if the proper food of birds were leaves, or if insects were permitted to devour the foliage unchecked ! our woods would be leafless, our gardens would become deserts.

THE BARRED WARBLER SYLVIA NISORIA (*Plate LXIX*)

Upper parts ashy grey ; upper tail-coverts barred with slate and white ; upper wing-coverts and inner secondaries tipped with white ; tail-feathers, except the two central ones, tipped with white ; under parts greyish white, with numerous transverse grey bars, deeper on the flanks ; bill brown ; feet brownish grey ; iris pale yellow. Female *browner and less barred.* Young *almost without bars and with iris dark greyish brown. Length six inches and a half. A scarce passage migrant through the British Isles, chiefly in autumn and on the east coast.*

THE DARTFORD WARBLER SYLVIA UNDATA (*Plate LII*)

Upper parts blackish brown ; under purplish red ; middle of the abdomen white ; tail long, dark brown, the outer feather tipped with white ; wings very short ; quills ash-grey on the inner web, dark brown on the outer ; feet yellowish ; bill yellowish white, with a black tip. Length five inches and a half.

Blackbird ♂ *imm.*

Blackbird ♀ ♂

Ring Ouzel ♂ ♀

XLIX

Stonechat ♀ ♂

Whinchat

Redstart ♂ ♀

Black Redstart ♀ ♂

L

Wheatear ♀ ♂
Nightingale

Hedgesparrow

Robin

LI

Reed Warbler   Marsh Warbler

Sedge Warbler   Dartford Warbler ♀ ♂

LII

Whitethroat ♂ ♂

Garden Warbler

Lesser Whitethroat

Blackcap ♂

LIII

Wood Warbler   Willow Warbler

Grasshopper Warbler   Chiffchaff

LIV

Pied Flycatcher ♂ *imm.* ♂   Spotted Flycatcher ♀
     Greenfinch ♂ *young* ♀   Waxwing ♂ ♂

LV

Blue-headed Wagtail ♂

White Wagtail ♂

Yellow Wagtail ♂

Grey Wagtail ♂

Pied Wagtail

LVI

Yellowhammer ♂

Meadow Pipit

Tree Pipit

Rock Pipit

LVII

Great Grey Shrike ♂

Woodchat Shrike ♂

Red-backed Shrike ♂

Nutcracker

LVIII

Rose-coloured Starling

Starling ♂

Dipper

Golden Oriole ♀ ♂

Cirl Bunting ♂   Lapland Bunting

Reed Bunting ♂ ♀

Corn Bunting   Snow Bunting ♂ ♀

Tree Sparrow

House Sparrow ♂

Linnet ♂

Brambling ♂

LXI

Siskin ♂ ♀ ♀
Chaffinch ♂ ♀

Goldfinch
Hawfinch ♀ ♂

LXII

Mealy Redpoll ♀ ♂

Lesser Redpoll ♂   Twite ♂ ♂
Bullfinch ♂

LXIII

Crossbill, *imm.* ♀♂   White-winged Crossbill ♂

Cuckoo ♂

LXIV

Eggs greenish white, speckled all over, and especially at the larger end, with brown and ash-grey. A local resident in some of the southern counties of England.

THIS species received its name from having been first shot on Bexley Heath, near Dartford, in 1773. It has since been observed on furzy commons in several of the southern and western counties, but is local and nowhere abundant. In its habits it resembles the Stone and Furze Chats, perching on the upper sprays of the furze and whitethorn, but never still for a minute, throwing itself into various attitudes, erecting its crest and tail at intervals, frequently rising into the air with most fantastic movements, catching insects on the wing, and either returning to the same twig, or making a short flight to some other convenient bush. The syllables ' *cha cha cha* ' are several times repeated when the bird is irritated. Its note is commonly *Pitchou*, hence its French name. It keeps quite aloof from human habitations, and is so timid that on the approach of an observer it creeps into a bush, and remains concealed until the danger is past. The nest of goose grass and soft bits of furze, wool, and moss is placed in the fork of a furze-bush selected for its thickness and difficulty of access. It is somewhat wandering, but may be called a resident in the South.

THE WOOD-WREN OR WOOD-WARBLER
PHYLLOSCOPUS SIBILÁTRIX (*Plate LIV*)

Upper plumage bright yellowish green ; a broad streak of sulphur-yellow over the eye ; sides of the head, throat, insertion of the wings and legs, bright yellow ; rest of the under plumage pure white ; second primary equal to the fourth, third and fourth with the outer web sloped off at the extremity ; legs pale brown. Length five inches and a half ; breadth eight and three-quarters. Eggs white, speckled so thickly with purplish brown as almost to conceal the ground. A summer visitor to the British Isles, breeding in most parts of England, Wales, and Scotland, but only very rarely in Ireland, and not in the Outer Hebrides, Orkneys, or Shetlands.

THE Wood-warbler, Willow-warbler, and Chiff-chaff resemble each other so closely in size, colour, and habits, that except by a practised observer, they are likely to be mistaken for one another. In song, however, they differ materially, and as this is begun early, and continued till very late in the season, it affords ready means of discriminating the species. The Wood-warbler, or Wood-wren as it is often called, arrives in England towards the end of April, and betakes itself to woodland districts, where it spends the greater portion of its time among the upper branches of lofty trees, constantly moving from place to place with rapid irregular flight, and frequently repeating its short and peculiar song. It feeds exclusively on insects, which it occasionally catches on the wing. Its song is difficult to describe. The name by which it is popularly known in some parts of France, *Touite*, is derived from the syllable ' *tweet* ', which, rapidly and continuously repeated many times, constitutes its song. These notes are uttered in a sweet

I

tone, and with a tremulous accent, and are unlike those of any other bird. Gilbert White, who appears to have been the first who noticed the bird, describes it as ' joyous, easy, and laughing '. The last notes of its strain are accompanied by a quivering of the wings and tail, which accounts for their tremulous sound.

The Wood-warbler is much less frequent than either the Willow-warbler or Chiff-chaff, and on a close inspection may be distinguished by its superior size, by the pure white of its under tail-coverts, and by the bright yellow line above the eye. The nest is composed of grass, ferns, and moss, and lined with fine grass and hair ; it is covered with a dome, an entrance being left sufficiently large to allow its contents to be seen, and is placed on the ground, in or near a wood, among thick herbage, or against the stump of a tree. The eggs are from five to seven in number, almost round, and so thickly spotted with purple-brown that the ground is almost invisible.

THE WILLOW-WREN OR WILLOW-WARBLER
PHYLLOSCOPUS TRÓCHILUS (*Plate LIV*)

Upper parts bright olive-green ; a narrow streak of yellow over the eye ; under parts yellowish white, palest in the middle ; feathers of the leg yellow ; second primary equal to the sixth ; third, fourth, and fifth, with the outer web sloped off at the extremity ; feet stoutish ; legs light brown.   Length nearly five inches ; breadth eight.   Eggs white, more or less speckled with rust-colour.   A summer visitor, breeding throughout the British Isles.

THERE seems to be no sufficient reason why this bird should be named Willow-warbler or Willow-wren, as it shows no special preference for willows, nor does it frequent watery places. The popular name, ' Hay-bird ', is, I think, the better of the two ; for, except in the extreme west of England, wherever there are hayfields and trees these birds are to be found ; they build their nest principally of hay, and very frequently place it in the border of a hay-field. But, by whatever name it is known, it is a cheerful and active little bird, to which our woods and groves are much indebted for their melody. It is abundant and generally diffused, arriving in England early in April, and remaining until the middle of September. During the greater part of this period, it may be seen fluttering about the tops of trees, hunting the twigs and leaves for insects, and occasionally catching flies on the wing. It often, too, descends to the ground, and picks up insects among the herbage. I have never heard it sing on the ground ; but while employing itself aloft, it rarely allows more than a few minutes to elapse without going through its short and sweet song. This, though very agreeable, possesses no great variety, and is composed of about twenty or thirty notes, the latter ones of which are repeated rapidly, and form a natural cadence. For many years this pleasant little melody, or the simpler song of the Chiff-chaff, has been the first sound I have heard to announce the arrival of the summer birds of passage ; perhaps it is on this account that it is with me, at all seasons, a favourite rural sound.

Ornithologists seem well agreed that the Willow-warbler's food consists entirely of insects. This may be so, but I am much mistaken if a brood of this species annually hatched in a bank of furze adjoining my garden, do not, in conjunction with Blackcaps and Whitethroats, pay daily visits to a certain row of red raspberries in my garden. It may be that they come only in quest of aphides, but I have certainly seen them in dangerous proximity to clusters of the ripest fruit, which, when they were scared away, bore evident marks of having been pecked by birds. The nest of the Hay-bird resembles that of the Wood-warbler, but it is lined with feathers. The eggs are usually from five to seven, and of the same size and shape, but the spots are rust-coloured and limited in number.

THE CHIFF-CHAFF PHYLLOSCOPUS COLLYBITA (*Plate LIV*)

Upper parts olive-green, tinged with yellow ; above the eyes a narrow, faint, yellowish, white streak ; under parts yellowish white ; feathers of the leg dirty white ; second primary equal to the seventh ; third, fourth, fifth, and sixth, with the outer web sloped off at the extremity ; under wing-coverts primrose-yellow ; feet slender ; legs nearly black. Length four inches and a half ; breadth seven and a quarter. Eggs white, sparingly spotted with dark purple. A summer visitor, breeding in England, Wales, Ireland and south-western Scotland. A few remain for the winter in southern England, Wales, and Ireland.

WHATEVER question there may be whether the name of Willow-warbler be appropriately applied to the last species, there can be no doubt that the Chiff-chaff is well named. Let any one be asked in the month of May to walk into a wood and to hold up his hand when he heard a bird call itself by its own name, ' Chiff-chaff ', he could not possibly fall into an error. The bird is so common in southern England that it would be difficult to walk a mile in a woodland district without passing near one or more, and having little to say, it seems never weary of repeating its tale, ' Chiff, chaff, cheff, chiff, chaff ' : the syllables have a harsh sound pronounced by human lips, but when chanted in the silvery notes of a little bird, in the season of primroses and wild hyacinths, and accompanied by the warble of the Hay-bird, the full song of the Thrush, and the whistle of the Blackbird, they contribute not a little to the harmony of the woods. For two successive years a little yellowish bird, scarcely bigger than a wren, has established himself in my garden about the middle of April, and sedulously devoted himself to clearing away the aphides which infested some China roses trained against the walls of my house. Occasionally he would flutter against the windows, and give his attention to the spiders and gnats which nestled in the corners of the panes. The first year I took him for a Hay-bird, but, only too grateful for his kind offices, I was careful not to molest him. When, however, he appeared a second year, exactly at the same season, and performed a series of manœuvres so precisely similar that it was impossible to doubt that the bird was not merely of the same species, but the same individual, I watched him

more closely.   The dark colour of his feet, as observed from within
the house, as he was fluttering against the glass, decided the point that
he was not a Hay-bird, and when he retired to an apple tree hard by
and treated himself to a song after his repast, no doubt remained that
he was a Chiff-chaff.   It is not often that the Chiff-chaff is thus familiar
in its habits.   More frequently it makes its abode in woods and groves,
resembling the Hay-bird so closely in size, colour, and habits, that to
distinguish the two is very difficult.   The difference of note, however,
is decisive ;   and the colour of the feet (when the bird is near enough
to admit of being thus distinguished) is another certain criterion.   The
two birds frequent the same trees without rivalry or jealousy.   The
Chiff-chaff is the earliest of our spring visitors, arriving the middle of
March, and it sings all through the summer ;   I have heard it as late
as the thirtieth of September.   The nests, popularly called ' wood-
ovens ', are alike and placed in similar situations ;   their eggs are of
the same size and shape, but those of the Chiff-chaff are spotted with
very dark purple instead of rust-colour.   A few occasionally remain
with us all the year, feeding on winter gnats and the pupæ of small
insects, but remaining wholly silent.   Other names by which it is
known are ' Chip-chop ' and Lesser Pettichaps.

THE YELLOW-BROWED WARBLER PHYLLOSCOPUS INORNATUS
(Plate LXIX)

*Upper parts greenish yellow ; a lighter streak passing from the base of the upper
mandible through the crown to the back of the head, a lemon-coloured streak over
each eye, a narrow dusky band through the eye, and a short lemon-coloured streak
below the eye ; two lemon-colour bands across the wing ; quills dusky, edged
with pale yellow ; under parts pale yellow.   Length four inches ; breadth six
and a half.   Eggs white, with fine spots of dark red-brown, chiefly at the large
end.   A scarce passage migrant in the British Isles, occurring chiefly in autumn
and on the east coast.*

FAMILY REGULIDÆ

THE GOLD-CREST REGULUS REGULUS (Plate XLV)

*Upper parts olive, tinged with yellow ; cheeks ash-colour, without streaks ;
wing greyish brown, with two transverse white bands ; crest bright yellow,
tipped with orange and bounded on each side by a black line ; under parts
yellowish grey.   In the* female *the crest is lemon-colour, and the other tints
are less brilliant.   Each nostril is covered by one buff feather.   Length three
inches and a half.   Eggs cream-colour, minutely mottled at one end.   Resident
throughout the British Isles, except the Orkneys and Shetlands ; also a winter
visitor and passage migrant.*

THE Gold-crest, Golden-crested Regulus, or Golden-crested Wren,
though not exceeding in dimensions some of the larger humming-

birds, and though decorated with a crest equalling in brilliancy of colour the gay plumage of tropical birds, is a hardy little fellow, able to bear without shrinking the cold of an English winter, and to keep his position among the branches of high trees in the stormiest weather. Even during a heavy gale I have watched Gold-crests fluttering from branch to branch, and busily hunting for food, though the trees were waving like reeds. They are most numerous in winter, as a considerable number migrate southwards in October, but a great many remain with us all the year, preferring those districts where there are fir plantations. Their whole life is spent in the air ; I at least have never observed one on the ground. Their food consists of the insects which infest the leaves and twigs of trees ; and I have seen them capture small moths on the wing. While hunting for food, which appears to be all day long, they are never still, fluttering from branch to branch, hanging in all attitudes, and peering in all directions. From time to time they utter their thin and wiry call-note, which is by some compared to the cry of the Shrew. It might be mistaken for the jarring noise made by two branches which cross one another, or that of a damp finger rubbed lightly along a pane of glass. Early in spring the song commences ; it is composed of about fifteen short notes, rapidly uttered at an exceedingly high pitch, and ending with a yet more rapid cadence. By the call-note or song the vicinity of the bird is far more frequently detected than by its actual appearance ; for the branches of firs in woods are mostly at a considerable height from the ground, and our ' little king ' (saving his majesty) is hard to be distinguished from a fir-cone, except when he is in motion. Gold-crests are eminently social birds ; they generally hunt in parties of half a dozen or more, and do not often change their hunting-ground ; at least I infer as much from the fact that on various occasions I have observed the same bird on the same clump of trees, at intervals extending over several weeks. I could scarcely have been mistaken in the identity of the bird, as it had lost a leg, by what accident I know not ; but the loss did not at all interfere with its activity or spirits. Their sociability extends sometimes to birds of other kinds, as the Creeper and the Tits of several species have been seen hunting in company with them. The habits of these birds being similar, they perhaps associate from a feeling of mutual protection, just as Sparrows, Buntings, and Finches make common cause, when they invade our rick-yards. The Gold-crests are, however, naturally less wary than any of the Tits. These last will at once decamp if disturbed, but Gold-crests will continue their hunting without taking any notice of a spectator. In autumn large flocks sometimes arrive on our east coast extending across England and on into Ireland. In April a return migration takes place. The nest of the Gold-crest is a beautiful structure. Its external form is nearly that of a globe, with a contracted opening at the top. It is composed of moss and lichens, interwoven with wool and lined thickly with feathers. It is usually placed among the boughs of a silver fir or spruce fir, in such a manner as to be partially suspended from one branch and supported by another. The bird seems neither to court nor to shun the vicinity of human beings ; as I have found nests in the most lonely woods, and I have seen one in the branches of a spruce fir, so close to my house that I could look into the nest from my bedroom windows, and watch the old birds feeding their young. The eggs vary in number from five to eight, they are almost globular, and smaller than those of any other British bird. This is scarcely surprising, seeing that the weight of a recently killed adult male which I have before me is eighty-seven grains; so that five and a half full-grown birds weigh but an ounce.

THE FIRE-CREST REGULUS IGNICAPILLUS (*Plate XLV*)

Upper parts olive-green; a dark streak passing through the eye, and another white one above and below; crest brilliant orange, bounded in front and on each side by a black streak; in other respects resembling the last. Female *with all the colours less brilliant. Length four inches.* Eggs cream-colour, *tinged with red and dotted. A scarce winter visitor to England and Wales, chiefly to the southern counties of England.*

THIS species both in size and habits resembles the last, from which it is best distinguished by three dark lines on each side of its head. Hence it is called in France ' *Roitelet à triple bandeau* '. It is far less common than the Gold-crest; in fact, it is only a rare straggler. Its call-note is shorter than that of the Gold-crest, not so shrill, and pitched in a different key. The nests of the two birds are much alike.

FAMILY MUSCICAPIDÆ

THE SPOTTED FLYCATCHER MÚSCICAPA STRIATA (*Plate LV*)

Upper plumage ash-brown; feathers of the head marked with a central dark line; under parts white, the sides marked with longitudinal brown streaks; flanks tinged with red. Length six inches; breadth ten inches. Eggs bluish white, mottled with reddish spots, which are deepest in colour towards the larger end. A summer visitor, breeding throughout the British Isles, except the Outer Hebrides, Orkneys, and Shetlands.

THERE are few birds with whose haunts and habits we are more familiar than those of the common Flycatcher. In the wooded parts of England there is scarcely a country house, perhaps, which has not in its neighbourhood at least a single pair of these birds, who, though their stay with us is but short, become as necessary appendages of the garden during the summer months as the Redbreast is in winter. They have neither song to recommend them nor brilliancy of colouring; yet the absence of these qualities is more than compensated by the confidence they repose in the innocent intentions of the human beings whose protection they claim, by their strong local attachments, and by their unceasing activity in the pursuit of flying insects. At any time during the months of June, July, and August, in most country and suburban gardens, one may observe perched on a railing, standard rose, or the low branch of an apple tree, a small brownish bird, with a speckled breast, about the size of a Sparrow, but more slender in form, taking no notice of human beings, but nevertheless evidently on the lookout for something. Suddenly it darts from its position, flies rapidly forwards for a few yards, performs an evolution in the air, and returns either to the exact spot which it had previously occupied or to a similar one hard by. After a rest of a few seconds, it performs the same manœuvre, and always with the same object and success. Every time it quitted its perch, some ill-fated fly or beetle was discovered, winging its way through the air, and captured to be devoured on the spot, or to form part of a pellet of insect food for a hungry nestling. The nest, composed of moss, straws, and hair, and lined with feathers, is usually placed either against a wall, hidden by the leaves of a trained fruit tree, or on the horizontal bough of a standard apple tree. During the year 1859, a pair of these birds had taken up their quarters in my own garden in a situation such as that first described, but becoming dissatisfied with the locality even after the nest had received its complement of eggs—five—deserted it, and built another nest in an apple tree a few yards off, choosing a position on a short branch, where their workmanship was concealed from the sight of passengers by a cluster of large apples. The bough overhung a path by which many persons passed to and fro every day ; but the nest was built, and the old birds hatched their eggs, neither noticed nor noticing, until one day when I happened to stop underneath, upon which the bird took flight, and so revealed her place of retreat. I do not mention this incident as anything remarkable, but simply to exemplify the habits of the bird when it has taken up its residence in a frequented garden, and in contrast with its treatment of intruders when it has chosen a more secluded spot for a home. A few days after, I happened to be fly-fishing on the bank of a stream close to which grew some tall elm trees. Under one of these I was pursuing my amusement, when a flycatcher darted from a tree on the opposite side of the stream, and flew so close to my face that to dip my head out of the way was unavoidable. The same movement was repeated again and again, making it impossible for me to persist. Suspecting that there was a nest somewhere very near me, I looked up and discovered, within a few inches of my head, a nest built against the bole of the tree, and containing four or five nearly fledged young ones, whose heads and breasts projected considerably beyond the edge of their mossy cradle. As I moved away, the parent bird hopped about uneasily in a neighbouring tree, uttering its monotonous and unmusical chirrup, but molested me no further. It would seem then that the garden bird, grown familiar with the human form, was unsuspicious of danger, while the other, who had not been accustomed to see her sanctuary approached, immediately took alarm. It is supposed that the same birds are in the habit of returning annually to their old resort. Both the above incidents tend to give weight to this opinion : one of the birds having been reared, probably in the garden, and so having been accustomed to the sight of men from the first ; the other having been always a recluse. The fact which fell under my own notice, that a nest was built, and a brood reared for three successive years in exactly the same spot, is, I think, conclusive evidence that either the same birds or their immediate descendants were the architects, it being scarcely credible that three several pairs of birds should have fixed on the same spot by accident. Mr. Denham Weir has observed that the Spotted Flycatcher consumes only a day and a half in the construction of its nest, and that a pair of birds which he watched fed their young no less than 537 times in one day, beginning at twenty-five minutes before four o'clock in the morning, and ending at ten minutes before nine in the evening. The young birds soon learn to hawk for their prey as well as their parents. I have recorded elsewhere an instance in which the parent birds contrived to feed a disabled young one after it had left the nest. The Flycatcher arrives in England about the end of April, and leaves about the end of September.

THE PIED FLYCATCHER MUSCÍCAPA HYPOLEUCA (*Plate LV*)

Upper plumage and tail black, the wings black, with the central coverts white ; scapulars edged with white ; under plumage white. In the female *the black is replaced by greyish brown, the white is dingy, and the three lateral tail-feathers are edged with white. Length five inches. Eggs pale blue, generally without spots. A summer visitor, breeding regularly in Wales, northern England, and southern Scotland, and occasionally elsewhere in England and Scotland ; also a passage migrant.*

THE Pied Flycatcher, so called from its feathers being varied with black and white, is a smaller bird than the preceding, and by no means so common, being very local as a breeder. It appears, indeed, to be mainly confined to the northern counties of England, where it arrives about the middle of April, and builds its nest of dry leaves, small roots, grass, and a little hair, loosely put together, in the hole of a tree. There it lays from five to seven pale blue eggs, very like, both in size and colour, those of the Redstart, which it also much resembles in habits. It has more claim to be considered a songster than the Spotted Flycatcher. In places where it is frequent it is often observed to settle on the decayed stump of a tree, constantly repeating its short, little varied, but far from unpleasing song, every now and then interrupted by the pursuit and capture of some passing insect. It is said also to be very noisy and clamorous when its nest is approached. It quits our shores in September.

THE RED-BREASTED FLYCATCHER MUSCÍCAPA PARVA
(*Plate LXIX*)

Forehead and crown brown, tinged with greyish ; rest of upper parts brown ; upper tail-coverts and tail brownish black, four outer pairs of tail-feathers with conspicuous white bases ; chin, throat, and upper breast, orange-red ; belly white ; sides and flanks pale buff ; bill brown ; legs and iris dark brown.

Female *without grey tinge on head ; throat and upper breast pale buff. Length five inches. Eggs pale bluish green, freckled with rusty brown. A rare passage migrant in the British Isles, chiefly on the east coast in autumn.*

FAMILY PRUNELLIDÆ

THE HEDGE SPARROW PRUNELLA MODULÁRIS (*Plate LI*)

Crown of the head ash-colour with brown streaks ; sides of the neck, throat and breast, bluish grey ; bill strong and broad at base ; wing-coverts and feathers on the back reddish brown, with a tawny spot in the centre ; middle wing-coverts tipped with yellowish white ; lower tail-coverts brown, with a whitish border ; middle of abdomen white. Length five and a half inches. Eggs greenish blue, without spots. Resident throughout the British Isles, except the Shetlands.

INVETERATE custom has so attached the name of Hedge Sparrow to this bird, that in spite of all the efforts of ornithologists to convince the world that it is no sparrow at all (a hard-beaked, grain-eating bird), it is still more frequently called by its popular name than by any of those that have been suggested. The gentle, innocent, confiding, little brown bird, which creeps like a mouse through our garden flower-beds, picks up a meagre fare in our roads and lanes, builds its nest in our thorn hedges, and though dingy itself, lays such brilliant blue eggs, has been known to us from our infancy as a ' Hedge Sparrow ', and we decline any innovation : the name is a time-honoured one, and no one will mistake us. Hedge Accentor, Hedge Warbler, Dunnock, and Shuffle-wing, are names open to those who prefer them, but we adhere to the old-fashioned designation of Hedge Sparrow. At all seasons his habits and food appear to be the same. All day long he is shuffling about on the ground picking up minute atoms, chiefly small seeds in winter, supplemented by insects in summer. Every day, nearly all the year round, he repairs at intervals to the nearest hedge, where he sings a song, soft and gentle like himself ; and every evening, when the Blackbird rings his curfew bell, he fails not to respond with his drowsy *cheep, cheep*, as he repairs to the bush he has selected for his night's rest. Very early in spring, he has chosen his mate, built his snug nest, and too probably commenced a second ; for, unsuspicious in nature, he does not retire to solitary places for this purpose, and the leafless hedges but ill conceal his labours from the peering eyes of all-destroying ploughboys. Such are nearly all his ' short and simple annals '. He quarrels with no one, he achieves no distinction, throwing no one into ecstasies with his song, and stealing no one's fruit ; unobtrusive and innocent, he claims no notice, and dreads no resentment ; and so, through all the even tenor of his way, he is, without knowing it, the favourite of children, and of all the good and gentle.

FAMILY MOTACILLIDÆ

THE PIED WAGTAIL MOTACILLA YARRELLII (*Plate LVI*)

Summer—all the plumage variegated with white and black ; back and scapulars, chin, throat, and neck, black ; a small portion of the side of the neck white. Winter—back and scapulars ash-grey ; chin and throat white, with a black, but not entirely isolated, gorget. Length seven inches and a half. Eggs bluish white, speckled with dark grey. A resident, breeding throughout the British Isles, but many individuals migrate south for the winter.

THE Pied Wagtail or Dishwasher is a familiar and favourite bird, best known by its habit of frequenting the banks of ponds and streams, where it runs, not hops, about, picking insects from the herbage, and frequently rising with a short jerking flight, to capture some winged insect, which its quick eye has detected hovering in the air. Its simple song consists of but few notes, but the tone is sweet and pleasing, and is frequently heard when the bird is cleaving its way through the air with its peculiar flight, in which it describes a series of arcs, as if it were every instant on the point of alighting, but had altered its mind. While hunting for food, it keeps its tail in perpetual motion. It shows little fear of man, and frequently approaches his dwelling. It may often be noticed running rapidly along the tiles or thatch of a country house, and it not infrequently takes its station on the point of a gable, or the ridge of the roof, and rehearses its song again and again. Very frequently, too, it perches in trees, especially such as are in the vicinity of ponds. Next to watery places, it delights in newly ploughed fields, and hunts for insects on the ground, utterly fearless of the ploughman and his implements. A newly mown garden lawn is another favourite resort ; so also is a meadow in which cows are feeding, and to these it is most serviceable, running in and out between their legs, and catching, in a short time, an incredible number of flies. The country scarcely furnishes a prettier sight than that afforded by a family of Wagtails on the short grass of a park, in July or August. A party of five or six imperfectly fledged birds may often be seen scattered over a small space of ground, running about with great activity, and picking up insects, while the parent birds perform short aerial journeys above and around them, frequently alighting, and transferring from their own mouths to those of their offspring, each in its turn, the insects they have just captured. They are at all times sociably disposed, being seen sometimes in small parties, and sometimes in large flocks. It has been noticed that when one of a party has been wounded by a discharge from a gun, another has flown down as if to aid it, or sympathize with it. They share, too, with Swallows the praise of being among the first to announce to other birds the approach of a Hawk, and join with them in mobbing and driving it away.

About the middle of April, the Pied Wagtail begins to build its nest. This is usually placed in a hole in a bank or hedge, among stones, or in the hollow of a tree ; it is composed of dry grass and withered leaves, mixed with moss, and lined with wool, hair, and a few feathers. It is a compact and solid structure, capable of protecting the eggs and young from the damp soil, but is not generally concealed with much art ; and hence perhaps it is frequently selected by the Cuckoo, to lay an egg in.

Towards autumn, Pied Wagtails for the most part migrate southwards. In the midland counties they may be often observed in large companies, in October, halting for a few days wherever food is abundant, and then suddenly disappearing ; after which only a few stragglers are seen until the spring. They return northwards about the beginning of March. In the extreme south of England they are numerous all the year round.

THE WHITE WAGTAIL MOTACILLA ALBA (*Plate LVI*)

Summer—head, breast, wings, and tail, variegated with black and white ; chin, throat, and neck, black ; back and scapulars pearl-grey ; side of the neck as low as the wings white. Winter—chin, throat, and neck, white, with an isolated black gorget. Length nearly seven inches and a half. Eggs bluish white, speckled with black. A passage migrant through the British Isles, occasionally remaining to breed.

THIS is the Continental representative of the Pied Wagtail, identical in habits and behaviour. The back and rump are clear pale grey. The males are therefore easily distinguished, but the females are much more alike and can only be distinguished with certainty by the colour of the rump. The young are indistinguishable. The two forms not infrequently interbreed and are generally regarded as geographical races of a single species though no intermediates are found.

THE GREY WAGTAIL MOTACILLA CINEREA (*Plate LVI*)

Summer—head and back bluish grey ; a pale streak above the eyes ; throat black ; under parts bright yellow ; tail very long. Winter—chin and throat whitish, passing into yellow. Length seven inches and three-quarters. Eggs bluish white, speckled with dark grey. A resident in the British Isles, not breeding in the Shetlands and Outer Hebrides and only sparingly in the eastern counties of England ; many migrate south for the winter.

GREY WAGTAIL is not a very happy name for this bird, as the bright yellow of its neck and breast are far more conspicuous than the more sober grey of the head and back ; yet, as there are other claimants for the more appropriate names ' Yellow ', and ' Greyheaded ', the young observer must be cautious while reading the descriptions of the several members of the family, or he may possibly fall into error. The Grey Wagtail is among the most elegant and graceful of British birds, and in delicacy of colouring is surpassed by few. Its habits are much the same as those of the Pied Wagtail, but it is even lighter and more active in its movements. It is less frequently observed away from water than that species, and though, like it, not altogether a permanent resident in England, it visits us at the opposite season, coming in autumn, and retiring northwards in spring. This partial migration seems to be characteristic of the family, and is difficult to account for. Why out of a certain number of birds of the same species, some should annually travel southwards, to supply the place of individuals belonging to an allied species, who have travelled yet farther to the south, and why, on the reappearance of the latter in spring, the first should return to their northern haunts, are questions more easily asked than answered.

The Grey Wagtail has been repeatedly observed to indulge in a fancy which might well obtain for it the name of ' window-bird '. The first recorded instance occurs in an early number of the *Zoologist*, where it is stated that every morning for a period of between three and four months, from the beginning of October to the end of January, a Grey Wagtail came to the window of a country house as soon as the blinds were drawn up, and darted against the panes of glass, pecking with its beak as if it saw some object. It would then retire, and after a pause repeat the operation, but from what motive no one could conjecture. A lady writes to me from Dewlish House, Dorsetshire : ' We are constantly being disturbed by a yellow-breasted Water-Wagtail, which comes tapping at the windows or skylights, from the first streak of light till evening. What may be his object no one can say. It is too cold at present (March) for flies or spiders, and had there been any hibernating there he would have eaten them long ago, he comes so frequently. When, on going upstairs, or when sitting down in my room, I hear this loud repeated tapping, it is vain for me to open the window and try to entice him in with crumbs ; he does not even notice them. This morning he woke me at about four o'clock. You would have said, " Some one rapping at my window as a signal that I must get up." An old servant tells me, " Ah, 'twere just the same last spring, when the family were in London ; they say that it do mean something." '

The Grey Wagtail does not commonly build its nest in the eastern counties of England, although instances have occurred. It prefers hilly and rocky districts. More frequently it repairs in spring to the north of England and south of Scotland, and builds its nest on the ground, or in the hole of a bank, or between large stones, and never at any great distance from the water. It is composed of stems and blades of grass, mixed with moss and wool, and lined with wool, hair, and feathers.

THE BLUE-HEADED (OR GREY-HEADED) WAGTAIL
MOTACILLA FLAVA (*Plate LVI*)

Top of the head, lore, and nape, lead-grey ; over the eye a white streak ; scapulars, back, and upper tail-coverts, greenish olive, tinged with yellow ; chin white, in the young male yellow ; under parts bright yellow. Length six inches and a half. Eggs mottled with yellow, brown, and grey. A rare summer visitor to the British Isles, a few pairs breeding regularly in south-eastern England and occasionally elsewhere.

THIS, one of the common Yellow Wagtails of the Continent, is a rare visitor in this country. Its habits, nest, and eggs, closely resemble those of the next species. It is the *Bergeronette printanière* ('Little shepherdess of the Spring') of the French, a pretty name, suggested by the habit, common to all the genus, of resorting to sheepfolds for the sake of feeding on the flies with which such places abound.

YELLOW, OR RAY'S, WAGTAIL MOTACILLA RAYI (*Plate LVI*)

Top of the head, lore, nape, back, and scapulars, pale olive ; over the eye a streak of bright yellow ; chin yellow ; lower parts of the same colour. Length six inches and a half. Eggs whitish, mottled with yellow, brown, and grey. A summer visitor to the British Isles, breeding in most parts of England and Wales, a few districts of southern and eastern Scotland, and round Lough Neagh in Ireland.

IN eastern and southern England Ray's Wagtail is, next to the Pied, the best known species, being a regular summer visitor, and everywhere tolerably common. It is said by most authors to frequent the water rather less than the other species, and to prefer fields of peas and tares, open downs, and sheep pastures ; but, as far as my own observation goes, I have seen it far more frequently near water than elsewhere, and if I wished to observe its habits, I should repair to the nearest canal or river, in the certain expectation of seeing a pair hunting among the aquatic weeds for their food, running along the sandy or muddy shore, perching on the broad leaves of the water-lily, and chasing each other with dipping flight through the air. I am inclined to believe that, though it may have often been noticed in dry pastures and stony places, yet that when so circumstanced, it is only engaged on an exploring expedition from its watery haunts ; for it is scarcely possible that a bird so thoroughly at home in a weedy pond, can ever be long absent from such a locality from choice. Its habits are precisely similar to those of the Pied Wagtail, except that it visits us in the summer exclusively, retiring southwards in autumn. It may often also be seen in company with that species. Besides its call-note, which consists of two shrill notes, the second of which is a musical tone lower than the first, it has a short and exceedingly sweet song, something like that of the Redbreast when at its best. This I have heard it utter whilst it was perched on a low bush over-hanging a pond. Its nest was probably somewhere in the neighbour-hood, for when disturbed it flew to a short distance only, alighted on another twig and repeated its warble again. This was in the first week in May, and is the only occasion on which I ever heard it really sing. The nest resembles that of the Pied Wagtail, and is placed on the ground, usually in water meadows. The popular name Washerwoman belongs to the whole family. The corresponding term, *Lavandière*,

is also found in France, and was given from the fanciful similarity
between the beating of the water with its tail by the bird while tripping
along the leaves of a water-lily, and the beating of linen in the water
by washerwomen, a custom still existing in France, and some parts
of England and Ireland.

THE TREE PIPIT ANTHUS TRIVIÁLIS (*Plate LVII*)

*Hind claw shorter than the toe, and curved so as to form the fourth of a circle ;
upper parts ash, tinged with olive, the centre of each feather dark brown ;
a double band across the wing, formed by the yellowish white tips of the lesser
and middle wing-coverts ; throat and region of the eye dull white ; breast
reddish yellow, spotted, and at the sides lightly streaked with dark brown.
Length six inches. Eggs dull white, variously mottled with purple brown. A
summer visitor, breeding in England, Wales, and the mainland of Scotland.*

THE name Titlark is popularly applied to three common species of
birds which were formerly placed in the same family with the Skylark. Modern ornithologists now place them in a distinct genus,
in the same family as the Wagtails. In colouring, however, in general
form, and, to a slight extent, in habits, namely, in the mode of feeding
and nesting, there is much similarity between the genera ; but in the
power of soaring, the Lark, though imitated by one species, is
unrivalled. The old name Titlark, then, must be understood to be
merged in the more distinctive title, Pipit, given to three common
kinds which severally frequent trees, meadows, and the seashore.
The Tree Pipit alone is a migratory species, arriving in this country
towards the end of April, and leaving us in the autumn. It is common
in most of the wooded counties of England, except the extreme west,
but attracts little notice, being unostentatious in size and colour,
while its song, except by the practised ear, is likely to be lost in the
general melody of the woods. Yarrell's succinct account of its most
characteristic habit is so comprehensive and accurate, that the observer
who wishes to make its acquaintance can scarcely fail by its help
to identify the bird on its very first occurrence. ' The male has a
pretty song, perhaps more attractive from the manner in which it is
given, than the quality of the song itself. He generally sings while
perched on the top of a bush, or one of the upper branches of an
elm tree standing in a hedgerow, from which, if watched for a short
time, he will be seen to ascend with quivering wing about as high
again as the tree ; then, stretching out his wings and expanding his
tail, he descends slowly by a half-circle, singing the whole time, to
the same branch from which he started, or to the top of the nearest
other tree ; and so constant is this habit with him, that if the observer
does not approach near enough to alarm him, the bird may be seen
to perform the same evolution twenty times in half an hour, and I
have witnessed it most frequently during and after a warm May
shower.' Its descent to the ground is generally performed in the
same manner. Its food consists of insects and small seeds, for which
it searches among the grass or newly ploughed ground, with the

walking and running gait of the Wagtails, but without their incessant waving movement of the tail. The nest, which is placed on the ground, under a tuft of grass or low bush, and very frequently on the skirt of a wood or copse, is composed of dry grass and small roots, and lined with finer grass and hair. The eggs are usually five in number, and vary so much that extreme specimens would scarcely seem to belong to the same bird. In the predominating brown hue a tinge of red is, however, always perceptible, and by this it may be distinguished from the egg of the Meadow Pipit.[1]

THE MEADOW PIPIT ANTHUS PRATENSIS (*Plate LVII*)

Hind claw longer than the toe, slightly curved ; upper parts ash, tinged with olive, especially in winter, the centre of each feather dark brown ; under parts reddish white, streaked with dark brown. Length five inches and three-quarters. Eggs dull white, variously spotted and mottled with brown. A resident, breeding throughout the British Isles, but many migrate south in winter.

IT may be thought at the first glimpse that a difference in the comparative length of the hinder claws of two birds so much alike as the Tree and Meadow Pipits is scarcely sufficient to justify a specific distinction ; but when it is considered that a short and curved claw enables a bird to retain a firm grasp of a small twig, while a long and almost straight one is best adapted for perching on the ground, it will appear at once that, however similar two birds may be in all other respects, yet the slight one in which they differ is the point on which hinges a complex scheme of habits. So the Tree Pipit frequents wooded districts, and passes a large portion of its time aloft among the branches, while the Meadow Pipit finds its happiness on the ground. It is not, indeed, confined to the unwooded country, for no bird is more generally diffused, and the nests of both species, constructed of similar materials, may frequently be found in the border of the same field, yet it often finds a home in wild, barren districts, frequented by no other small birds but the Wheatear and Ring Ouzel. I have even more than once seen it alight on a tree, but this was apparently as a resting-place on which it perched previously to descending to roost among the heath on a common. Had I not been near, it would most probably have dropped at once to its hiding-place as some of its companions did. From its attachment to commons and waste lands, the Meadow Pipit has received the names of Ling-bird and Moss-cheeper. In winter it is more abundant in the plains, where it may often be seen in small parties searching for seeds and insects in recently ploughed lands, well marked by its running gait and the olive tinge of its upper plumage. Its song, which is not frequently heard, is a short and simple

[1] ' Amongst our land birds ', says Hewitson, ' there is no species the eggs of which present so many, or such distinct varieties, as those of the Tree Pipit. No one would at first believe them to be eggs of the same species ; and it was not till I had captured the bird upon each of the varieties, and also received them from Mr. H. Doubleday, similarly attested, that I felt satisfactorily convinced upon the subject.'

strain, sometimes uttered on the ground, but more generally, while rising or falling, at no great height in the air. Its nest is only to be distinguished from that of the Tree Pipit by the dark brown hue of the eggs, which are somewhat similar to those of the Skylark, only smaller. 'The egg of the Cuckoo is more frequently deposited and hatched in the nest of the Meadow Pipit than in that of any other bird,' says Yarrell.

THE ROCK PIPIT ANTHUS PETROSUS (*Plate LVII*)

Hind claw about equal in length to the toe, much curved; upper plumage greenish brown, the centre of each feather darker brown; a whitish streak over the eye; under parts dull white, spotted, and streaked with dark brown. Length six inches and three-quarters. Eggs dull white, mottled with dingy brown. A resident on the coasts of the British Isles.

EXCEPT that it is somewhat larger, the Rock Pipit is very similar in form and colour to the last species. It is, however, far more local, being confined exclusively to the seashore, but there of very common occurrence. Every one familiar with the sea-coast, must have observed it moving through the air with a jerking flight, occasionally alighting on a rock or on the beach near the line of high-water mark, searching busily for marine insects. In spring, it frequently takes little flights inland, never to a great distance, repeating its simple song all the while, and chasing as if in sport some one or other of its companions. In winter, it seems to act as a guide to the smaller land birds, who, finding their supply of food diminished or altogether cut off by the frost, are attracted by its movements, and join it in searching for insects among the unfrozen

'ridge of all things vile,'

left on the shore by the receding tide. If not gregarious, it is at least sociable, and that, too, at seasons when the flocks could hardly have been family gatherings only. The same remark holds good of the Meadow Pipit. A migration southwards takes place in October along our east coast.

THE WATER PIPIT ANTHUS SPINOLETTA (*Plate LXVIII*)

Upper parts greyish brown; wings and tail dark brown, the outer tail-feathers white on the outer portion; chin and stripe over the eye white; throat and breast buffish pink; belly and under tail-coverts whitish; bill and legs brown. Length six and a half inches. Eggs greyish white, mottled with brown. A scarce passage migrant and winter visitor to the British Isles.

THE TAWNY PIPIT ANTHUS CAMPESTRIS (*Plate LXVIII*)

Upper parts sandy brown with dull dark centres to the feathers; tail-feathers dark brown, outer pair creamy white on the outer portion; stripe over the eye cream-coloured ; breast and flanks buff ; chin and belly cream-colour ; bill brown, above, yellowish below ; legs yellowish brown. Length six and a half inches. Eggs whitish, closely spotted and mottled with brown. A very rare visitor to the British Isles, except Sussex, where it formerly occurred almost annually and nested on at least one occasion.

FAMILY BOMBYCILLIDÆ

THE WAXWING BOMBYCILLA GARRULUS (*Plate LV*)

Feathers of the head elongated, forming a crest ; upper plumage purplish red ; lower the same, but of a lighter tint ; throat and lore black ; greater wing-coverts black, tipped with white ; primaries black, with a yellow or white angular spot near the extremity, six or eight of the secondaries and tertiaries having the shaft prolonged and terminating in a substance resembling red sealing-wax ; tail black, tipped with yellow. Length eight inches. Eggs pale blue, with a few streaks of brown and lilac. An irregular winter visitor to the British Isles, chiefly to the eastern counties of Scotland and England.

THE Waxwing is an elegant bird, of about the size of a Thrush. It visits this country, and in fact every other European country where it is known at all, at irregular intervals, generally in flocks, which vary in number from eight or ten to some scores. Thus it is everywhere a stranger ; and little was known till recently of its nesting habits. It is perhaps on account of this ignorance of its natural history, that it has borne a variety of names which are as inappropriate as possible. Temminck describes it under the name Bombycivora, or devourer of Bombyx, a large moth, a name quite unfit for a bird which lives exclusively on fruits and berries. This was softened into Bombycilla, which means, I presume, a little Bombyx, though the bird in question is far larger than any known moth. Its French name *Jaseur,* equivalent to the English one, Chatterer, is quite as inappropriate, as it is singularly silent. Why again it should be called Bohemian, no one seems to know ; for it is no more a resident in Bohemia, or even more frequent there, than in England. In default of all certain information, then, I venture to surmise that, coming in parties no one knows whence, and going no one knows whither, they may have received the name Bohemian, because they resemble in their habits the wandering tribes of gypsies, who were formerly called indifferently Egyptians and Bohemians. Taken in this sense, the Bohemian or *Wandering* Waxwing, as it used to be called, is a name open to no exception. The plumage of the bird is silky, and that of the head is remarkable for forming a crest, and being capable of being elevated, as in the Cardinal. Its black gorget and tiara, the patches of white, yellow, and black described above, make it very conspicuous for colouring, and the singularity of its appearance is much increased by the appendages to its secondaries and tertiaries, which resemble in colour and substance red sealing-wax. In very old birds these waxen appendages are also to be found at the extremities of the tail-feathers, being no more than the shafts of the feathers, condensed with the web. It feeds on insects, fruit, berries, and seeds. Its call-note is a twitter, which it rarely utters, except when taking flight and alighting. The Waxwing is a northern bird, and one of its German names, *Schneevogel* (snowbird), was evidently given in this belief. It is a stupid, lazy bird, occupied only in eating and reposing for digestion. Its song is weak and uncertain.

FAMILY LANIIDÆ

THE GREAT GREY SHRIKE LANIUS EXCÚBITOR (*Plate LVIII*)

Head, nape, and back, bright ash-grey ; a broad black band beneath the eyes ; under plumage pure white ; wings short, black ; base of the primaries and tips of the secondaries white ; tail with the two middle feathers black, and the outer on each side white with a black spot at the base, the rest black and white ; bill and feet black. Female—of a more dingy hue above ; below, dull white, the proportion of black in the feathers increasing as they approach the middle ; each feather of the breast terminating in a crescent-shaped ash-grey spot. Length ten inches ; breadth fourteen inches. Eggs bluish white, spotted at the larger end with two shades of brown. Young barred below. A scarce winter visitor to the British Isles, chiefly to the east of Scotland and England.

THE family of Shrikes, or Butcher-birds, would seem to occupy an intermediate station between birds of prey and insectivorous birds. The subject of the present chapter especially, though little resembling a Hawk in appearance, has, on account of its habits, some pretension to be ranked among birds of prey ; from which, however, it differs in the essential particular that, as well as the rest of the family, it seizes and carries off its prey with its beak and not with its claws. It derives its name *excubitor* (sentinel) from its favourite habit of posting itself on the topmost twig of a poplar or other lofty tree, whence it keeps up a watchful look-out, not only for its prey, but for any bird of the Hawk tribe, against which it wages incessant and deadly hostility. When it descries one of these birds, which it does at a great distance, it utters a shriek, as if for the purpose of giving an alarm, a cry which is instantly repeated by all birds of the same species which happen to be within hearing. This antipathy against birds of prey is taken advantage of by fowlers in France, who, when setting their nets for Hawks, take with them a ' sentinel ' Shrike and station it near the living bird, which they employ as a lure. So rapid is the swoop of the Falcon that but for the warning cry of the Shrike it would descend and carry off its victim before the fowler had time to close his nets ; but the keen eye of the sentinel detects, and his shrill cry announces, the approach of his enemy, and the fowler has time to prepare. The principal food of this bird appears to be mice, frogs, lizards, and insects, especially the stag-beetle and grasshopper, though in its natural state it will capture and destroy any birds inferior to itself in strength and courage. Its name *Lanius* (Latin for butcher) and

Butcher-bird were given to it from its habit of impaling beetles and small birds on thorns in the vicinity of its nest. Its flight is peculiar, being composed of a series of dips, like that of the Wagtail; and when it quits its perch on the summit of one tall tree to fly to another, it drops and rises again so as to form a curve like that of a loose rope hung from two tall masts. Another peculiarity of the Shrike is a remarkable power of imitating the song of other birds, which it is said to exercise in order to obtain its food more easily, by beguiling the nestlings of the smaller birds into answering it by a chirrup, and so betraying their retreat. The notes which it has been observed to imitate are those of the Nightingale, Robin, Swallow, and Stonechat. Its proper note is harsh, resembling somewhat that of the Kestrel.

THE RED-BACKED SHRIKE LANIUS COLLURIO (*Plate LVIII*)

Head, nape, shoulders and upper tail-coverts, ash-grey, a black band reaching from the gape to beyond the ears; back, scapulars, and wing-coverts, reddish brown; throat white, passing into rose-red on the breast and flanks; wings blackish, edged with reddish brown; tail nearly even at the end, four middle feathers black, tipped with reddish grey, the rest white from the base through two-thirds of their length, the other third black with a white tip; second primary longer than the fifth. Female—upper plumage rusty brown, tinged near the nape and tail with ash-grey; lower, white, the sides barred transversely by narrow curved lines; outer webs and tips of the outer tail-feathers yellowish white, four middle ones uniform dusky brown. Length seven inches; breadth eleven inches. Eggs cream-coloured, greenish, or delicate grey, variously mottled and spotted with light brown and ash-grey. A summer visitor, breeding in England and Wales, but only a rare straggler to Scotland and Ireland.

THE Red-backed Shrike, though not generally diffused throughout England, is in certain localities far from uncommon. In the wooded districts of the midland and southern counties many specimens may be annually observed, and the nest is of frequent occurrence. This is usually placed a few feet from the ground, in the middle of a thick bush or hedge; and, very unlike that of the rapacious birds, is a massive, well-built structure of twigs, dry grass, and moss, lined with hair and fine roots. This bird is called in France *l'écorcheur* (the flayer), from the custom ascribed to it of skinning the bodies of its victims before devouring them. Its habits and food are similar to those of the last species, and it is said also to possess the same imitative power. That it impales insects and even young birds on thorns there is no doubt.

A professional bird-catcher told how a Red-backed Shrike once pounced on one of his call-birds (a Linnet), and attempted to carry it off; but being prevented from doing so by the Linnet being fastened to the ground by a string and wooden peg, the Shrike tore off the head of its victim, with which it made its escape. The bird-catcher then drew out from the ground the peg which held down the Linnet, and left the dead bird lying in the net. In about half an hour the Shrike again appeared, pounced upon the body of the dead Linnet, and carried it off in its beak, with the string and peg hanging to it ; the weight of the latter was probably the cause of the Shrike not carrying its prey quite away, as it dropped it after flying about fifteen yards, when the bird-catcher again picked up the dead Linnet, and replaced it in the net. The Shrike in the meantime retreated to some neighbouring bushes, from which it soon made a third pounce upon the nets, this time attacking the second call-bird, which was a Sparrow. On this occasion, however, the bird-catcher was on the watch, and, drawing his nets, captured the Shrike, which proved to be an adult female. This daring act was observed late in the month of June, when, perhaps, the courage of the mother bird was unusually excited by the cravings of her brood at home, and further stimulated by the impression that the call-birds were in trouble, and consequently offered an easy prey.

An amiable trait in the character of this Shrike is its attachment to its mate and young. A female has been known to approach so close to the cage in which her captured lord was confined, that she was herself easily taken ; and when a nest of young birds is molested, both parents defend their offspring with astonishing intrepidity.

The Red-backed Shrike is known to us only as a summer visitor, departing early in autumn. Its note is a harsh *chuck !* but the song of the male is somewhat pleasant.

THE WOODCHAT SHRIKE LANIUS SENATOR (*Plate LVIII*)

Forehead and cheeks black ; nape bright rust-colour ; back and wings variegated with black, white, and reddish brown ; under parts white ; outer tail-feathers white, with a square black spot at the base on the inner web, the two next with the black spot larger, and on both webs, the two middle ones wholly black, the rest black tipped with white ; tail slightly rounded ; second primary equal in length to the fifth. Female—all her colours dingy ; breast marked transversely with fine brown lines. Length seven and a half inches. Eggs bluish white, spotted at the larger end with brown and ash-grey. An occasional summer visitor to the British Isles, chiefly to south and east England, said to have nested in the Isle of Wight.

THE habits of this bird, which is a very rare visitant to the British Isles, differ in no material respect from those of the foregoing species. On the Continent it is more frequent in the south than the north, where it frequents trees rather than bushes, and generally places its nest, which it constructs of twigs, moss, and white lichen, in the forked branch of an oak.

FAMILY STURNIDÆ

THE STARLING STURNUS VULGÁRIS (*Plate LIX*)

Plumage black, with brilliant purple and green reflections, the upper feathers tipped with cream-colour ; under tail-coverts edged with white ; beak yellow ; feet flesh-colour, tinged with brown.   Female—spotted below as well as above. Young—uniform ash-brown, without spots.   Length eight and a half inches ; width fifteen inches.   Eggs uniform pale greenish blue.   A resident throughout the British Isles, also a winter visitor and passage migrant.

THE Starling is a citizen of the world.   From the North Cape to the Sahara and from Ireland to Kamchatka, he is almost everywhere at home, and too familiar with the dealings of man to come within a dangerous distance of his arm, though he fully avails himself of all the advantages which human civilization offers, having discovered, long ago, that far more grubs and worms are to be procured on a newly mown meadow than on the bare hillside, and that the flavour of May-dukes and Coroons immeasurably excels that of the wild cherries in the wood.   That dove-cots, holes in walls, and obsolete water-spouts are convenient resting-places for a nest, appears to be a traditional piece of knowledge, and that where sheep and oxen are kept, there savoury insects abound, is a fact generally known and improved on accordingly.   So, in suburban gardens, where even the Redbreast and Tits are unknown, Starlings are periodical visitors and afford much amusement by their shambling gait, and industrious boring on the lawn for larvæ—in cherry orchards they are regarded with terror, on account of the amount of mischief they will accomplish in a short space of time ;   and in the sheep-fold they are doubtless most cordially welcomed and their services thankfully received, as they rid the poor tormented animals of many an evil ' tick '.

The Starling is a handsome bird ;   seen at a distance it appears to be of a uniform black hue, but on closer inspection its sable coat is found to be lustrous with reflections of purple and green, and every feather is tipped with white, or cream-colour—a mantle of shot-silk garnished with pearls.

Except during the nesting season, a Starling is rarely seen alone ; most commonly perhaps they are observed in parties of from six to twelve, hunting in orchards or meadows for whichsoever article of their diet happens to be in season.   Wherever a colony of Rooks, Jackdaws, or Rock Pigeons has established itself, there most probably, or somewhere in the neighbourhood, a large party will assemble to roost, and will attend the others on all their foraging expeditions.   In spring the flocks, small and great, break up into pairs, each with-drawing to a convenient nesting-place, which is sometimes a hole in a tree, sometimes in a building, a cliff, or a cave.   The nest itself is a simple structure, being composed of dry grass and roots, and contains generally five eggs.   At this season the male bird adds to the chirping and twittering notes of both sexes a soft, and not unmusical note, which resembles more closely than any other sound with which I am acquainted the piping of a boatswain's whistle, and it is not uncommon to hear a party of choristers thus engaged, perched meanwhile on some high tree, even while incubation is going on.   Starlings, also, mimic the notes of other singers.   The breeding season over, they become nomad in their habits.   Many families unite into a flock, and explore the country far and wide for suitable feeding-places, their diet being, up to this time, exclusively worms and insects.   But no sooner does the fruit begin to ripen in the cherry districts, than the flocks, now assembled in countless multitudes, descend on the trees, and, if not observed and scared away, appropriate the whole crop.

Newly fledged Starlings are so different from their parents that they might be mistaken for a different species.   The plumage is of a uniform greyish brown, lighter beneath.   It is not till the end of July or the beginning of August that the adult plumage begins to show itself, and then the young birds present a singular appearance, as the glossy black feathers, tipped with pearl, appear in irregular patches on various parts of the body.   Starlings do not usually roost near the scene of their depredations, but from this season and thence until late in autumn they repair, as if by some preconcerted scheme, to a rendez-vous common to many detachments.   A writer in the *Zoologist* states that there were formerly, near Melbourne in Cambridgeshire, some large patches of reeds, which were rented at a certain annual sum, and which the tenant sold to builders to use in making plaster-floors and ceilings of rooms.   Towards autumn, Starlings resorted to them in such numbers to roost that unless scared away, they settled upon the reeds, broke them down and rendered them completely useless. It required a person to keep watch every evening for some time, and fire at them repeatedly with a gun as they were settling down ; but as the spot was a favourite one, they showed considerable reluctance in quitting it.

THE ROSE-COLOURED STARLING PASTOR ROSEUS
(*Plate LIX*)

Head crested ;   crest and neck black, lustrous with violet reflections ;   back and lower parts rose-colour ;   wings and tail lustrous brown.   Length eight inches.   Eggs very pale blue or bluish-white, unspotted.   A rare, irregular visitor to the British Isles, chiefly in summer and autumn.

FAMILY PLOCEIDÆ

THE HOUSE SPARROW PASSER DOMESTICUS (*Plate LXI*)

Crown and back of the head dark bluish ash ;   lore, throat, and front of the neck, black ;   above the eyes a band of uniform reddish brown, intermixed with a few small white feathers ;   upper feathers dark brown, edged with reddish brown ; a single transverse white bar on the wing ; cheeks, sides of the neck, and under parts, greyish white. Female—head, nape, neck, and breast, ash-brown ; above the eye a light yellowish brown streak ; rest of the plumage less bright. Length five inches and three-quarters. Eggs white, spotted and speckled with dark grey and brown. A resident throughout the British Isles wherever there are human habitations.

WHAT were the haunts of the Sparrow at the period when men dwelt in tents, and there were neither farmhouses nor villages, much less towns and cities, it were hard to say. Certain it is now that thoroughly wild Sparrows are not to be met with in districts remote from human dwellings and cultivation ; they have left the hillside and forest as if by common consent, and have pitched their tents where man builds, or ploughs, or digs, and nowhere else. In the city, the seaport town, the fishing village, the hamlet, the farmhouse, nay, near the cot on the lone waste and by the roadside smithy, they are always present, varying in the amount of confidence they place in their patrons, but all depending on man to a certain extent. And not only do they court his society, but they have adopted his diet. Whatever is the staple food of a household, the Sparrows that nestle around will be right pleased to share it ; bread, meat, potatoes, rice, pastry, raisins, nuts, if they could have these for the asking, they would not trouble them-selves to search further ; but obliged, as they are, to provide for them-selves, they must be content with humble fare ; and so skilful are they as caterers, that whatever other birds may chance to die of starvation, a Sparrow is always round and plump, while not a few have paid for their voracity by their lives. Much difference of opinion exists as to whether Sparrows should be courted by man as allies, or exterminated as enemies. The best authorities on this point have come to the con-clusion that their numbers must be lessened, and that the most humane way to do this is to tear down nests before the young are hatched out. That Sparrows consume a very large quantity of corn in summer there can be no doubt ; as soon as the grain has attained its full size, and long before it is ripe, they make descents on the standing corn, and if undisturbed will clear so effectually of their contents the ears nearest to the hedges, that this portion of the crop is sometimes scarcely worth the threshing. During harvest they transfer their attention to the sheaves, while the reapers and binders are occupied elsewhere ; as gleaners they are indefatigable ; they participate, too, in the joys of harvest home, for their food is then brought to their very doors. The most skilful binder leaves at least a few ears exposed at the wrong end of the sheaf, and these are searched for diligently in the rick ; and the barns must be well closed indeed into which they cannot find admission. At threshings and winnowings they are constant attend-ants, feeding among the poultry, and snatching up the scattered grains under the formidable beak of Chanticleer himself. At seed-time their depredations are yet more serious, as they now come in not simply for a share of the produce, but undermine the very foundations of the future crop. I once had the curiosity to examine the crop of a Sparrow which had been shot as it flew up from a newly sown field, and found no less than forty-two grains of wheat. A writer in the *Zoologist*, who professes himself a deadly enemy of the Sparrow, states that he once took 180 grains of good wheat from the crops of five birds, giving an *average* of thirty-six for a meal. Now if Sparrows had the opportunity of feeding on grain all the year round, they would be unmitigated pests, and a war of extermination against them could not be waged too vigorously ; but during the far greater portion of the year they have not the power of doing mischief, and all this time they have to find food for themselves. Against their will, perhaps, they now hunt for the seeds of various weeds, especially the wild mustard ; and these being smaller than grains of corn and less nutritive, they consume an immense number of them, varying their repast with myriads of cater-pillars, wireworms, and other noxious grubs ; also they devour small beetles (called hay-chaffers) when the hay lies in swathes on the field. They thus compensate, certainly in part, perhaps wholly, for the mischief they do at other seasons ; and it is even questionable whether, if a balance were struck between them and the agriculturists, the obligation would not be on the side of the latter.

It is scarcely necessary to say much of the habits of a bird which stands on such familiar terms with the human race as the Sparrow. During no period of the year do Sparrows live together in perfect amity ; if half a dozen descend to pick up a handful of scattered crumbs, each in his turn will peck at any other who comes too near his share of the feast, and, with a peculiar sidelong shuffle or hop, will show his intention of appropriating as large a portion of the feeding-ground as he can. In spring, this bickering assumes a more formidable character. A duel is commenced among the branches of a tree, obstinate and noisy ; all the Sparrows within hearing flock to the scene of combat, joining at first with their voices, and finally with their beaks ; a general riot ensues, with as little object seemingly as an Irish ' row ' ; for suddenly the outcry ceases, and the combatants return to their various occupations. A writer in the *Naturalist* gives an account of a fray of this kind, during which three male birds fell at his feet one after another either dead or dying ; but cases of this kind are very rare.

Sparrows build their nests at a considerable elevation from the ground, but are by no means particular as to the locality. At the period when most farmhouses and cottages were thatched, the eaves were their favourite resort, and here they hollowed out for themselves most comfortable dwellings. The general employment of tiles or slates has interfered with this arrangement ; but they will fix upon any projection, niche, crack, or hole which will hold a nest, and if these are all occupied, content themselves with a tree ; but, as far as my own observation goes, the number built in trees far exceeds that to be found in other localities. Very frequently they appropriate the nest of the House Martin. The nest itself is a rude structure, composed mainly of straw and hay, and lined with feathers and any other soft materials which they can find. Two or three broods are reared every year, the number of eggs being usually five. The young are fed on worms, caterpillars, and insects of various kinds.

THE MOUNTAIN OR TREE SPARROW PASSER MONTÁNUS
(Plate LXI)

Crown and back of the head chestnut-brown ; lore, ear-coverts, and throat, black ; neck almost surrounded by a white collar ; upper plumage resembling the last ; wing with two transverse white bars. The female scarcely differs from the male. Length five inches and a half. Eggs as in the last. A local resident in many parts of the British Isles, also a winter visitor.

THE Mountain Sparrow seems scarcely to deserve its name, as it is by no means confined to mountainous districts. It is abundant all over the European continent, and is to be met with here and there in many parts of England, in the east of Scotland, and of late years in Ireland and in the Hebrides ; but it is nowhere so abundant as the House Sparrow, which it resembles in all respects, except that the head is of a bright chestnut colour, and the neck wears a white collar. I have never seen it except in society with the common species, and could never detect any difference either in flight or note ; but other observers state that the flight is slow and constrained, and the note assumes more the character of a song. The nest is placed in soft rotten wood of pollard willows and other trees, in holes in walls and under the thatch of buildings.

FAMILY FRINGILLIDÆ

THE LAPLAND BUNTING CALCARIUS LAPPÓNICUS (Plate LX)

Crown of the head black, speckled with red ; throat and breast black, a broad white band extending from the eye down the sides of the neck ; nape bright chestnut ; back, wings, and tail, variegated with brown, white, and black ; under parts white, spotted at the sides with dark brown. Length six inches and three-quarters. Eggs pale ochre-yellow, spotted with brown. A scarce winter visitor and passage migrant in the British Isles, chiefly on the coasts and most frequent in autumn.

THIS bird, as its name denotes, is an inhabitant of high northern latitudes ; and its occurrence in this country is very rare. In the Arctic regions it inhabits hilly and mountainous districts, and spends most of its time on the ground, where it runs in the manner of Larks, and where also it builds its nest. The male is said to have a pleasing song, combining that of the Skylark and of the Linnet.

THE SNOW BUNTING PLECTROPHENAX NIVALIS (Plate LX)

Head, neck, portion of the wings, and lower parts, white ; upper parts black, tinged here and there with red. Length six inches and three-quarters. Eggs pale reddish white, speckled and spotted with brown and pale red. A resident in the Highlands of Scotland, breeding in small numbers on the higher mountains. Elsewhere in the British Isles a winter visitor, chiefly to coasts or on hills inland.

THIS, though a northern bird also, does not confine itself so closely to the Arctic regions as the preceding species ; but is of common occurrence in many parts of Scotland during autumn and winter and later in the season in various parts of England. Macgillivray wrote : ' About the end of October it makes its appearance along the coasts or on the higher grounds of the south of Scotland, and about the same period in the south of England, although it is there of much less frequent occurrence. Assembled in large straggling flocks, or scattered in small detachments, these birds may be seen flying rather low along the shore, somewhat in the manner of Larks, moving in an undulating line by means of repeated flappings and short intervals of cessation, and uttering a soft and rather low cry, consisting of a few mellow notes, not unlike those of the Common Linnet, but intermixed at times with a sort of stifled scream or *churr*. When they have found a fitting place, they wheel suddenly round, and alight rather abruptly, on which occasion the white of the wings and tail becomes very conspicuous. They run with great celerity along the sand, not by hops, like the Sparrows and Finches, but in a manner resembling that of the Larks and Pipits ; and when thus occupied, it is not in general difficult to approach them, so that specimens are easily procured. At intervals they make excursions into the neighbouring fields, alight in cornyards, at barn-doors, or even on the roads, where they obtain seeds of oats, wheat, and weeds, which I have found in them. In the villages along the coast of Lothian, they are sometimes, in spring, nearly as common as Sparrows, and almost as familiar. About the middle of April, or sometimes a week later, these birds disappear and betake themselves to their summer residence.' Its habits, as observed in England, are similar ; but the flocks are generally smaller. In the Arctic regions, it is abundant from the middle or end of April to the end of September. Its nest is composed of dry grass, neatly lined with deer's hair, and a few feathers, and is generally fixed in the crevice of a rock or in a loose pile of timber or stones. In spring it feeds principally on the buds of *Saxifraga oppositifolia*, one of the earliest of the Arctic plants ; during winter, on grass seeds. Peculiar interest attaches to the Snow Bunting, from the fact that it is (according to Linnæus) the only living animal that has been seen two thousand feet above the line of perpetual snow in the Lapland Alps. Mention of it frequently occurs in books of Arctic travels. I must not omit to state that the specimens obtained in Great Britain vary so considerably in the proportions of white and tawny in their plumage, that there were at one time considered to be three several species. In Norfolk, I have seen them in severe weather flocking with Larks, among which they make themselves so conspicuous by the white portion of their plumage, as to be popularly known by the name of ' White-winged Larks '.

THE CORN (OR COMMON) BUNTING EMBERÍZA CALANDRA
(*Plate LX*)

Upper parts yellowish brown, with dusky spots ; under parts yellowish white, spotted and streaked with dusky. Length seven inches and a half. Eggs dull white, tinged with yellow, or pink, and spotted and streaked with dark purple brown. A resident in many districts throughout the British Isles.

THOUGH called the Common Bunting, this bird is by no means so abundant in England as the Yellow Bunting ; its name, however, is not misapplied, as it appears to be the most generally diffused of the family, being found all over the European continent, in the islands of the Mediterranean, in Asia Minor, and the north of Africa. In the latter district it appears as a bird of passage in November ; and about Martinmas it is so abundant as to become a staple article of food. At this season, all the trees in the public roads and squares of the villages are literally covered with these birds. Macgillivray informs us that it is more abundant in the outer Hebrides than in any other part of the country he has visited ; and that it is there generally known by the name of Sparrow. In England it is a constant resident ; but as it is much more abundant in autumn and winter than in summer, it probably receives accessions to its numbers from the north. From its habit of congregating in large flocks in the winter and alighting on arable land to feed, after the manner of the Skylark, it is sometimes called ' Lark Bunting ', and, from its favourite food, ' Corn Bunting.' It builds its nest in a tuft of grass, often under the shelter of briers or a low bush, constructing it of dry grass with a lining of hair. Its song, which is harsh and unmelodious, consists of a number of short repetitions of the same note, terminating with a long one lower in tone, and is generally uttered by the bird perched the while on some slight elevation, such as a stone or the topmost twig of a furze-bush. On first rising, it allows its legs to drop as if broken.

THE REED BUNTING EMBERÍZA SCHŒNICLUS (*Plate LX*)

Head, throat, and gorget, black (in winter speckled with light brown) ; nape, sides of the neck, and a line extending to the base of the beak on each side, white ; upper parts variegated with reddish brown and dusky ; under parts white, streaked with dusky on the flanks. Female—head reddish brown, with dusky spots ; the white on the neck less distinct ; under parts reddish white, with dusky spots. Length six inches. Eggs purplish grey, blotched and lined with dark purple-brown. A resident throughout the British Isles, except the Shetlands.

WHEREVER there is water, in the shape of a lake, canal, or river, lined by bushes and rushes, there this black-headed Bunting is pretty sure to be seen at most seasons of the year. The male is strongly marked by his black head and white collar ; the head of the female is of the same colour as the body ; but the white collar, of a less bright hue, she shares with her mate. ' Reed Sparrow ' is another name for this bird. In summer it rarely quits the vicinity of water. At this season its food consists of various seeds and insects ; but on the approach of winter it either forms small parties, or joins itself on to flocks of Yellow Hammers, Sparrows, and Finches, and visits the stack-yards in search of grain. It builds its nest in low bushes, or among aquatic plants, very near the ground, employing bents, bits of straw, reeds, etc., and lining it with hair. The eggs are four or five in number, of a dull, livid purple colour, marked with irregular curves or blotches of darker purple, which remind one of the figure of the lines, so often seen on bramble leaves, made by leaf-eating grubs. Its note resembles that of the other Buntings, and is pleasant from its association with walks by the river's side rather than for tone or melody. In Scotland the Reed Bunting is migratory, repairing southwards in October and returning in March.

THE LITTLE BUNTING EMBERÍZA PUSILLA (*Plate LXVIII*)

Crown and sides of the head chestnut, a broad black stripe on each side of the head above the eye ; upper parts reddish brown with blackish streaks ; tail-feathers ashy brown, two other pairs with longitudinal white terminal patches ; under parts buff, streaked black. Length five inches and a quarter. Eggs very variable in ground colour, blotched and scrawled with dark brown or reddish brown. A scarce migrant through the British Isles chiefly in autumn and on the east coast of Scotland and England.

THE YELLOW BUNTING (OR YELLOW HAMMER)
EMBERÍZA CITRINÉLLA (*Plate LVII*)

Head, neck, breast, and lower parts, bright yellow, more or less streaked with dusky ; flanks streaked with brownish red ; upper parts reddish brown, spotted with dusky. Female—the yellow parts less vivid, and spotted with dull reddish brown. Length six inches and a quarter. Eggs purplish or yellowish white, speckled and lined with dark purple-brown. Resident throughout the British Isles, except the Outer Hebrides and Shetlands.

THIS familiar and pretty bird appears to be generally diffused throughout all parts of the country, except the mountains. With its bright yellow head and breast it can scarcely fail to attract the attention of those even who are least observant of birds, and being by no means shy it will allow itself to be examined from a short distance. It may often be detected by its bright yellow plumage among the leaves of a hedge, neither fluttering nor hunting for food, but apparently waiting to be admired. As we approach within a few yards it darts out into the lane with rapid flight, displaying the white feathers of its tail, with tawny tail-coverts, perches on another twig some fifty yards in advance, and, after one or two such manœuvres, wheels away with rapid flight uttering two or three short notes as it passes over our head. In summer, especially during the hot afternoons of July, when most other birds have closed their concert for the season, it loves to perch on the top of a furze bush or other shrub, and repeat its simple song. This consists of about a dozen short notes, rapidly repeated and closed by a longer note, which I believe to be a musical minor third below. Sometimes this last note is preceded by another which is a third above. The effect is in some measure plaintive, and gives the idea that the bird is preferring a petition. In Devonshire it goes by the names of ' Little-bread-and-no-cheese ', and ' Gladdy '. Of the latter name I do not know the origin ; that of the former is clear enough ; for if the words ' A little bit of bread and no cheese ' be chanted rapidly in one note, descending at the word ' *cheese, chee-ese* ', the performance, both in matter and style, will bear a close resemblance to the bird's song. It has been noticed that the song of the Yellow Hammer may always be heard about three o'clock in the afternoon.

In winter, Yellow Hammers assemble in large flocks, often mixed with other hard-billed birds, and resort to ploughed fields, or rick-yards. Macgillivray describes with singular accuracy their move-ments on these occasions. ' When the ground is covered with snow, they congregate about houses, and frequent corn-yards along with other birds, retiring to the trees and hedges in the vicinity when alarmed. Their flight is undulated, light, strong, and graceful, and they alight abruptly, jerking out their tail-feathers. It is indeed surprising to see with what velocity they descend at once from a considerable height, to settle on the twigs of a tree which had attracted their notice as they were flying over it, and with what dexterity all the individuals of a flock perch in their selected places.'

The nest and eggs of the Yellow Hammer resemble those of the Corn Bunting, but are smaller. The nest is most frequently placed close to the ground, or actually on the ground, among grass on the skirt of a meadow. Yarrell suggested that the name ' Yellow Hammer ' should be written ' Yellow Ammer '—the word Ammer being a well-known German term for Bunting.

Collectors of eggs should carefully avoid cleaning the eggs of the Buntings, as the dark colouring matter with which they are blotched is easily rubbed off with a damp cloth.

THE ORTOLAN BUNTING EMBERÍZA HORTULANA
(*Plate LXVIII*)

Head and neck olive-grey, spotted with brown ; throat, orbits, and a narrow band stretching downwards from the gape, greenish yellow ; feathers of the back black, with reddish edges ; those of the lower parts brownish red, edged with ash-grey. Length six inches and a half. Eggs reddish white, spotted and lined with dark brown. A passage migrant in the British Isles, chiefly in autumn on the east coast of England and Scotland and the northern isles.

THE CIRL BUNTING EMBERÍZA CIRLUS (*Plate LX*)

Crown dark olive, streaked with black ; gorget and band above and below the eye bright yellow ; throat, neck, and band across the eye, black ; breast olive-

grey, bounded towards the sides by chestnut ; abdomen dull yellow ; back brownish red, with dusky spots. Female—the distinct patches of black and yellow wanting ; the dusky spots on the back larger. Eggs greyish, marked with ash-coloured and black blotches and lines. A local resident in southern and western England and Wales.

WITH the exception of its black chin and throat, this bird closely resembles the Yellow Hammer. Its habits, too, are much the same, so that little can be said of it which does not equally apply to its congener. It appears, however, to be much less patient of cold, and is consequently mostly confined to the southern counties of England, from Cornwall to Kent, and in the valley of the Thames. In the south of Europe, in the islands of the Mediterranean, and in Asia Minor, it replaces the Yellow Hammer. It is in the habit of perching higher than the Yellow Hammer, and is said to be partial to elm trees.

THE CHAFFINCH FRINGILLA CŒLEBS (*Plate LXII*)

Forehead black ; crown and nape greyish blue ; back and scapulars chestnut, tinged with green ; rump green ; breast wine-red, fading towards the abdomen into white ; wings black, with two white bands ; coverts of the secondaries tipped with yellow ; tail black, the two middle feathers ash-grey, the two outer on each side black, with a broad oblique white band. Female—head, back, and scapulars, ash-brown, tinged with olive ; lower parts greyish white ; the transverse bands less distinct. Length six inches. Eggs greenish purple, streaked and spotted with purple-brown. A resident throughout the British Isles, except the Shetlands.

' GAI comme Pinson ', as gay as a Chaffinch, is a familiar French proverb, which describes not only the character of the bird, but the peculiar temperament which in France is an essential part of gaiety. The Chaffinch is a smart, lively, active bird, always in a bustle, flitting here and there incessantly and staying long nowhere, always wearing a holiday look, so trim and spruce is he, and rattling through his song with wondrous volubility. It received the name *cœlebs*, bachelor, from Linnæus, who observed that the flocks in winter are composed for the most part either exclusively of males or of females. Large flocks arrive on our east coast each year from the Continent, and others coming from the north spread themselves over the country to the southward. During the open weather of autumn and early winter, Chaffinches frequent stubble and ploughed fields, where they busily collect grain and the seeds of various weeds, and are not, I fear, very scrupulous whether they are engaged as gleaners of what is lost, or robbers of what is sown. In severe weather they resort to farmyards and homesteads, where, along with Sparrows, Buntings, and Greenfinches, they equally consider all they can find as provided for their own especial use. On the return of spring, they feed upon the young shoots, and for a few weeks show themselves great enemies to horticulture. Their visits to our flower-gardens, paid very early in the morning, are attested by scattered buds of polyanthuses, which they attack and pull to pieces as soon as they begin to push from between the leaves. In the kitchen-garden they are yet more mischievous, showing a strong inclination for all pungent seeds. Woe to the unthrifty gardener, who, while drilling in his mustard, or cress, or radishes, scatters a few seeds on the surface ! The quick eye of some passing Chaffinch will surely detect them ; so surely will the stray grains serve as a clue to the treasure concealed beneath, and so surely will a hungry band of companions rush to ' the diggings ', and leave the luckless proprietor a poor tithe of his expected crop. Yet so large is the number of the seeds of weeds that the Chaffinch consumes, in the course of a year, more particularly of groundsel, chickweed, and buttercup, that he, without doubt, more than compensates for all his misdeeds ; and as his summer food partially, and that of his young family exclusively, consists of cater-pillars and other noxious insects, he is in reality among the gardener's best friends, who should be scared away at the seasons when his visits are not welcome, and encouraged at all other times. The Chaffinch, though a wary bird, does not stand greatly in fear of man ; for if disturbed at a meal, he is generally satisfied with the protection afforded by the branches of the nearest tree, on which he hops about until the danger is past, uttering his simple but not unpleasing note, ' *twink* ' or ' *pink* ' or ' *spink, spink, spink* ' as it is variously translated. To this cry it adds the syllable ' *tweet* ', frequently repeated in an anxious tone and with a peculiar restlessness of manner, which always indicate that its nest is somewhere very near at hand, and by which indeed it is very often betrayed.

Its proper song commences very early in spring, and is continued until June or later. This must be the song which the poet had in view when he sang :

> Then as a little helpless innocent bird,
> That has but one plain passage of few notes,
> Will sing the simple passage o'er and o'er,
> For all one April morning, till the ear
> Wearies to hear it.—TENNYSON.

It consists of from ten to twelve notes of the same tone, and about the same length, with the last but one elevated and accented, uttered rapidly at short intervals, and without the least variation.

The nest of the Chaffinch is an exquisite piece of workmanship, composed of moss, dry grass, fine roots felted together with wool, decorated externally with scraps of white lichens, and lined with hair and feathers. It is placed sometimes in the fork of a tree, sometimes against the bole, but more frequently than anywhere else it is built in among the twigs of an apple-tree ; but in every case it is attached to its support by wool interwoven with the other materials. The Chaffinch usually lays five eggs.

THE BRAMBLING FRINGILLA MONTIFRINGÍLLA (*Plate LXI*)

Head, cheeks, nape, and upper part of the back, black, the feathers (in winter) tipped with light brown or ash-grey ; neck and scapulars pale orange-brown ;

wings black, variegated with orange-brown and white ; rump and lower parts white, the flanks reddish, with a few dark spots. Female—crown reddish brown, the feathers tipped with grey, a black streak over the eyes ; cheeks and neck ash-grey ; all the other colours less bright. Length six inches and a half. Eggs yellowish white, spotted and streaked with dark red. A winter visitor to the British Isles, occasional pairs remaining to breed in the north of Scotland.

IN winter this bird occurs over the whole continent of Europe, and not infrequently in enormous flocks. Pennant mentions an instance in which eighteen were killed at one shot—a statement which I can well believe, having seen in the winter of 1853 by far the largest flock of small birds I ever beheld, and which was composed entirely of Bramblings. They were employed in searching for food on the ground in a beech wood, and, as I approached, flew up into the branches in thousands. The Brambling, called also the Bramble Finch and Mountain Finch, is a fairly regular autumn and winter visitor to many parts of Scotland and England. Its presence in our country in any numbers depends on the severity of the weather on the Continent. Sometimes it is fairly numerous with us, especially where there are many beech woods. Few visit Ireland. It resembles the Chaffinch in habits, size, and general tone of colour ; and as it often feeds in company with it, is probably sometimes confounded with it by an inexperienced eye. It arrives in this country in November, and takes its departure early in spring.

THE GREENFINCH CHLORIS CHLORIS (*Plate LV*)

All the plumage yellowish green, variegated with yellow and ash-grey. Length six inches. Eggs bluish white, speckled and spotted with purplish grey and dark brown. Resident throughout the British Isles, except the Shetlands.

THE Greenfinch, or Green Linnet, is one of our most generally diffused birds. No bird is a more frequent inhabitant of country gardens during the summer than this, being attracted, it would seem, not so much by the prospect of abundance of food, as by its fondness for building its nest in evergreens and the thick hedges of shrubberies. The lively greenish yellow tint of the plumage on its throat and breast sufficiently distinguish it from any other British bird ; and its note, when once identified, can be confounded with no other song. Let any one who wishes to obtain a sight of one, walk anywhere in the country where there are trees, on a bright sunny day in May or June, and listen for a monotonous long-drawn croak, trying to pronounce the syllable ' *twe-e-e* ' or ' *bree-eze* '. No matter what other birds may be tuning their lays, the harsh monotone of the Greenfinch, if one be near, will be heard among them, harmonizing with none, and suggestive of heat and weariness. In a few seconds it will be repeated, without a shadow of variation either in tone or duration ; and if it be traced out, the author of the noise (music I cannot call it) will be discovered perched among the branches of a moderately high tree, repeating his mournful ditty with extreme complacency

Mute Swan   Canada Goose
Glossy Ibis

Little Ringed Plover

Sabine's Gull

Dusky Redshank

Sooty Shearwater   Long-tailed Skua
Iceland Gull

LXVII

Little Bunting
Water Pipit
Tawny Pipit

Little Owl
Ortolan Bunting

Yellow-browed Warbler
Red-breasted Flycatcher

Bluethroat
Barred Warbler

LXIX

for an hour together.   Very often he takes advantage of the midday
silence of the groves, and pipes away without any other competitor
than the Yellow Hammer, whose song, like his own, is a constant
accompaniment of sultry weather.   The Greenfinch has another note
which is heard most frequently, but not exclusively, in spring.   This
is a single plaintive chirp which may be easily imitated by human
whistling ; it resembles somewhat one of the call-notes of the Canary-
bird or Brown Linnet, and, being full and sweet, harmonizes with
the woodland chorus far better than the monotonous croak described
above.   Another of the notes is a double one, and closely resembles
that of the ' Pee-wit ', hence it is called in some places ' Pee-sweep '.
The Greenfinch builds its nest, when not among evergreens, in some
tall thick bush either in a hedge or coppice.   Less neatly finished
than that of the Chaffinch, it is nevertheless a beautiful structure.
It is composed externally of a framework of light twigs and roots,
interleaved with moss and wool, to which succeeds a denser layer
of the same materials lined with hair.   It lays five eggs, which are
of a light grey colour, almost white, variously speckled with purple,
and of a long shape.   In winter, Greenfinches congregate in large
numbers, and feed together on the seeds of various weeds in stubble
fields, or not infrequently they descend on newly sown fields of wheat,
where they are very troublesome.   If disturbed, they rise simultaneously, fly rapidly only a few feet from the ground to another part
of the field, but before they alight wheel about several times with
singular precision of movement, disappearing from the sight and
reappearing according as the dark or light portion of their plumage
is turned towards the spectator ; and by this peculiarity they may
be distinguished from flocks of other small birds at a great distance.
If repeatedly disturbed, they alter their tactics, and take refuge in
the top branches of the neighbouring trees until their persecutor has
turned his back, when they return to the charge with the same perseverance which they display in the repetition of their summer song.
These flocks, probably, are composed of individuals which have
banded together in some more northern climate, and emigrated
southwards in quest of food ; for smaller parties, either unmixed, or
associated with Sparrows, Chaffinches, and Buntings, frequent our
farmyards and gardens in undiminished numbers.

THE HAWFINCH COCCOTHRAUSTES COCCOTHRAUSTES (*Plate LXII*)

Lore, throat, and plumage at the base of the bill, black ; crown and cheeks
reddish brown ; nape ash-grey ; back dark reddish brown ; wings black,
great coverts white ; some of the quills truncated at the extremity ; under
parts light purplish red ; tail short.   Length seven inches.   Eggs light olive-
green, with a few brown spots and numerous irregular lines of a lighter tint.
A resident in England (except Cornwall), eastern Wales, and southern Scotland ;
elsewhere in the British Isles an occasional visitor.

JUDGING from its conformation, one would, without knowing anything
of the habits of this bird, pronounce it to be a professor of some labori-

ous occupation.   Its short tail and wings unfit it for long aerial voyages, and its thick neck and ponderous bill denote the presence of great muscular power, and such, indeed, it both has and requires.   It is not a common bird.   In Berkshire I have several times seen two or three together busily occupied in picking up the seeds which had fallen from the cones of a spruce fir.   On one occasion a nest was brought to me by a man who had found it built on some twigs which grew from the trunk of a tall oak tree ;   it was built of the tangled white lichens which grow on trees, on a foundation of a few roots, and contained five eggs.   I afterwards discovered another nest of exactly similar structure, which I believed must have been built by the same bird, but it was empty.   In Hertfordshire a single Hawfinch visited my garden one winter for several days in succession, and diligently picked up and cracked the stones of laurel cherries, from which Blackbirds had, a few months before, as busily stripped the pulp.   In the cherry orchards in the neighbourhood they are not uncommon, where, even if not seen, their visits are detected by the ground being strewn with halves of cherry-stones, which these birds split with their powerful beaks as cleverly as a workman with the chisel.   Their note I have never heard, but the proprietor of the orchards assured me that he had often detected their presence by the low twittering noise which they made.   I have never seen a nest in Hertfordshire, but on several occasions have observed their eggs among the collections made by the country boys in the neighbourhood.   Besides cherry-stones, Hawfinches feed on hazelnuts, hornbeam seeds, the kernels of the fruit of the hawthorn, seeds of various kinds, and, when they can get them, green peas, for the sake of which they often venture into gardens.   They usually build their nests in trees at an elevation varying from twenty-five to thirty feet, and the nest is composed of dead twigs, intermixed with pieces of grey lichen ;   this last material varying much in quantity in different nests, but being never absent.

THE GOLDFINCH CARDUÉLIS CARDUÉLIS (*Plate LXII*)

Back of the head, nape, and feathers round the base of the bill, black ; forehead and throat blood-red ; cheeks, forepart of the neck, and lower parts, white ; back and scapulars dark brown ; wings variegated with black, white, and yellow ; tail black, tipped with white.   Length five inches.   Eggs bluish white, speckled with pale purple and brown.   A resident in England and Wales, Ireland, and some districts of the mainland of Scotland.

THIS little bird, as sprightly in its habits as it is brilliant in its colouring, is perhaps a more general favourite than any other British bird. Though in its natural state less familiar with man than the Redbreast, and inferior as a musician to the Lark, the Thrush, and others of our resident birds, it is more frequent as a caged bird than either, and thus is known to tens of thousands of city folk who never heard the wild song of the Thrush, nor saw a Redbreast under any circumstances.   In a cage it is attractive from its lively movements, its agreeable song, and yet more from its docility, as it not only is readily tamed, but may be taught to perform various tricks and manœuvres utterly repugnant to the nature of birds. Its affection, too, for its owner is not less remarkable. Of this many instances are, I doubt not, familiar to the reader ; but the following is not so well known. There was some years since in a small town, about twelve leagues from Paris, a tame Goldfinch, which belonged to a carrier, and which for many years regularly accompanied his master twice a week to and from the metropolis. At first it used to content itself with perching on the driver's seat, and from time to time flying a short distance ahead, or gambolling with other birds of the same kind that it encountered on the way. By and by it seemed to grow dissatisfied with the slow pace of the wagon, and took long flights in advance, still returning from time to time to its accustomed perch. At length, becoming more enterprising, it would leave its master in the lurch, and fly in advance the whole of the way, and announce his approach at the house in the city where he put up. If the weather was stormy, it would quietly await his arrival, taking up its quarters by the fireside ; but if the weather was fine, it would, after making a brief stay, return to meet him. At every meeting, caresses and congratulations were exchanged, as fondly as if they had been separated for years. This romantic attachment was at length terminated by the disappearance of the bird, but whether through the instrumentality of a cat, a Hawk, or some mischievous boy, was never discovered.

Whatever doubt may exist as to the services rendered to man by the Sparrow and Chaffinch, about the Goldfinch there can be no difference of opinion. The farmer has no better friend, and yet an abundance of Goldfinches on an estate is anything but a welcome sight ; for it denotes abundance of its favourite food, the seeds of thistles. Where these weeds flourish, there, for the most part, Goldfinches are to be met with in considerable numbers. The French name, *Chardonneret*, denotes ' a frequenter of thistles ', and the ancient Greek and Latin name for it, *Acanthis*, is of similar import ; the *Acanthis*, Pliny tells us,[1] bears animosity against no living creature but the donkey, a beast which eats the flowers of thistles, and so deprives it of its food. To this dietary it adds the seeds of dandelions, centaury, and other weeds, but shows a decided preference for the seeds of the compound flowers. Its nest is among the most beautiful that birds construct. One now before me is placed among the terminal branches cut from the bough of a Scotch fir which grew at an elevation of about twenty feet from the ground. It is encircled by upwards of a dozen leafy twigs which unite beneath its base, and form both a firm support and effectual shelter. The substance is composed of tufted white lichens (*Usnea* and *Evernia*), and a few fine roots and wiry stems of garden-thyme, felted together with wool so securely, that it is scarcely possible to remove one of them without damaging the whole. With these is intermixed a piece of worsted, and a thread of sewing cotton ; a few horsehairs succeed, and the whole of the interior is thickly matted with the white silky down of the coltsfoot.

[1] *Nat. Hist.* lib. x. cap. lxxiv.

Other nests vary in the materials employed, moss being sometimes used instead of white lichen, and willow-cotton or feathers instead of the down of the coltsfoot. Thistle-down is sometimes named as the material of the lining ; but this must be under unusual circumstances, that substance being generally unattainable in spring. Besides fir trees, the apple and elm are often selected by Goldfinches to build their nests in, and they not infrequently resort to any low tree in a hedge or shrubbery, also to young oak trees. In autumn, Goldfinches assemble in flocks of from ten to twenty or more, and resort to waste places, or the borders of fields, where thistles abound, and it is hard to imagine a prettier sight than a party of these innocent and brilliant hunters, perching, all heedless of spines and prickles, on the thistle heads, plucking out the seeds with the pappus attached, and cleverly separating the former from their appendage. While thus employed, they seem to take it for granted that no one will molest them, but continue their useful labour, twittering pleasantly all the while, until the spectator comes within a few yards of them, when they fly off like butterflies to another prickly bed.

Owing to more efficient bird-protection the Goldfinch, which was decreasing largely in numbers, is now on the increase again.

THE SISKIN CARDUÉLIS SPINUS (*Plate LXII*)

Crown black ; behind the eye a broad yellow streak ; all the plumage variegated with grey, dusky, and various shades of yellow and yellowish green ; wings dusky, with a transverse greenish yellow bar, and a black one above, and another black one across the middle of the tertiaries ; tail dusky, the base and edge of the inner web greenish yellow. Female—all the colours less bright, and no black on the head. Length four and a half inches. Eggs greyish white, speckled with purplish brown. Resident in north-eastern Scotland, and, locally, in western and southern Scotland and in Ireland ; has also nested occasionally in various parts of England and Wales. A winter visitor to all parts of the British Isles, fluctuating in numbers.

THE Siskin, or Aberdevine, is best known as a cage-bird, and during the period of its stay is retiring in its habits. Siskins are more frequently met with in the northern than the southern counties of England, but they are common in neither, and will only nest where pine woods abound. They are generally observed to keep together in small flocks of from twelve to fifteen, and may be heard from a considerable distance, as they rarely intermit uttering their call-note, which, though little more than a soft twittering, is as clear as that of the Bullfinch, to which it has been compared. Their flight is rapid and irregular, like that of the Linnet. They leave their roosting-places early in the morning, and usually alight on the branches of alder trees, where they remain all day. The seeds of the alder, enclosed within scales something like those of the coniferous trees, form the principal food of these pretty little birds, who are obliged to hang at the extremities of the twigs in order to explore the seed-vessels on all sides. Occasionally, but less frequently, they are seen

visiting heads of thistles and burdocks, and not infrequently they
descend to the ground for the sake of picking up scattered seeds.
During the whole of their feeding time, they never cease twittering
and fluttering about joyously from twig to twig. Now and then,
as if by preconcerted signal given by a leader, they all take flight
to another tree or, after a short evolution, return to the same from
which they started. Should it happen that, while one little band
is occupied in despoiling a tree, another is heard in the air, the latter
is immediately invited by general acclamation to take part in the
banquet, and rarely fails to accept the invitation. Owing to this
sociability of character they are easily entrapped, provided that one
of their own species be employed as a decoy bird. They soon become
reconciled to captivity, and are valued for their readiness to pair
with the Canary-bird, the note of which the joint offspring is thought
to improve. The nest, which in some respects resembles those of
the Greenfinch and Chaffinch, is concealed with great care in the
fork formed by two branches of a fir, with which it is so skilfully made
to assimilate, that it is almost impossible to discern it from below.

THE LINNET CARDUÉLIS CANNABÍNA (*Plate LXI*)

*Winter—head ash-brown, the feathers dusky in the middle, those of the
forehead more or less tinged with crimson ; back chestnut-brown, becoming
brighter towards the scapulars and duller towards the tail ; tail-feathers black,
edged towards the tip with reddish grey, the outer ones bordered with white ;
primaries black, the first five with very narrow, the next five with broad, white
edges, the rest of the wing-feathers tinged with red, all tipped with ash-grey ;
under parts—breast-feathers dull crimson or brown, edged with yellowish red ;
abdomen dull white ; flanks reddish yellow ; beak brownish horn-colour ;
feet and toes brown ; tail moderate. In* summer *the beak is of a bluish
lead colour ; feathers of the forehead and crown greyish brown, tipped with
crimson ; upper plumage uniform rich chestnut-brown ; breast crimson, with
a few pale brown feathers intermixed. Length five inches. Eggs pale bluish
grey, speckled with deep red. Resident throughout the British Isles, also a
winter visitor.*

IT is not unusual in the country to hear mention made of the Brown,
the Grey, and the Rose or Red Linnet, and the Common Linnet,
as if these were all different birds. Such, however, is not the case.
The Linnet is a bird which varies its plumage considerably at different
seasons of the year, in consequence of which, at a period when little
attention was paid to ornithology, the same individual was known
by whichever of these names best described its characteristic colouring.
Even by the earlier ornithologists there were supposed to be two
species, one of which was called Linota, probably from its having
been observed feeding on flax-seed (*Linum*) ; the other Cannabina,
from having been seen to feed on hemp-seed (*Cannabis*). Linnets
offer themselves to our notice in the evenings of autumn and winter
more than at any other time. Large flocks of them may then be
observed making their way, with rapid and irregular flight, towards

tall trees which happen to stand in the vicinity of a common or a furzebrake. On the summits of these they alight, with their heads, in stormy weather, always turned towards the wind, and after keeping up a continuous twittering for a few minutes, suddenly drop into their roosting-places among the furze and thick shrubs. At the return of dawn, they issue forth to their feeding-grounds, still congregated in large flocks, and spend the whole of the day in hunting on the ground for food. This consists principally of the seeds of various weeds, especially wild-mustard or charlock, wild-cabbage, and other plants of the same tribe, thistle and dandelion ; chance grains of corn no doubt are not passed by, but any injury which may be done by these birds, either to standing crops or newly sowed lands, must be far outweighed by their services as destroyers of weeds and insects, which latter also enter into their dietary. At this season their only note is a simple call, mellow and pleasant, which they utter both while flying and when perched. In spring, the flocks break up, and the members betake themselves in pairs to the commons and heaths, which afforded them night-lodging during winter. Here they build their nests at a moderate distance from the ground, more frequently in a furze-bush than anywhere else, but occasionally in other shrubs or an adjoining hedge. The nest is constructed of small twigs, moss, roots, and wool ; and is lined with hair, feathers, and sometimes vegetable down. The Linnet lays four or five eggs. The spring and summer song of the Linnet is remarkable neither for compass nor power ; it is, however, very sweet, and on this account the Linnet is a favourite cage-bird.

THE REDPOLL CARDUÉLIS FLAMMEA (*Plate LXIII*)

Forehead, throat, and lore, black ; crown deep crimson ; under parts light crimson tinged with buff, fading towards the tail into white ; upper parts reddish brown, with dusky streaks ; wings and tail dusky, edged with pale reddish brown. Female—all the colours less bright. Length five and a quarter inches. Eggs bluish white, speckled at the larger end with reddish brown. Resident throughout the British Isles except Cornwall and the Shetlands, also a winter visitor.

OF this small finch three distinct races occur in the British Isles. The description above is that of the Lesser Redpoll (*C. f. cabaret*) which is resident in the British Isles and the mountains of central Europe. In northern Europe, Siberia, and Canada the breeding form is larger and considerably paler. This race, the Mealy Redpoll (*C. f. flammea*), is an irregular visitor to the British Isles in winter, chiefly to northern and eastern Scotland and north-eastern England. In Greenland and Iceland the breeding form is still larger, with a stouter bill, but not so pale. This race, the Greater Redpoll (*C. f. rostrata*), is a rare visitor in autumn to the coasts of Scotland and Ireland.

The Lesser Redpoll so closely resembles the Siskin in its habits and temperament, that a description of either of these birds would serve well for the other. Like that bird it congregates in small flocks ; it frequents damp valleys where alder trees abound ; it feeds on the seeds of the same trees ; like it, hangs at the extremities of the twigs to explore the catkins, twitters merrily as it flies, and is quite as easily reconciled to captivity. But for the yellow plumage and larger size of the Siskin, they might well be mistaken one for the other. The Redpoll, however, is a much more frequent bird, as its annual visits to the southern counties of England in winter are as regular as those of Swallows in summer. Though a northern bird, it does not repair to high latitudes, but in summer remains to breed in Scotland and the northern counties of England. As far south as Yorkshire it is not infrequent, but in the Midlands, the southern counties, and Wales it is very local in the breeding season. The nest, which is remarkably small, is placed in the fork of a small tree or shrub, loosely constructed of dry grass and weeds, and lined either with the cotton of the willow or the pappus of some compound flower, stated by some to be dandelion, by others, thistle, but perhaps, in reality, coltsfoot. In captivity, Redpolls are prized for their liveliness and remarkable affection for each other, and, indeed, for all little birds who do not disdain their attentions. They can be taught many little tricks also.

THE MOUNTAIN LINNET OR TWITE
CARDUÉLIS FLAVIROSTRIS (*Plate LXIII*)

Upper plumage dark brown, edged with light brown ; no crimson either on the forehead or breast ; rump of the male tinged with red ; throat tawny brown, without streaks ; breast and abdomen dull white, streaked on the flanks with dark brown ; beak yellow ; feet and claws dark brown ; tail long. Length five inches and a quarter. Eggs pale bluish white, speckled with purple-red. Resident in Scotland, Ireland, and northern England. A winter visitor to southern England, chiefly along the east coast.

ANOTHER northern bird, inhabiting the Arctic Regions, Scandinavia, and Russia, and travelling southwards in autumn. In the Orkney and Shetland Islands it is the most common, if not the only, species, and builds its nest among the corn or heath. It breeds from Derbyshire and northwards, but is very local ; at one time it was very common on the Lancashire moors. Yellow-neb Lintie is a Scotch name given to it. In the countries where it is resident all the year round, it is very destructive to wheat in winter, and to turnips in summer. As soon as the latter plants appear above ground, the bird pulls them up, nips off the seed-leaves, and the field remains strewn with the fragments of the young plants. In winter, Mountain Linnets assemble in very large flocks, and in their habits resemble Common Linnets, from which they are best distinguished (at a distance) by their longer tails. During severe weather I have observed them in Norfolk, flocking to the salt-marshes, and feeding on the seeds of saline plants, especially those of the shrubby sea-blite. At this season their note resembles the twitter of the Common Linnet, but is less mellow. The nest is placed among heath or grass, or in bushes.

It is constructed of dry grass, moss, and roots, and lined with various soft substances. The Mountain Linnet is generally called the Twite, a syllable which its simple note is thought to resemble. It is more shy as a rule than the Lesser Redpoll.

THE BULLFINCH PÝRRHULA PÝRRHULA (*Plate LXIII*)

Crown, throat, plumage round the bill, wings, and tail, lustrous purple-black ; upper part of the back bluish ash ; cheeks, neck, breast, and flanks, red (in the female *reddish brown) ; rump and abdomen pure white ; a broad buff and grey band across the wings. Length six and a quarter inches. Eggs light greenish blue, speckled and streaked with light red and dark purple. Resident throughout the British Isles, except the Outer Hebrides, Orkneys, and Shetlands.*

' THE Bullfinch ', said Macgillivray, usually so accurate an observer, ' is not very common anywhere.' From this last remark I infer that the author in question was never either proprietor or occupant of a fruit-garden in a wooded district, or he would have reported very differently of the frequency of the Bullfinch. During winter the food of these birds consists exclusively of berries of various kinds and seeds, especially of such weeds as thistle, ragwort, duckweed, plantains, etc., either picked up from the ground or gathered from herbs and shrubs. In spring, unfortunately for the gardener, their taste alters, and nothing will satisfy them but the blossom-buds of fruit trees, especially those which are cultivated. They attack, indeed, the buds of the sloe and hawthorn as well ; but of these, being value-less, no one takes note. Still keeping together in small family parties, all uninvited, they pay most unwelcome visits to gooseberries, plums, and cherries, and, if undisturbed, continue to haunt the same trees until all hope of a crop is destroyed. Gooseberry-bushes are left denuded of flower-buds, which have been deliberately picked off and crushed between their strong mandibles, while the leaf-buds, situated principally at the extremities of the branches, are neglected. Plum and cherry trees are treated in like manner, the ground being strewn with the bud-scales and rudiments of flowers. Some persons endeavour to deter them by whitewashing the trees, and are said to find this plan effectual. Others wind a straw rope round the goose-berry-bushes, so disguising their natural appearance. This plan I found perfectly successful one year, but the next it was entirely with-out effect. A new one which I have adopted this year is somewhat more complex. In addition to the straw bands, I have stretched long strings, with feathers attached here and there, so as to resemble the tail of a paper kite ; and, by way of offering them an inducement to stay away, I have sprinkled peas on the ground in an adjoining lane, in the hope that they will partially, at least, satisfy their hunger on these. A bird with so strong a beak as that of the Bullfinch is evidently designed to crush its food, not to swallow it whole ; accord-ingly, I find my peas disappearing, but the parchment-like rind is left on the ground, a substance too indigestible even for the gizzard of a Bullfinch. This bird has, however, justly many friends, who assert that the buds he attacks are infested with concealed insects, and that the tree he strips one season will be heavily laden the following year. When not occupied in disbudding fruit trees, Bullfinches are most frequently observed in tall and thick hedges, either in small flocks as described above, or in pairs. They are rarely met with singly, and yet less frequently associated with birds of another species. Occasionally a pair may be seen feeding with Sparrows and Chaffinches in the farmyard ; but this society seems one of accident rather than of choice. When disturbed in a hedge they are singularly methodical in their movements : first one flies out, bounds, as it were, through the air in a direction away from the spectator, perches on a twig in the thick part of the hedge, and is followed by the rest of the party in single file. When the passenger has approached within what the bird considers a safe distance, the same manœuvre is repeated, each bird following, with dipping flight, the line marked out by its predecessor.

THE CROSSBILL LOXIA CURVIRÓSTRA (*Plate LXIV*)

Bill equalling in length the middle toe, point of the lower mandible extending beyond the ridge of the upper mandible ; plumage variegated, according to age and sex, with green, yellow, orange, and brick-red. Length six and a half inches. Eggs bluish white, speckled with red-brown. A resident in certain districts of England, Scotland, and Ireland where pine trees are plentiful ; also an irregular immigrant in late summer and autumn, sometimes in large flocks which spread all over the British Isles and remain for the winter. After such irruptions a few pairs often remain to breed in districts where they are not normally found.

THE beak of this bird was pronounced by Buffon ' an error and defect of Nature, and a useless deformity '. A less dogmatic, but more trustworthy authority, our countryman, Yarrell, is of a different opinion. ' During a series of observations ', he says, ' on the habits and structure of British birds, I have never met with a more interesting or more beautiful example of the adaptation of means to an end, than is to be found in the beak, the tongue, and their muscles, in the Crossbill.' No one can read the chapter of Yarrell's *British Birds* devoted to the Crossbill (in which the accomplished author has displayed even more than his usual amount of research and accurate observation) without giving a ready assent to the propriety of the latter opinion. Unfortunately the bird is not of common occurrence in this country, or there are few who would not make an effort to watch it in its haunts, and endeavour to verify, by the evidence of their own eyes, the interesting details which have been recorded of its habits.

The Crossbill is about the size of the Corn Bunting, and, like it and the Hawfinch, is a remarkably stout bird, having a strong bill, a large head, short, thick neck, compact ovate body, short feet of considerable strength, rather long wings, and moderately large tail. Its plumage, in which green or red predominates, according to the age and sex of the bird, is much more gaudy than that of our common birds, and approaches that of the Parrots, a tribe which it also resembles in some of its habits. They are occasionally mischievous in orchards and gardens, on account of their partiality to the seeds of apples, which they reach by splitting the fruit with one or two blows of their stout bills. Food of this kind, however, they can only obtain in autumn ; at other seasons, and, indeed, all the year round in districts remote from orchards, they feed principally on the seeds of coniferous trees, which they extract from the cone by the joint action of their beak and tongue. The alder and other trees are also sometimes visited, and they have been noticed to resort to thistles and pick the seeds from them. ' In the autumn of 1821,' says Macgillivray, ' when walking from Aberdeen to Elgin, by the way of Glenlivat, and along the Spey, I had the pleasure of observing, near the influx of a tributary of that river, a flock of several hundreds of Crossbills, busily engaged in shelling the seeds of the berries which hung in clusters on a clump of rowan (mountain ash) trees. So intent were they on satisfying their hunger that they seemed not to take the least heed of me ; and as I had not a gun, I was content with gazing on them without offering them any molestation. They clung to the twigs in all sorts of positions, and went through the operation of feeding in a quiet and business-like manner, each attending to his own affairs without interfering with his neighbours. It was, indeed, a pleasant sight to see how the little creatures fluttered among the twigs, all in continued action, like so many bees on a cluster of flowers in sunshine after rain.' A writer in the *Zoologist* thus describes the manœuvres of a flock which he observed in 1849, in the county of Durham : ' On the fifteenth of July when taking a drive in the western part of the county, where there are many thousand acres of fir plantations, I had the good fortune to see a flock of birds cross my path, which appeared to be Crossbills ; so, leaving the gig, I followed some distance into a fir plantation, where, to my great gratification, I found perhaps thirty or more feeding on some Scotch firs. The day being fine, and as they were the first I had seen in a state of wild nature, I watched them for about twenty minutes. Their actions are very graceful while feeding, hanging in every imaginable attitude, peering into the cones, which, if they contain seeds, are instantly severed from the branch ; clutched with one foot, they are instantly emptied of their contents, when down they come. So rapidly did they fall, that I could compare it to nothing better than being beneath an oak tree in autumn, when the acorns are falling in showers about one's head, but that the cones were rather heavier. No sooner are they on the wing than they, one and all, commence a fretful, unhappy chirl, not unlike the Red-poll's, but louder.' Another writer, in the *Magazine of Natural History*, thus records his experience : ' From October, 1821, to the middle of May, 1822, Crossbills were very numerous in this county (Suffolk), and, I believe, extended their flight into many parts of England. Large flocks frequented some fir plantations in this vicinity, from the beginning of November to the following April. I had almost daily opportunities of watching their movements ; and so remarkably tame were they, that, when feeding on fir trees not more than fifteen or twenty feet high, I have often stood in the midst of the flock, unnoticed and unsuspected. I have seen them hundreds of times, when on the larch, cut the cone from the branch with their beak, and, holding it firmly in both claws, as a hawk would a bird, extract the seeds with the most surprising dexterity and quickness. I do not mean to assert this to be their general habit ; but it was very frequently done when feeding on the larch. I have never seen them adopt the like method with cones of the Scotch or other species of pine, which would be too bulky for them to manage. Their method with these, and, of course, most frequently with the larch, was to hold firmly on the cone with their claws ; and, while they were busily engaged in this manner, I have captured great numbers ; many with a horsehair noose fixed to the end of a fishing-rod, which I managed to slip over their head when they were feeding, and, by drawing it quickly towards the body, I easily secured them ; others I took with a limed twig, fixed in such a manner in the end of a rod that, on touching the bird, the twig quickly became disengaged, adhered to the feathers, rendered the wings useless, and caused the poor bird to fall perfectly helpless on the ground. In this manner, in windy weather, I have taken several from the same tree, without causing any suspicion of danger. On warm sunny days, after feeding a considerable time, they would suddenly take wing, and, after flying round for a short time, in full chorus, alight on some lofty tree in the neighbourhood of the plantations, warbling to each other in low pleasing strains. They would also fly from the trees occasionally for the purpose of drinking, their food being of so dry a nature. To captivity they were quickly reconciled, and soon became very familiar. As, at first, I was not aware what food would suit them, I fixed branches of the larch against the sides of the room in which I confined them, and threw them a quantity of the cones on the floor. I found that they not only closely searched the cones on the branches but, in a few days, not one was left in the room that had not been pried into. I gave them canary and hemp-seed ; but thinking the cones were both amusement and employment, I continued to furnish them with a plentiful supply. I had about four dozen of them ; and frequently, whilst I have been in the room, they would fly down, seize a cone with their beak, carry it to a perch, quickly transfer it to their claws, and in a very short time empty it of its seeds, as I have very many times witnessed to my surprise and amusement.' These accounts are most interesting, yet they are all equally defective in failing to describe the mode in which Buffon's ' useless deformity ', the crossed bill, is employed in the work of splitting open a cone. This defect is supplied partially by Mr. Townson's description, quoted by Yarrell, and partly by the latter author in his own words. ' Their mode of operation is thus :— They first fix themselves across the cone, then bring the points of the mandibles from their crossed or lateral position, to be immediately over each other. In this reduced compass they insinuate their beaks between the scales, and then, opening them—not in the usual manner, but by drawing the inferior mandible sideways—force open the scales.'

'At this stage,' Yarrell proceeds to say, ' the end of the tongue becomes necessary ; and this organ is no less admirably adapted for the service required. . . . While the points of the beak press the scale from the body of the cone, the tongue is enabled to direct and insert its cutting scoop underneath the seed, and the food thus dislodged is transferred to the mouth ; and when the mandibles are separated laterally in this operation the bird has an uninterrupted view of the seed in the cavity with the eye on that side to which the under mandible is curved.'

The beak of the Crossbill then, far from being a defect in the organization of the bird, is a perfect implement always at its owner's command, faultless alike in design and execution, and exquisitely adapted to its work, not an easy one, of performing, by a single process, the office of splitting, opening, and securing the contents of a fir-cone, and he must be a bold man who could venture to suggest an improvement in its mechanism.

It has been observed that young birds in the nest have not their mandibles crossed, and at this period such an arrangement would be useless, as they are dependent for food on the parent birds.. It has also been observed that the side on which the upper mandible crosses the lower varies in different individuals ; in some it descends on the right side of the lower mandible, in others on the left. The bird appears to have no choice in the matter, but whatever direction it takes at first, the same it always retains.

The nest of the Crossbill is constructed of slender twigs of fir and coarse dry grass, and lined with fine grass and a few hairs, and concealed among the upper branches of a Scotch fir.

TWO-BARRED (OR WHITE-WINGED) CROSSBILL
LOXIA LEUCOPTERA (*Plate LXIV*)

Somewhat smaller than the common Crossbill and in full plumage the red male has a pink rather than an orange tinge. At all ages and in both sexes it is at once distinguished by two white bars across the wings. Length five inches and three-quarters. Eggs greenish white, with a few dark purple spots. An occasional visitor to the British Isles, usually with irruptions of the common Crossbill.

GLOSSARY OF COMMON AND PROVINCIAL NAMES AND OF TECHNICAL TERMS

♂ : male　　　　♀ : female

Aberdeen Sandpiper : a name for the Knot

Aberdevine : a name for the Siskin

Accentor, Hedge : the Hedge Sparrow

Alk : the Razor-bill

Allamotte : the Petrel

Allan : the Skua

Alp : a name for the Bullfinch

Annet : the Kittiwake Gull

Arctic-bird : the Skua

Assilag : the Petrel

Awl : the Woodpecker

Badock : the Skua

Bankjug : the Chiff-chaff and Willow-warbler

Bargander : the Sheldrake

Barley-bird : the Siskin and Wryneck

Barred or **Lesser-spotted Woodpecker**

Basal : at or near the base

Beam-bird : the Spotted Flycatcher

Bean Crake : the Land Rail

Bearded Reedling, or **Bearded Tit**

Bee-bird : a name sometimes given to the Flycatcher ; sometimes to the Willow-warbler

Beech-finch : the Chaffinch

Bee-hawk : the Honey Buzzard

Bergander : the Sheldrake

Bernacle Goose, or **Barnacle Goose**

Billy : the Hedge Sparrow

Billy-whitethroat : the Whitethroat

Black-a-top : the Stonechat

Black-billed Auk : a name given to the Razor-bill in the winter plumage of the first year

Blackcap : a name sometimes given to the Black-headed Gull, the Marsh Tit, and Cole Tit

Black Duck : the Scoter

Blacky-top : the Stonechat

Blind Dorbie : the Purple Sandpiper

Bloodulf : the Bullfinch

Blue-backed Falcon : the Peregrine Falcon

Bluebird : the Fieldfare

Blue-cap : the Blue Tit

Blue Darr : the Black Tern

Blue Hawk : the Peregrine Falcon

Blue-winged Shoveler : the Shoveler

Boatswain : the Skua

Brake-hopper : the Grasshopper Warbler

Brambling, or **Bramble-finch**

Bran : the Crow

Brancher : the Goldfinch in its first year

Brantail : the Redstart

Broad-bill : the Shoveler

Bronzie : the Cormorant

Brook Ouzel : a name given to the Dipper, and incorrectly to the Water Rail

Brown-headed Gull : Black-headed Gull, Red-legged Gull, or Hooded Gull

Brown Owl, or **Tawny Owl**

Brown Starling : a name sometimes given to the young of the Starling

Brown Tern : the Tern in its immature plumage

Budfinch : the Bullfinch

Bunting, Lapland, or **Finch**

Burgomaster : the Glaucous Gull

Burrow Duck : the Sheldrake

Cackareer : the Kittiwake Gull

Caddaw : the Jackdaw

Calloo : the Long-tailed Duck

Cargoose : the Great Crested Grebe

Carinate : in the form of a keel

Car-swallow : the Black Tern

Cere : the wax-like membrane which covers the base of the bill in the Falconidæ

Chaldrick, or **Chalder :** the Oyster Catcher

Chanchider : the Spotted Flycatcher

Chank and **Chank-daw :** the Chough

269

Channel Goose: the Gannet
Chanter, Hedge: the Hedge Sparrow
Charlie Miftie: the Wheatear
Chepster: the Starling
Cherry-finch: the Hawfinch
Cherry-sucker, Cherry-chopper, and Cherry-Snipe: the Spotted Flycatcher
Chevy Lin: the Redpoll
Chickell: the Wheatear
Chickstone: the Stonechat
Chippet Linnet: the Redpoll
Church Owl: the Barn Owl
Churn Owl: the Nightjar
Churr: the Dunlin
Clack Goose, Clakes: the Brent Goose
Clatter Goose: the Brent Goose
Clee: the Redshank
Cleff: the Tern
Clinker: the Avocet
Cloven-footed Gull: the Tern
Coal-and-candle-Light: the Long-tailed Duck
Coal Goose: the Cormorant
Coaly Hood: the Bullfinch or Cole Tit
Cob: the male Swan
Cob: the Great Black-backed Gull
Cobble: the Great Northern Diver
Cobbler's Awl: the Avocet
Cobweb: the Spotted Flycatcher
Cockandy: the Puffin
Cock-winder: the Wigeon
Coddy Moddy: the common Gull in its first year's plumage
Coldfinch: the Pied Flycatcher
Colin: a name in America for Quail
Compressed: flattened vertically
Coot-foot: the Phalarope
Copperfinch: the Chaffinch
Corbie: the Raven
Corndrake: the Land Rail
Cornish Crow, or **Daw:** the Chough
Cornwall Kae: the Chough
Coulterneb: the Puffin
Courser Gull: the Glaucous Gull
Crank bird: the Lesser Spotted Woodpecker
Craw: part of the stomach in birds
Cream-coloured Plover: Swift-foot or Courser
Creeper, Creep-tree, or **Tree-creeper:** these names are in some places given to the Nuthatch

Crested Cormorant: the Shag
Crested Heron: Common or Grey
Cricket-bird: the Grasshopper Warbler
Cricket Teal: the Garganey
Crooked Bill: the Avocet
Cuckoo's Leader or **Mate:** the Wryneck
Culmen: the ridge of the upper mandible
Cultrate: in the form of a billhook or pruning knife
Curlew-Jack: the Whimbrel
Curwillet: the Sanderling
Cushat: the Ring Dove
Cutty Wren: the Common Wren
Cygnet: the young Swan

Daker Hen: the Land Rail
Danish Crow: the Hooded Crow
Darr, Blue: the Black Tern
Depressed: flattened horizontally
Deviling: the Swift
Dick Dunnock: the Hedge Sparrow
Dippearl: the Tern
Dirty Allen: the Skua
Dishwasher: the Wagtail
Diving Pigeon: the Guillemot
Dobbler and **Dabchick:** the Little Grebe
Door-Hawk and **Dorr-Hawk:** the Nightjar
Dorbie: the Dunlin
Doucker: a popular name for a Grebe or Diver
Dove-coloured Falcon: the Peregrine Falcon
Doveky: the Black Guillemot
Draine: the Mistle Thrush
Duck Hawk: the Marsh Harrier
Ducker: a popular name for a Grebe or Diver
Dulwilly: the Ringed Plover
Dun Crow: the Hooded Crow
Dundiver: the female and young of the Merganser
Dung Hunter: the Skua
Dunkir and **Dunair:** the Pochard
Dunnock: the Hedge Sparrow

Earl Duck: the Red-breasted Merganser
Easterling: the Smew
Ebb: the Bunting
Ecorcheur: the Shrike

Egret : a tuft of long narrow feathers found on the lower part of the neck of the Herons. The name is also sometimes extended to the two tufts of feathers, resembling ears or horns, in some of the Owls

Elk : the Hooper Swan

Emmer or **Ember Goose :** the Great Northern Diver

Emmet Hunter : the Wryneck

Erne : the Sea Eagle

Falk or **Falc :** the Razor-bill

Faller : the Hen Harrier

Fallow Chat, Fallow Finch, Fallow Lunch, or **Fallow Smich :** the Wheatear

Fanny Redtail : the Redstart

Fauvette : the Garden Warbler, also applied to others of the Warblers

Feather-poke : i.e. ' sack of feathers ' is the Chiff-chaff, so called from the materials and form of the nest

Felt and **Feltyfare :** the Fieldfare

Fiddler : the Common Sandpiper

Field Lark : the Skylark

Fiery Linnet : the Common Linnet

Finch, Lapland or **Bunting**

Fire-crested Regulus or **Wren :** the Fire-crest

Fire-tail : the Redstart

Flapper : a young Duck

Flopwing : the Lapwing

Flusher : the Butcher-bird

Foot : The foot of a bird consists of four, never less than three, toes, with their claws, and the joint next above, called the ' tarsus '

French Linnet : the Redpoll

French Magpie : the Red-backed Shrike

French Pie : the Great Spotted Woodpecker

Gaggle : a flight of Wild Geese

Gairfowl : the Auk and the Razor-bill

Gallinule : the Moor-hen ; this name is sometimes applied to the Crakes

Gallwell Drake : the Land Rail

Gardenian Heron : the young of the Night Heron

Garden Ouzel : the Blackbird

Gaunt : the Great Crested Grebe

Gidd : the Jack Snipe

Gillhowter : the Barn Owl

Gladdy : the Yellow Hammer

Glead, Gled, or **Glade :** the Kite

Goat Owl and **Goat-sucker :** the Nightjar

Golden-crested Regulus, Warbler, or **Wren :** the Gold-crest

Golden Oriole or **Thrush**

Gorock : the Red Grouse

Gorse-duck : the Corn Crake

Gorsehatch : the Wheatear

Gorse Linnet : the Common Linnet

Goud Spink : the Goldfinch

Gouk : the Cuckoo

Gouldring : the Yellow Hammer

Gourer : the Petrel

Graduated : a term applied to the tail of. a bird when the middle feathers are longest and the outer ones are shorter in gradation

Greenwich Sandpiper : the Ruff

Grey : the Gadwall

Grey-bird : the Song Thrush

Grey Coot-footed Tringa : the Phalarope

Grey Crow : the Hooded Crow

Grey-Duck : the Gadwall

Grey Falcon : the Hen Harrier

Grey Heron : Common or Crested Heron

Grey-lag : Fen, Stubble, or Wild Goose

Grey Lapwing, or **Sandpiper :** the Grey Plover

Grey Linnet : the Common Linnet

Grey Owl : the Barn Owl

Grey Partridge : the Common Partridge

Grey Skit : the Water Rail

Grisette : the Whitethroat

Ground Lark : the Pipit and Bunting

Ground Wren : the Willow-warbler

Guldenhead : the Puffin

Gull-tormentor : the Skua

Gunner : the Great Northern Diver

Gurfel : the Razor-bill

Gustarda : the Bustard

Hackbolt : the Great Shearwater

Hadji : the Swift

Hagdown : the Great Shearwater

Haggard : the Peregrine Falcon

Hagister : the Magpie

Half-Curlew : the Whimbrel and Godwit

Half-Duck: the Wigeon, Pochard, etc.

Half-Snipe: the Jack Snipe

Harle: the Red-breasted Merganser

Harpy: the Marsh Harrier

Hawk-Owl: this name is sometimes given to the Short-eared Owl

Hay-bird, or **Hay-Tit:** the Willow-warbler

Hay-Jack: the Garden Warbler and Whitethroat

Heather-bleater: the Snipe

Heath Throstle: the Ring Ouzel

Hebridal Sandpiper: the Turn-stone

Heckimal: the Blue Tit

Hedge-Chicken: the Wheatear

Hedge-Jug: the Long-tailed Tit

Hegrilskip: the Heron

Helegug: the Puffin

Hellejay: the Razor-bill

Hern, Hernshaw, Heronshaw: the Heron

Heronsewgh: the Heron

Herring-bar: perhaps a corruption of Herring-bird, Diver

Herring Gant: the Gannet

Hew-hole: the Woodpecker

Hickwall: the Lesser Spotted Wood-pecker

High-hoo: the Woodpecker

Hiogga: the Razor-bill

Hissing Owl: the Barn Owl

Hoarse Gowk: the Snipe

Hoddy: the Crow

Holm Cock and **Holm Screech:** the Mistle Thrush

Hoop: the Bullfinch

Hornfinch: the Petrel

Horniwinks: the Lapwing

Horra: the Brent Goose

Horsefinch: the Chaffinch

Horsmatch: the Red-backed Shrike, the Wheatear and Whinchat

Howlet: the Tawny Owl

Howster: the Knot

Huckmuck: the Long-tailed Tit

Hullat: the Owl

Icebird: the Little Auk

Imber, or **Great Northern Diver**

Iris (*plural*, Irides)**:** the coloured circle of the eye surrounding the pupil

Isaac: the Hedge Sparrow

Isle of Wight Parson: the Cor-morant

Ivy Owl: the Barn Owl

Jack Curlew: the Whimbrel

Jack-nicker: the Goldfinch

Jack Saw: the Goosander

Jar Owl: the Nightjar

Jay, Jay Pie, or **Jay Pyet**

Jenny: the Wren

Jid, or **Judcock:** the Jack Snipe

Kadder and **Kae:** the Jackdaw

Kamchatka Tern: the Black Tern

Katabella: the Hen Harrier

Kate: the Hawfinch

Katogle: the Eagle Owl

Kiddaw: the Guillemot

King-Harry: the Goldfinch

Kip: the Tern

Kirktullock: the Shoveler

Kirmew and **Kirmow:** the Tern

Knee: a name often given, though inaccurately, to the junction of the tarsus and tibia of a bird

Lamhi or **Lavy:** the Guillemot

Land Curlew: the Stone Curlew

Lary: the Guillemot

Laughing Goose: the White-fronted Goose

Lavrock: the Skylark

Leg-bird: the Sedge Warbler

Lesser wing-coverts: the feathers which overlie the greater wing-coverts, or those next the quills

Ling-bird: the Meadow Pipit

Linlet: a young Linnet

Lobefoot: the Phalarope

Long-tongue: the Wryneck

Loom, or **Loon:** the Diver

Lore: the space between the beak and the eye

Lough Diver: the Smew

Lum, Lungy: the Guillemot

Lumme: the Diver

Lyre: the Manx Shearwater

Madge Howlet: the Barn Owl

Maglowan: a name for the Divers

Magpie Diver: the Smew

Malduck, or **Malmarsh:** the Ful-mar

Mallemoke: the Fulmar

Mandibles : upper and under, the two portions of a bird's bill
Man-of-war bird : the Skua
Marketjew Crow : the Chough
Marrot : the Guillemot and Razor-bill
Mavis : the Song Thrush
May-bird, or **Mayfowl :** the Whimbrel
Meadow Crake or **Drake :** the Moor-hen
Meggy-cut-throat : the White-throat
Merlie : the Blackbird
Mew, or **Mow :** a Gull
Millithrum : the Long-tailed Tit
Minute Gallinule : the Little Crake
Minute Merganser : the young Smew
Minute Tringa, the Little Stint
Mire Snipe : the Snipe
Mistle Thrush, or **Mistletoe Thrush**
Mitty : the Petrel
Mock-bird : the Sedge Warbler
Mock Nightingale : the Blackcap and Garden Warbler
Monk : the Bullfinch
Moor Blackbird or **Ouzel :** the Ring Ouzel
Morrot : the Guillemot
Moss-cheeper : the Meadow Pipit
Mother Carey's Chickens : the Petrels
Mountain Linnet : the Twite
Mountain Ouzel : the Ring Ouzel
Mouse Hawk, or **Owl :** the Short-eared Owl
Mow : a Gull
Mud-plover : the Grey Plover
Muggy : the Whitethroat
Mullet : the Puffin
Mumruffin : the Long-tailed Tit
Murdering-bird : the Butcher-bird

Nape : the upper part of the neck behind
Neck-a-pecker and **Nickle :** the Woodpecker
Night-crow, or **Night-hawk :** the Nightjar
Nope : the Bullfinch
Norfolk Plover : the Thick-knee or Stone Curlew
Norie : the Cormorant
Northern Crow : the Hooded Crow

Norway Lark : the Snow Bunting
Nun : the Blue Tit

Oke : the Auk
Olive : the Oyster Catcher
Olive-tufted Duck : the Golden Eye
Operculum : a lid or covering
Orbit : the skin that surrounds the eye, and in some birds is destitute of feathers
Oven-bird : the Chiff-chaff, Willow-warbler, and Wood-warbler

Padge and **Padge Owl :** the Barn Owl
Palmipedes : web-footed birds
Pandle-whew : the Wigeon
Parasitic Gull : the Skua
Parrot, Ailsa : the Puffin
Parrot, Sea : the Puffin
Parson Mew : the Black-backed Gull
Passerine : belonging to the order Passeres
Passerine Warbler : the Garden Warbler
Pea-finch : the Chaffinch
Pearl : the Tern
Pease Crow : the Tern
Peck : the Bar-tailed Godwit
Pectinated : cut like a comb
Peese-weep : the Lapwing or Pee-wit, also sometimes given to the Greenfinch
Peggy : the Wren, Whitethroat, and the Garden Warbler
Peggy cut-throat : the Whitethroat
Petrel : the name Petrel is in some places given to the Godwit
Pettychaps, Greater : the Garden Warbler
Pettychaps, Lesser : the Chiff-chaff
Philomel : the Nightingale
Pianet : the Magpie, and Oyster Catcher
Picarini : the Avocet
Pick-cheese : the Blue Tit and Great Tit
Pickmire : the Black-headed Gull
Picktarney and **Picket :** the Tern
Pictarn : the Black-headed Gull
Pie, Sea : the Oyster Catcher
Pied Diver : the Smew
Pied Wigeon : the Garganey, and Golden Eye

Pie-finch: the Chaffinch
Pienet and Piet: the Magpie
Piet, Water: the Dipper
Pigeon Hawk: the Sparrow-Hawk
Pigeon Mow, Red-legged: the Black-headed Gull in its winter plumage
Pigmy Curloo, the Curlew Sandpiper
Pink: the Chaffinch
Pinnock: a Tit
Pint: the Laughing Gull
Pirenet: the Sheldrake
Plover's Page: the Purple Sandpiper or Dunlin
Pocker, or Poker: the Pochard
Poke-Pudding: the Long-tailed Tit
Poor-willie: the Godwit
Pop: the Redwing
Pope: the Puffin
Popinjay: the Green Woodpecker
Port-Egmont Hen: the Great Skua
Post-bird: the Spotted Flycatcher
Primaries: the quills, usually ten, of the terminal joint of a bird's wing
Proud-tailor: the Goldfinch
Provence Furzel: the Dartford Warbler
Puckeridge: the Nightjar
Pudding-poke: the Long-tailed Tit
Puffinet: the Black Guillemot
Purre: the Dunlin
Puttock: the Buzzard and Kite
Pywipe: the Lapwing

Quaketail: the Wagtail
Que: the Night Heron
Queest, or Quest: the Ring Dove
Queet: the Coot and Guillemot
Quill-coverts: a row of feathers immediately covering the base of the quills above and below, and therefore called upper and under
Quills: the large feathers of the wing, called primary, or digital; secondary, or cubital; and tertiary, or humeral; according as they arise from the terminal, middle, or inner joint
Quinck: the Goose

Rafter-bird: the Spotted Flycatcher
Rain-bird: the Green Woodpecker
Rain-Goose: the Red-throated Diver
Raptores: Birds of Prey
Rasores: Gallinaceous Birds

Rattle-wings: the Golden Eye
Redcap: the Goldfinch
Red Godwit: the Bar-tailed Godwit
Red-headed Linnet: the Linnet and Redpoll
Red-headed Pochard: the Pochard
Red-headed Wigeon: the Wigeon
Red Hoop: the Bullfinch
Red-legged Crow: the Chough
Red-legged Godwit: the Spotted Redshank
Red-legged Gull, the Black-headed Gull
Red-necked Coot-foot, Lobe-foot, or Phalarope
Red Sandpiper: the Knot in its summer plumage
Reed-bird: the Sedge Warbler
Reed Fauvette: the Sedge Warbler
Reed Pheasant: the Bearded Tit
Reed Sparrow: the Reed Bunting
Reeve: the female of the Ruff
Richel Bird: the Little Tern
Rind-tabberer: the Green Woodpecker
Ring Blackbird: the Ring Ouzel
Ring Dove: the Wood Pigeon
Ringed Dotterel, or Plover
Ringed-necked or Great Northern Diver
Ring-tailed Eagle: the Golden Eagle in its second year's plumage
Rippock: the Tern
Rochie: the Little Auk
Rock-birds: the Auk, Puffin, and Guillemot
Rock Dove, Rocker Dove, Rockier Dove
Rock Hawk: the Merlin
Rock Lark, or Pipit
Rock Ouzel: the Ring Ouzel
Rock Sandpiper: the Purple Sandpiper
Rodge: the Gadwall
Rood Goose, or Brent Goose
Rose-coloured Linnet: the Redpoll, and Common Linnet
Rose-coloured Ouzel, Pastor, Starling, or Thrush
Rotck, or Rotcke: the Little Auk
Rothermuck: the Bernacle Goose
Ruddock: the Redbreast, Robin
Ruddy Plover: the Bar-tailed Godwit
Runner: the Water Rail
Runner, Stone: the Ringed Plover

St. Cuthbert's Duck: the Eider
St. Martin's Snipe: the Jack Snipe
Sandcock: the Redshank
Sandsnipe: a Sandpiper
Sandy-loo: the Ringed Plover
Sandy Poker: the Pochard
Sarcelle: the Long-tailed Duck
Saw-bill: the Merganser
Scale Drake: the Sheldrake
Scallop-toed Sandpiper: the Phalarope
Scammel: the Bar-tailed Godwit
Scapulars: the feathers which rise from the shoulders and cover the sides of the back
Scar Crow: the Black Tern
Scarf and **Scart:** the Shag
Scaurie: the Herring Gull
Scooper: the Avocet
Scotch Goose: the Brent Goose
Scout: the Common Guillemot
Scrabe: the Manx Shearwater
Scraber: the Black Guillemot
Scraye: the Tern
Screamer and **Screecher:** the Swift
Screech: the Mistle Thrush
Screech Martin: the Swift
Screech-Owl: the Barn Owl
Scull: the Skua
Scurrit: the Little Tern
Scuttock: the Guillemot
Sea Crow: the Cormorant, and Black-headed Gull
Sea Dotterel: the Turnstone
Seaford Goose: the Brent Goose
Sea Hen: the Guillemot
Sea Lark: the Rock Pipit and Ringed Plover
Sea Mall, Mew, or **Mow:** the Gull
Sea Parrot: the Puffin
Sea Pheasant: the Pintail Duck
Sea Pie: the Oyster Catcher
Sea Sandpiper: the Purple Sandpiper
Sea Snipe: the Dunlin
Sea Swallow: the Tern
Sea Titling: the Rock Pipit
Sea Turtle-dove: the Guillemot and Little Auk
Sea Wigeon: the Scaup
Sea Woodcock: the Godwit
Secondaries: the quill-feathers arising from the second joint of the wing

Sedge-bird, Sedge Warbler, or **Sedge Wren**
Selninger Sandpiper: the Purple Sandpiper
Serrated: toothed like a saw
Serrator: the Ivory Gull
Serrula: the Red-breasted Merganser
Sheldapple: the Crossbill. This name and 'Shelley' are sometimes given to the Chaffinch
Shepster: the Starling
Shilfa: the Chaffinch
Shoeing-horn: the Avocet
Shore-bird: the Sand Martin
Shore Pipit: the Rock Pipit
Shrieker: the Black-tailed Godwit
Shrimp-catcher: the Little Tern
Shrite: the Mistle Thrush
Silvery Gull: the Herring Gull
Skart: the Cormorant, and Shag
Skein: a flight of Geese
Skiddaw: the Guillemot
Skiddy Cock, Skilty, or **Skit:** the Water Rail
Skite: the Yellow Hammer
Skitty: the Spotted Crake
Skrabe: the Black Guillemot
Snake-bird: the Wryneck
Snite: the Snipe
Snow-bird: the Ivory Gull
Snow-Bunting: Flake, or Fleck
Snuff-headed Wigeon: the Pochard
Solan, or **Solent Goose:** the Gannet
Solitary Snipe: the Great Snipe
Sparling-fowl: the female Merganser
Speckled-bellied Goose: the White-fronted Goose
Speckled Diver: the young of the Red-throated Diver
Spectacle Duck: the Golden Eye
Speculum: the bright feathers which form a kind of disc of the wing of the Ducks
Speney: the Petrel
Spider-diver: the Dabchick
Spink: the Chaffinch
Spotted-necked Turtle Dove: the Turtle Dove
Sprat Loon, the young of the Great Northern Diver
Sprat Mew: the Kittiwake Gull
Spurre: the Tern
Standgale, or **Stannel:** the Kestrel

Starling, Common, Stare, or **Starenil**
Staynil: the Starling
Steel Duck, Larger: the Goosander
Steel Duck, Lesser: the Merganser
Stint: the Dunlin, or any similar bird, is often so called on the coast
Stonechacker, or **Stoneclink:** Stonechat
Stonegale: the Kestrel
Stone Hawk: the Merlin
Stone-smirch: the Wheatear
Storm Cock: the Mistle Thrush
Storm Petrel, or **Storm Finch**
Straney: the Guillemot
Summer Duck, or **Sheldrake:** the Long-tailed Duck
Summer Snipe: the Sandpiper
Summer Teal: the Garganey
Sweet William: the Goldfinch
Swiftfoot: the Courser
Swimmer, Little: the Phalarope
Swine-pipe: the Redwing

Tail-coverts: upper and under feathers covering the basal portion of the tail-feathers above and below
Tailor, Proud: the Goldfinch
Tammie Cheekie and **Tammie Norie:** the Puffin
Tangle-picker: the Turnstone
Tang-waup: the Whimbrel
Taring, Tarrot: the Tern
Tarrock: the young of the Kittiwake Gull
Tarse: the male Falcon, a name used in falconry
Tarsus: the bone of a bird's foot next above the toes. In a domestic fowl the tarsus is the portion between what is called the ' drumstick ' and the toes ; the shank
Tatler: a Sandpiper
Teal Cricket: the Garganey
Teaser: the Skua
Teewit: the Peewit
Tertiaries: the quills which spring from the third or inner joint of a bird's wing
Thistlefinch: the Goldfinch
Thrice-cock: the Mistle Thrush
Throstle: the Song Thrush
Tibia: the joint of a bird's leg next above the tarsus ; the ' drumstick '
Tick: the Whinchat

Tidley: the Wren
Tinkershere, or **Tinker's hue:** the Guillemot
Tippet Grebe: the Great Crested Grebe
Titlark and **Titling :** the Meadow Pipit
Titlark, Sea: the Rock Pipit
Tom Harry: the Skua
Tommy Norie: the Puffin
Tom Pudding: the Dabchick
Tomtit: the Blue Tit
Tonite: the Wood-warbler
Tony Hoop: the Bullfinch
Tope: the Wren
Tor-Ouzel: the Ring Ouzel
Towilly: the Sanderling
Tree Pipit, or **Lark**
Tree Sheeler: the Tree Creeper
Tuchit: the Lapwing Plover
Tuliac: the Skua
Turkey-bird: the Wryneck
Turtle, Sea: the Black Guillemot and Little Auk
Twink: the Chaffinch
Twit Lark: the Meadow Pipit
Tystie: the Black Guillemot

Ulnia: the Tawny Owl
Under tail-coverts : the feathers which overlap the base of the tail beneath
Under wing-coverts : the feathers which cover the wings beneath
Upper tail-coverts: the feathers which overlap the base of the tail above
Upper wing-coverts: the feathers which overlap the base of the quills
Utick: the Whinchat

Vare Wigeon: the Smew
Velvet Runner: the Water Rail

Wagell: the young of the Great Black-backed Gull
Wall Hick: the Lesser Spotted Woodpecker
Wash-dish and **Washerwoman:** the Pied Wagtail
Water Crow, the Dipper
Water-hen: the Moor-hen
Water Junket: the Common Sandpiper
Water Ouzel, or **Dipper**
Water Sparrow: the Sedge Warbler

Water Tie: the Wagtail
Water Wagtail: the Pied Wagtail
Waxen Chatterer, or **Waxwing**
Wease-alley: the Skua
Weasel Coot: the young Smew
Weasel Duck: the Smew
Weet-weet: the Common Sandpiper
Wellplum: the Red-headed Pochard
Whaup: the Curlew
Whautie: the Whitethroat
Wheel-bird, or **Wheeler:** the Nightjar
Wheety-why: the Whitethroat
Whewer: the Wigeon
Whey-bird: the Whitethroat
Whilk: the Scoter
Whim: the Wigeon
Whin Linnet: the Common Linnet
Whistling Plover: the Golden Plover
Whistling Swan: the Whooper Swan
White Baker: the Spotted Flycatcher
White-breasted Blackbird: the Ring or Water Ouzel
White-faced Duck: the Pochard
White Finch: the Chaffinch
White-headed Cormorant: the Common Cormorant
White-headed Goosander: the Smew
White-headed Harpy: the Marsh Harrier
White Nun: the Smew
White-spot Cormorant: the Common Cormorant
White-tail: the Wheatear
White-winged Black Duck : the Velvet Scoter
Whit-ile, i.e. **Whittle:** the Green Woodpecker
Whitterick: the Curlew
Whitty-beard: the Whitethroat
Whitwall and **Witwall:** the Green Woodpecker
Wierangel: the Great Grey Shrike
Willock and **Willy:** the Guillemot
Willow-biter: the Blue Tit
Willywicket: the Common Sandpiper
Windhover and **Windfanner:** the Kestrel
Windle, Winnard, and **Windthrush:** the Redwing

Wing-coverts: several rows of feathers covering the basal part of the quills above and below, and called the upper and under wing-coverts ; the feathers outside these are called the lesser wing-coverts
Winglet: a process arising from near the base of the terminal joint of the wing, answering to the thumb in the human hand
Winnel and **Windle-Straw:** the Whitethroat
Winter-bonnet: the Common Gull
Winter Duck: the Pintail Duck
Winter-Gull, or **Mew :** the Common Gull in its winter plumage
Winter Wagtail: the Grey Wagtail
Winthrush: the Redwing
Witch: the Petrel
Witwall: the Green Woodpecker
Woodcock, Sea: the Godwit
Woodcock-Owl: the Short-eared Owl
Woodcock-Snipe: the Great Snipe
Woodcracker: the Nuthatch
Wood Grouse: the Capercaillie
Woodpie: the Green Woodpecker
Wood Shrike: the Woodchat
Woodspite, Woodwall, and **Woodwele:** the Green Woodpecker
Writing Lark: the Bunting, so called from the markings of the eggs

Yaffil, Yaffle, Yaffler, Yappingale: the Green Woodpecker
Yardkeep and **Yarwhip:** the Bar-tailed Godwit
Yarwhelp: the Stone Curlew and Godwit
Yeldrin and **Yeldrock:** the Yellow Hammer
Yellow-legged Gull: the Lesser Black-backed Gull
Yellow Owl: the Barn Owl
Yellow Plover: the Golden Plover
Yellow Poll: the Wigeon
Yellow Sandpiper: the young of the Ruff
Yellow Warbler: the Willow-warbler
Yellow Yeldock, Yoit, Yoldrin, and **Yowley:** the Yellow Hammer
Yelper: the Avocet

INDEX